CYCLOPAEDIA OF COLDWATER FISH AND POND LIFE

OTHER BOOKS AVAILABLE

Fancy Goldfish Culture
Frank W. Orme

Profitable Fishkeeping
Guy N. Smith

Boys' Book of Angling
Major-General R. N. Stewart

Animals of the Countryside
Guy N. Smith

Modern Wildfowling
Eric Begbie

Practical Beekeeping
R. J. & W. E. Howe

Guide to Cage Birds
David Alderton

The Peafowl of the World
Josef Bergmann

The Incubation Book
Dr. A. F. Anderson Brown

Pictorial Poultry Keeping
Revised by Dr. J. Batty

CYCLOPAEDIA OF COLDWATER FISH AND POND LIFE

by

Frank W. Orme

Coloured Plates by Michael Stringer

SAIGA PUBLISHING CO. LTD.,
1 Royal Parade, Hindhead, Surrey GU26 6TD
England.

ISBN 0 904558 84 3

Typeset by: Heather FitzGibbon
5 Frensham Avenue, Fleet, Aldershot, Hants.
Printed and bound by
Robert Hartnoll Limited Bodmin Cornwall

Published by
SAIGA PUBLISHING CO. LTD.,
1 Royal Parade, Hindhead, Surrey, GU26 6TD
England.

PREFACE

Although not everything is covered within the pages of this book, I have nevertheless endeavoured to make it as comprehensive as possible. Many sources have been consulted to supplement my own knowledge, and much time devoted to collating the information into the form in which it is now presented. Where possible the use of 'technical jargon' has been avoided in order to make each subject easily understood, for the reader of this book will, one assumes, be seeking an explanation – not further confusion.

The subject matter covers a wide range including cold freshwater life, both animal and plant, from the microscopic up to the fishes of our British waters; some foreign coldwater fishes are also described, for these are popular with many aquarist's; the anatomy of the fish is covered in some detail, together with various complaints and suggested treatments; the definition of a little understood word or term may be found herein. In order that the required information may be quickly and easily found the text has been arranged in alphabetical order, many of the subjects being cross-referenced.

It must be mentioned that the illustrations which accompany the text are mostly representational and few, if any, are reproduced life-size – they are either greatly enlarged or reduced in comparison to the real-life subject.

Having long felt that there was a need for an easily understood book that dealt specifically, and comprehensively, with coldwater life, I hope that the enquiring mind of the reader will find at least some of the answers that are sought, and will consider this work a welcome addition to the bookshelf.

Frank W. Orme,

Rubery, Birmingham.

MONOCHROME ILLUSTRATIONS

COLOURED ILLUSTRATIONS

Between pages 24 and 25.

A. Often used as an abbreviation for anal fin.

ABDOMEN. In vertebrates – the part containing the digestive organs. The belly.

ABRAMIS. Generic name for the Bream.

ACANTHOCEPHALIA. Spiny-headed or thorny-headed worms. A small phylum of endoparasitic worms which are parasitic to fish. They live in the intestines where they attach themselves by means of a ring of hooks which surrounds their proboscis. The Freshwater Shrimp *Gammarus* acts as an intermediate host, on which the infection appears as red spots or streaks on the upper side of its back.

ACCESSORY BREATHING. Most species of fish rely upon their gills for the intake of oxygen. However, there are some which do not rely upon their gills. The latter fishes have the ability to breathe through an accessory organ which enables them to live in conditions that would prove difficult for the gill-breathing species. The substitute breathing organ usually appears either as a sac with walls through which there is a very good flow of blood, sac-like folds in addition to the gills or intestines, or special lung-like bags. These ancillary organs allow the fish to take in atmospheric air, from the water surface, when conditions prevent a sufficient oxygen intake through the gills.

ACCRESCENT. Botanical term for an organ, especially a calyx, that enlarges after flowering.

ACHENE. Small, dry one-seeded fruit.

ACILIUS. Genus of diving beetles, or *Dystiscidae.*

ACORUS. Genus of the reed family ***Araceae.*** Marsh plants found on the low banks of ponds and lakes. Hardy, with a creeping root-stock. *See under* **Plants.**

A. calamus Linne– This species originated from East Asia but is now found growing wild in many parts of the world. Suitable only for ponds, it is very hardy and has grass-like leaves with wavy edges which distinguish it from similar plants. The aromatic root-stock is sometimes used for medicine and can grow to a thickness of 1½ inches (38mm).

A. gramineus Solander– **The Japanese Rush.** A small, delicate species suitable for the aquarium; it can be grown submerged. The plant originates from the Far East and has hard, bright green to dark green, narrow, grass-like, pointed leaves that grow fan-wise from a creeping root-stock. *See* **Plants.**

ACROSOME. That part of the head of spermatozoon in the form of a cap over the nucleus.

ADEPHAGA. Predatory beetles, (Insecta: *COLEOPTERA*). Sub-order of carnivorous beetles which includes diving beetles, ***Dytiscidae;*** whirligigs, ***Gyrinidae*** and the smaller water beetles, ***Haliplidae.*** *See* ***Dytiscus.***

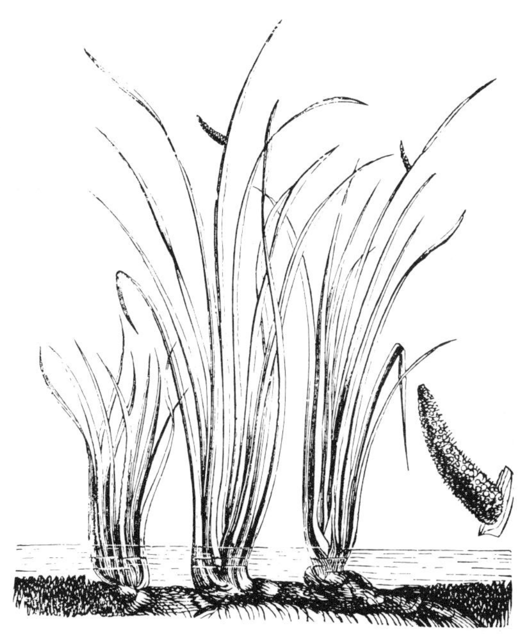

Figure 1 *Acorus calamus Linne* – **the Sweet Flag.**

ADVENTITIOUS. Appearing irregularly.

AERATION. Artificially creating water current, or turbulence, to present a larger proportion of the water to the air than is possible with still water. This movement allows an increased escape of any noxious gas and a greater intake of essential oxygen.

AERATOR. A mechanical device, usually an air-pump, used in conjuction with a porous silica stone. Air is forced through the stone to form a stream of small air-bubbles. These create a circulation of the water.

AERIAL LEAF. Leaf that rises above the water surface.

AEROBE. Organisms, especially bacteria, which need oxygen.

AEROBIC BACTERIA. *See* **Bacteria.**

AKA BEKKO. *See* **Koi.**

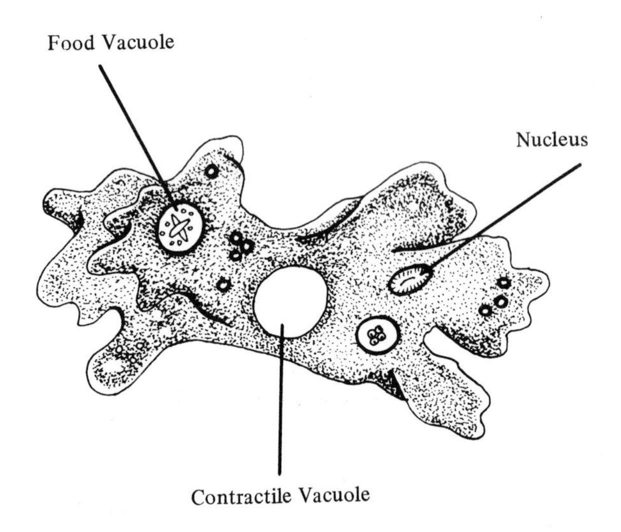

Figure 2 **Amoeba**

AKA MUJI. *See* **Koi.**

ALBINISM. An absence of pigment cells; a condition that can be inherited by future generations. In a pure albino there is no external colour to any part of the fish. The body and eyes may appear pinkish due to the red colour of the blood showing through.

ALBUMEN. The material surrounding an embryo.

ALBURNUS. Genus of the ***Cyprinidae*** family, or carp-like fishes.

A. lucidus– The Bleak.

ALDER-FLY. Species of smoky-brown winged insect. The common Alder-fly is a familiar sight around ponds, lakes and streams in Britain, during May and June. Females lay up to 2,000 eggs in clusters on stones and plants at the waters' edge. The larvae remain in the water for about two years, spending their time crawling through the bottom mud. They will attack any smaller creature and seize their prey in powerful mandibles.

ALGAE. A large number of lower plants, at one time regarded as a single group but now classified in a number of different divisions, or phyla. These include the blue-green algae (CYANOPHYTA), green algae (CHLOROPHYTA), brown algae (PHAEOPHYTA), red algae (RHODOPHYTA), diatoms and their allies (CHRYSOPHYTA). Algae represent the beginning of the development of higher organisms. In fresh water they normally take the form of threadlike or small to microscopic bodies. Reproduction may be either sexually or asexually.

ALGIVOROUS. Feeding on algae.

ALIMENTARY CANAL. The digestive tube that begins at the mouth and passes through the length of the body to the vent.

ALLELS (or Allelomorphs). Genes, in pairs of sets, on homologous chromosomes that control certain characteristics.

ALTERNATE. Leaves or flowers which grow alternately along the stem.

ALTERNIFOLIA. Varying leaves.

AMEIURUS NEBULOSUS. Genus of North American Catfish. *See* **Catfish.**

AMERICAN SUNFISHES. *See* ***Centrarchidae.***

AMITOSIS. Cell division without the cell nuclei being loosened in the chromosomes.

AMOEBA. Possibly the best known protozoan. A minute animal composed of an irregularly shaped protoplasm which is capable of changing shape whilst it moves. It multiplies by dividing into two new individuals.

AMPHIBIAN. Cold-blooded vertebrate, whose body temperature adjusts according to its surrounding temperatures.

Two orders exist in Britain: *CAUDATA,* the newts, and *SALIENTIA* which comprises frogs and toads. Although the adults have lungs and spend much time out of water they must, nevertheless, return to that environment to breed. Most have an aquatic larval stage in their development which breathes through gills. This showing that they have evolved from fishlike ancestors which left the water and colonized the land.

Newts– There are three British species: *Triturus vulgaris,* the Smooth Newt; *Triturus cristatus,* the Great Crested Newt; and *Triturus helveticus,* the Palmate Newt.

The **Smooth Newt** is also known as the Common Newt, and can be found over most of the British Isles. It reaches a length of about 4 inches (102mm) and spends much of its time on land where it is seldom seen. The female is a dull brownish colour, the male being more brightly coloured with a reddish belly and heavy black spotting over the body.

During the spring they take to the water when the males coloration becomes much more vivid and a pronounced serrated crest develops on the back. At this time the creatures are more easily found. Conical sperm capsules are deposited in the water by the males, the females take one of these and release the sperms into their vent. Thus the eggs are fertilized before release. Single eggs are laid on under-water plants, these take about fourteen days to hatch.

Great Crested Newts tend to spend more time in the water, apart from that they have a similar life history to the Smooth Newt. Both male and female are darker than the other species and have a skin covered with small tubercles; the tubercles excrete a protective substance which is distasteful to other creatures. They grow to around 6 inches (152mm).

Palmate Newts can easily be confused with the Smooth Newt although they are smaller in size, being approximately 3 inches (76mm) in length. During the breeding season the male develops webbing between the toes of the hind feet, and a thread-like filament appears at the end of the tail – at other times of the year these features are greatly reduced.

On land newts feed on insects, worms and similar foods. When in the water they and their tadpole larvae eat any small creatures that they can catch.

Frogs– Three species are found in Britain: *Rana temporaria,* the Common Frog; *Rana esculenta,* the Edible Frog; and *Rana ridibunda,* the Marsh frog.

The **Common Frog** has a wide variation of colour, ranging through yellows, greens and browns. They grow to 3 inches (76mm) or more.

Edible Frogs are not native, they have been introduced from the Continent. This frog is a much more aquatic creature than the Common Frog, is slightly larger and somewhat greener, although its colour can vary.

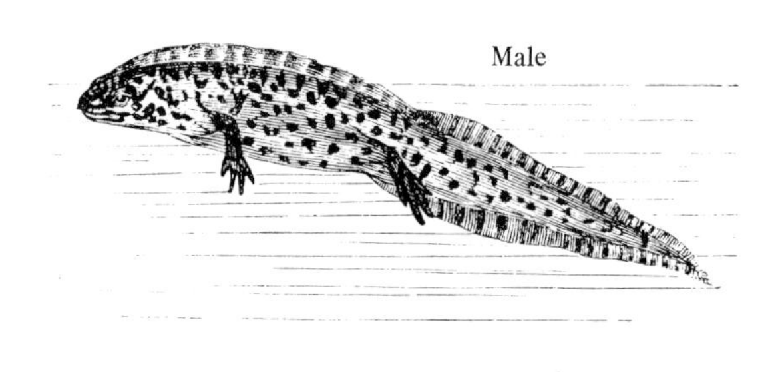

Figure 3 **Smooth Newt** *(Triturus vulgaris)* – showing male and female

The **Marsh Frog** is also an introduced species; they are thought to have descended from stock imported from Hungary in 1935. The brownish-green body is usually spotted with black. It is a large creature and the female can reach around 5 inches (127mm), the male being smaller.

Frogs deposit their masses of spawn early in the year; the tadpoles take around three months to complete their development into tiny replicas of the adult.

Toads– These can be distinguished from frogs by their warty skin; they do not hop but, instead, they crawl and their legs are much shorter.

Bufo bufo, the **Common Toad**, spends most of its time on land, hibernating in a deep hole from October to March. With the coming of spring both male and female return to water where eggs are laid in long strings of jelly-like matter.

Bufo calamita, the **Natterjack Toad**, is rarer. It has a green body with a yellow line down the middle of the back; very agile, it can run quite

Figure 4 **Common Toad** *(Bufo bufo)*

rapidly. It normally hides during the day. During the breeding period, around May time, it gives vent to an exceptionally loud, gurgling croak.

ANADROMOUS. Fish which ascend rivers, from the sea, to spawn and then return.

ANAEROBE. Bacteria which can live and multiply without oxygen. *See* **Bacteria.**

ANAEROBIC BACTERIA. *See* **Bacteria.**

ANAESTHETIC. It is sometimes necessary to temporarily immobilize a fish, or some other cold-blooded animal, before treating it for an ailment – or transferring it from one place to another. **MS-222** is much used nowadays for this purpose. It is a fine white crystalline powder, which is mixed with water at varying strengths, and may be used by spraying the gills, or as a bath in which the animal is immersed. Generally, fish are subdued within five minutes, or less, after being placed in the bath. Recovery is usually complete and takes only a short time.

Koi keepers have found this anaesthetic very useful when handling large, slippery Koi. The stress of being handled, which an active lively fish would suffer, is greatly reduced and allows easier treatment of an injured or sick fish.

ANASTOMOSING. Describes, botanically, the veins of a plant leaf which curls round to loop into the next and so create a network of intertwined leaves.

ANATOMY OF FISH. Generally, a fish is described in four parts, distinguished as the head, the trunk, the tail (or peduncle), and the fins. The boundary between the head and trunk is determined by the gill opening, and between the trunk and the tail by the vent.

The skeleton basically consists of a backbone which supports the skull, provides an attachment for the ribs and a support for the fins. The vertebrae of the backbone are so arranged that they allow flexibility of the body, especially in the region of the tail. The first four vertebrae are modified to such an extent that they appear to be almost a part of the skull. They have certain curiously shaped elements on each side which provide contact between the ear and the swim-bladder, known as the **Weberian ossicles.** The rear end of the backbone is modified to form the structure of the rays of the **caudal fin.**

The skull is made up of a number of bones. The cranium is a box-like structure in which the brain is contained; a large opening at the back allows the spinal cord to pass out backwards. Other apertures allow egress of the nerves to nasal organs and the eyes. Appended from both sides of the cranium, behind the eye openings, is a chain of bones (the **suspensorium**), and the lower jaw is hinged from the lowest of these bones. The lower jaw consists of three bones on each side; the upper jaw has four bones – a premaxillary on either side and, behind each, a maxillary. They move forwards when the jaw opens.

The eye openings are surrounded externally by a ring of circumorbital bones, which contain channels for certain sensory canals. Behind these, hinged to the cranium, are the gill covers – composed of four flat bones that are plainly visible – known as the **operculum**. The operculum protects and covers the gill cavities, and can be raised and lowered during the process of breathing.

There are five gill arches, four of which support the gills. The first is the **hyoid arch**, and consists of large flat bones that form a strong frame for the gill-cavities. The gill arches also have a series of sabre-shaped bones **(branchiostegal rays)** that open like a fan below the operculum to protect the gills. From the junction of the hyoid arches a bone projects, from near the chin, forward into the mouth to support what may be called the tongue, whilst another bone passes backwards to form a firm connection with the shoulder-girdle. Each gill arch comprises a number of slender bones which are suspended in a chain below the cranium, and are linked together.

The shoulder-girdle consists of the **pectoral arches**, which are attached to the back of the skull on each side and meet below. Each arch is made up of several bones joined together and supports a pectoral fin. Set further back, on the belly, is a pair of **pelvic fins**, supported by two flat pelvic bones. The pelvic bones are not attached directly to any part of the skeleton.

The fins are supported by rays, each ray being built up from short segments of bone which are very flexible. Each ray of the **dorsal**, **caudal** and **anal fins** are actually double and are formed by elements from each side of the body. Most of the rays are branched, but in some fish there may be some which are stiff and spine-like. The fin rays are hinged upon their supporting bones to allow movement in one or more directions.

Moveable bones are bound together with ligaments and generally cushioned against shock by cartilage.

The muscular system is not over-complex, consisting mainly of two muscle masses along each side of the central axis. One mass lies above and the other below the axis and each consists of an upper and lower section. The muscles are in segments known as **myotomes**, the number of segments corresponding to the number of vertebrae. The **dorsal mass** is attached to the back of the skull and extends the full length of the body. The **ventral mass** is weakly developed at the forward end and shows the strongest development in the region of the tail.

The dorsal and anal fins are controlled by a number of small muscles which expand or contract

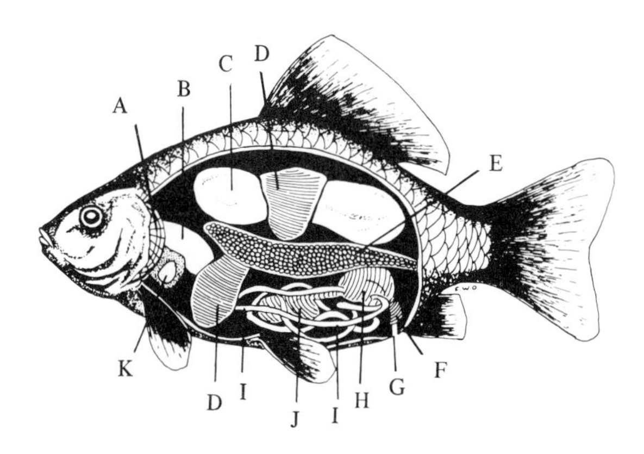

A	Gills	E	Gonad	I	Intestine
B	Gullet	F	Sexual Vent	J	Spleen
C	Swim Bladder	G	Anal Vent	K	Heart
D	Kidney	H	Liver		

Figure 5 **Anatomy of a fish**

the fins. The muscle which controls the expansion, or elevation, is the stronger. Therefore, in a healthy fish the dorsal and anal fins are seldom folded. The caudal fin is controlled by similar muscles which are also used to move the upper and lower rays from side to side. The pectoral fins perform a number of movements and thus the controlling muscles are strong and complex. Those of the pelvic fins are small, merely being required to spread the fin fan-wise.

The muscles of the skull perform a number of functions, such as operating the gill system, moving

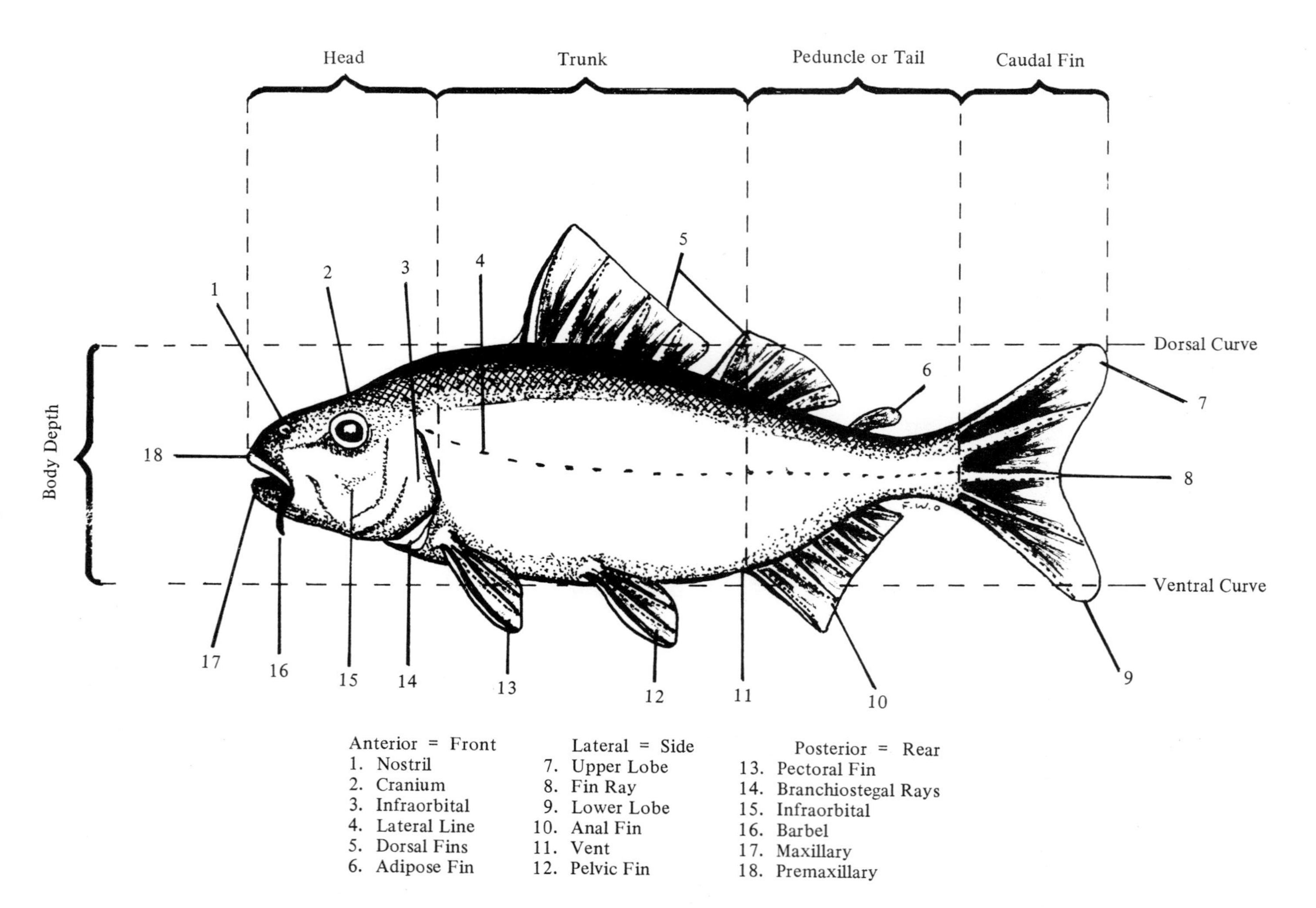

Figure 6 **External Features of Fish**

the eyes, opening and closing the mouth; these muscles are, therefore, quite complicated.

The structure of the eye shows clearly that, when compared to human vision, the fish is short-sighted. Although somewhat similar to the eyes of man they are, however, more globular and have flatter corneas. The outer wall of the eye is formed by a sclerotic coat in the eye socket, and, externally, by the transparent cornea. Behind the cornea is the iris. Light passes through the pupil of the iris to be focussed by the globular lens upon the retina. Adjustment to varying distances is

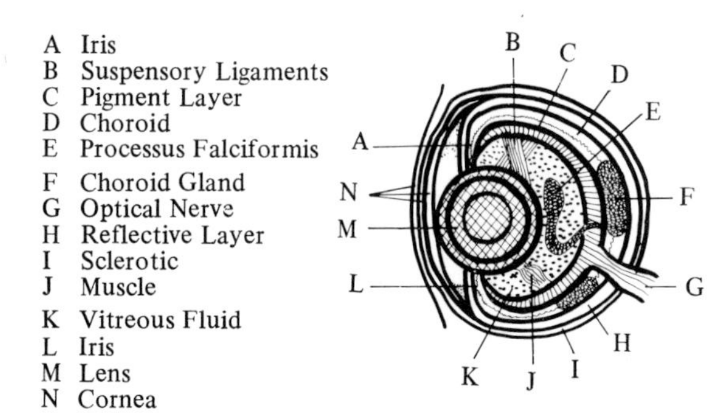

Figure 7 **Eye of a Fish**

accomplished by moving the lens, by means of a special muscle, either nearer or further from the retina.

The organ of smell is not used for respiration, but it does have the faculty of smell, which allows a fish to be attracted or repelled when it is near certain odours.

In fish the external and middle ear are non-existent, and the inner ear consists only of a labyrinth with three semi-circular canals. The vestibule of the labyrinth is delated into one or more sacs that contain the ear-stones, or **otoliths.** This arrangement is connected to the **swim-bladder.** There is no cochlea. Fish cannot hear in the way that man does for their auditory organ is mainly used as a balancing organ. When the labyrinth is damaged or injured, the fish loses its power to balance the body.

Just behind the shoulder girdle lies the liver, a large, dark red gland. Bedded in the liver is the pancreas; its duct enters the intestine close to the bile-duct. Near the stomach is the spleen. The kidneys are long and thin, deep red in colour, immediately below the vertebral column. Their duct (**the ureter**) passes down the back end of the abdominal cavity.

The swim- (or air) bladder lies below the vertebral column at the centre of gravity. It is a membranous sac filled with oxygen, nitrogen and a small amount of carbon dioxide. By adjusting its contents the fish is able to alter its specific gravity, so that it can float at any desired level without difficulty. Not all species are equipped with this organ and, therefore, spend much of their time on the bottom.

The stomach is an extension of the alimentary tract and lies just below the liver; it is connected to the intestine. The intestine occupies a position in the lowest part of the body cavity, and this leads to the anus.

Food is not chewed; fish 'bolt' their food and pass it from the mouth to the gullet. From the gullet it passes through the stomach, where the solid matter is acted upon by an acid medium and various enzymes reduce the food to a liquid state; it then passes into the intestine. Nutritive material is passed into the blood and the indigestible matter is passed out through the anus, a vent just in front of the anal fin.

The blood contains haemoglobin and is, therefore, red in colour. The red blood corpuscles when leaving the heart are deep red (arterial blood), but during the circulatory process the blood gathers carbon dioxide and becomes bluish-red (venous blood).

Venous blood passes through the veins to enter the heart, which is rather small. The heart lies forward in the body, in the **pericardial cavity** (a special chamber), below the gullet. The blood is received into a single auricle, and is pumped out by a single muscular ventricle. The heart, therefore, deals only with venous blood, which is pumped along the ventral aorta, through arteries and spreads out over a large area of the gills. There the red corpuscles discard the carbon dioxide and replace it with oxygen. It is then passed along further arteries into the great dorsal aorta, which lies below the vertebral column and branches off to supply blood to all parts of the body.

Respiration is, in general, accomplished by means of the gills which are highly vascular structures. The blood is circulated over the bronchial almellae and the blood is aerated and re-oxygenated.

The nervous system is a comparatively simple affair. The main centre is the brain, with lobes. From the front lobe (the **presencephalon**), the olfactory nerves pass forward to the nasal organs. On either side is a large optic lobe, giving rise to the optic nerve which is responsible for sight. Below is the **infundibulum**, a lobe from which is suspended the important ductless pituitary gland. Behind the optic lobes, on the upper side, is the **cerebellum**, or hind brain, which co-ordinates muscular activity in response to stimuli received through the senses. Below the cerebellum is the **medulla oblongata**, which enters the spinal chord where it leaves the cranium. In the region of the medulla a similar pair of nerves is situated, above and below, at each vertebral segment. The nerves divide, root-like, to serve all parts of the body in a complex manner.

Nerve fibres either control the muscular response, or they are sensory, conveying stimuli to the brain or other centres.

The reproductive organs consist of ovaries in the female, and testes in the male (hard and soft roe, respectively, as they are sometimes called). The ovaries are yellowish in colour and have a granular texture. The testes have a soft, creamy texture and are much paler in colour. Both ovaries and testes occupy much the same position in the body of the fish, lying just below and behind the swim-bladder. They are paired and elongated in shape, and connected to the kidneys. *See* **Scales,** *and* **Egg, Development of.**

ANCHOR WORM. *See Lernaea cyprinacea.*

ANGIOSPERMAE. Plants characterised by having seeds enclosed in a fruit knot. The larger and more advanced flowering plants which are divided into monocotyledons and dicotyledons.

ANGUILLA. The eel.

ANGUILLARIS. Shaped like an eel.

ANGUILLA VULGARIS. The **Common Eel.** It has a wide distribution and is readily recognised by the elongated, snake-shaped body with an absence of pelvic fins. In British species the vertical fins are confluent with the caudal fin. Most of the eel family are marine; the Common Eel, however, is born in the sea and enters fresh water where it spends the greater portion of its life.

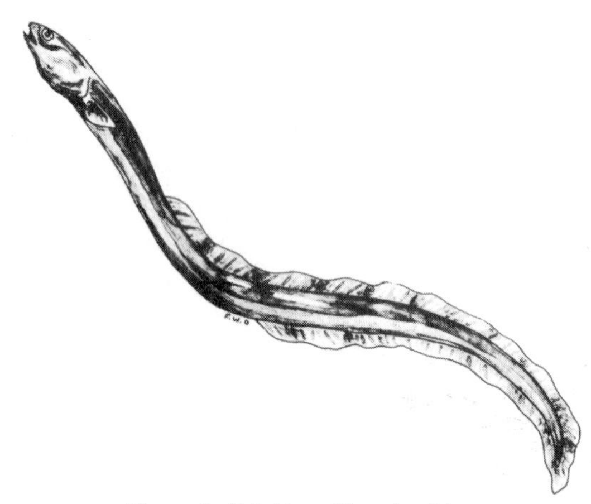

Figure 8 Eel *(Anguilla vulgaris)*

During the summer months tiny eels, or elvers, appear at the mouths of rivers. They are nearly transparent, about 2 inches (51mm) long and as thick as a piece of string. They swarm up the rivers, wriggling over obstacles and at night they will pass over wet grass to reach land-locked waters. They prefer muddy areas where they can hide during the daytime, concealed in the muds, under stones, or hidden in holes and roots of the bank. The young eels grow slowly; after the third summer they are a little over 7 inches (178mm) long. The males reach sexual maturity after about five years; the females mature when around six years old. It is not uncommon for an adult female eel to be 3 feet (0.9m) long and the males about 20 inches (51cm).

There are two colour variations: yellow eels which are the non-migratory eels in their ordinary living conditions; and silver eels, which are eels in their breeding dress. The larger yellow types often have an excessive development of the jaw-muscles.

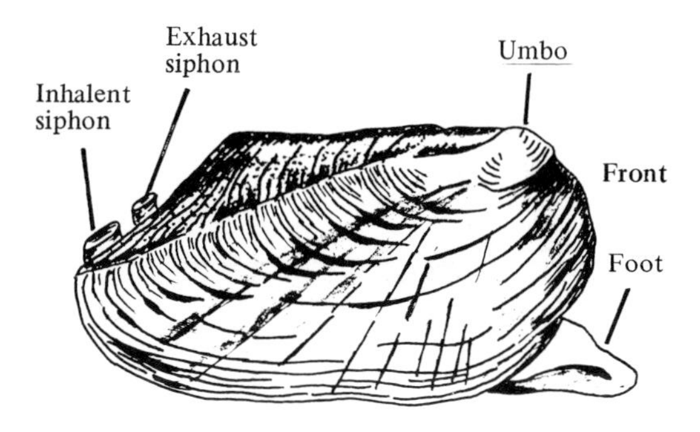

Figure 9 **Anodonata Mussel**

This is due to their extreme voracity, and gives the characteristic appearance which gives rise to such names as Broad-nosed Eel or Frog-mouthed Eel. Mainly they feed at night on such things as worms, crayfish, fish, offal, fish spawn, water birds, rats, voles, frogs and newts.

ANGUILLULA. Micro-worms.

ANIMALCULAE. Microscopic animals.

ANNELIDA. Phylum containing the segmented, ringed or bristle worms. The body is distinguished by externally visible rings, the number is indeterminate. Each segment is self-contained and protected by a tough cuticle. Of interest to the aquarist are the freshwater ***HIRUDINEA*** (leeches) and the ***OLIGOCHAETA,*** which includes the Earthworm. Most annelids are hermaphrodites.

ANNUAL. Living not more than twelve months.

ANODONTA. Pond Mussels.

ANTENNAE. The two feelers which insects carry on their head; they carry the sensory organs of touch and smell.

ANTHER. The, usually enlarged, upper portion of the stamen which contains the pollen.

ANTHOCYANIN. The red, blue and purple pigments contained in the sap of plants.

ANTIBIOTIC. A substance produced by living organisms, such as bacteria and fungi, that inhibits or kills other micro-organisms.

ANUS. The lower orifice (vent) of the digestive tube. *See* **Alimentary Canal.**

APELTES. Genus of North American Four-spined Stickleback, pertaining to ***Gasterosteidae.***

APICULATE. Leaf with small blunt point at its apex.

APODES. Order of bony elongated fishes which includes eels.

AQUARIUM. From the Latin *aqua,* meaning water. Describes an installation, often housed in a special building, used jointly for scientific purposes and to educate the public about life in the water. The term aquarium is also used to describe glass fronted tanks, which allow easy viewing of the contents, containing various forms of water life.

Henry Gosse was the first person to use the word 'aquarium' in 1853. **P. H. Gosse,** ALS., was a pioneer aquarist and author of *A Manual of Marine Zoology.* In 1850 he helped to establish the original aquarium at the gardens of the London Zoological Society. This English naturalist helped to make the keeping of an aquarium popular with the Victorian generation who used it as an instructive parlour ornament.

The modern ornamental home aquariums are available in the form of either moulded, clear plastic tanks or constructions of glass. The latter are the better proposition, being less liable to loss of clarity due to scratching. Although for many years the glass was framed in angle iron, the framed tank has given way to the 'all-glass' type. These are constructed from sheets of glass held together, very strongly, with silicone rubber adhesive. This silicone sealant makes a strong, flexible, water-tight joint and avoids the need for a supporting frame. Such tanks are ideal for use in the home because of their neat appearance. However, the tank should sit upon a cushion of thinnish expanded polystyrene to even out the base pressure. Without this bed, any slightly raised area on the supporting surface could result in the base of the filled aquarium cracking under the pressure of its contents.

Careful consideration should be given to the siting of the aquarium. Coldwater fish and plants benefit from a certain amount of sunlight but too much will encourage an excess of algae to develop. If possible, place the aquarium in a position that will allow about an hour of sunlight to reach the tank. Make sure that whatever is used to support the tank has sufficient strength to withstand, safely, the considerable load which it will have to bear. Furthermore, ensure that it is perfectly level in all directions – nothing is worse than finding that the completed aquarium has a sloping water level.

In general, coldwater fish require reasonably spacious quarters. For instance, the Goldfish should be allowed not less than 24 square inches (155cm^2) of water surface for every inch (25mm) of the fish's body length. The Goldfish would benefit from a larger proportion of the water surface area and, for many other coldwater fish, this is essential. In view of this requirement the coldwater aquarium should be the largest size feasible – certainly no smaller than 24 x 12 x 12 inches (610 x 305 x 305mm).

Apart from the cost of the tank it will be necessary to supply a light hood, together with fittings, in which to house a fluorescent light tube and, preferably, two tungsten light bulbs. Gravel, at the rate of 12lb (5.44kg) per square foot (929cm^2), will be required to give an average depth of 2 inches (51mm) over the base of the aquarium. Although not essential, a water filter will help preserve the clarity of the water. There are basically three types available: undergravel, the inside and the outside. The undergravel filter works upon biological principles and consists of a perforated grid which is buried beneath the gravel. By means of an air-pump water is drawn through the gravel strata into the perforated grid and returned via a discharge pipe – which is also the main tube of the pump-operated air-lift. After a time, provided the filter is run continuously, bacteria form in the gravel and break down the water-borne impurities. Once installed this type of filter requires a minimum of attention.

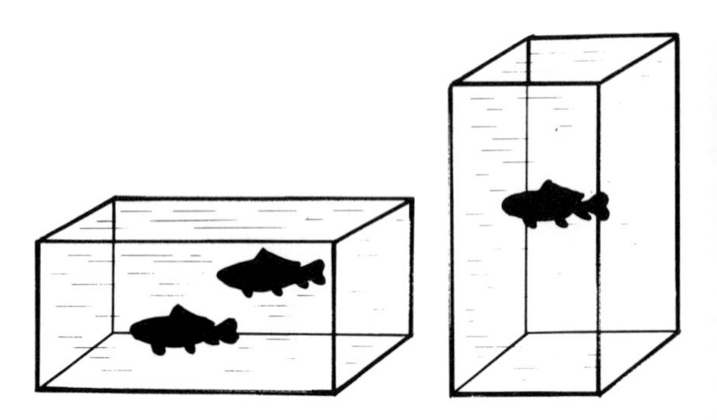

Both tanks are identical in size and water capacity, however, (a) has twice the surface area of (b) which allows it to accommodate twice as many inches of fish.

Figure 10 Water Surface Areas

The inside and outside filters are mechanical types and rely upon the use of materials such as activated carbon and nylon floss. These materials are held in a container that is positioned either inside the aquarium or hung on the outside, hence their respective names. Both types are powered by an air-pump, although there are some outside filters that have a built-in water pump. The designs may differ but the operating principle is the same. A siphon tube draws water from the aquarium into the filter, it then gravitates through the filtering medium; this process removes suspended solids, and the filtered water is then returned to the aquarium. If maximum efficiency is to be maintained the material must be cleaned and/or renewed at regular intervals.

Before assembling the tank it should be cleaned to remove any marks from the surfaces of upright walls; it can then be placed into the position selected for it. If the floor upon which it is to stand is boarded it would be a wise precaution to spread the combined weight of the aquarium and its stand. This can be done by placing it upon two strong battens of sufficient length to span two of the floor joists.

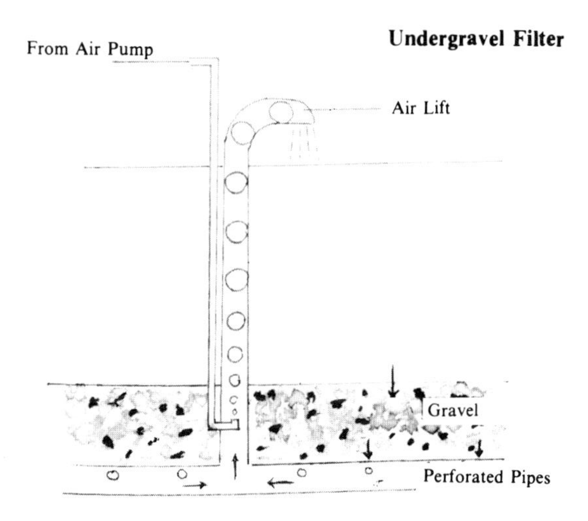

Figure 11 **Airlift Undergravel Filter**

Wash the gravel thoroughly to remove all dust and other unwanted matter, before placing it gently into the tank. Any rocks should be given a good scrub – limestone is not suitable for aquarium use – and if obtained from an underwater situation care should be taken to remove any snails, jelly-like matter, or anything else adhering to the surface. Failure to ensure absolute cleanliness at this stage can lead to future problems.

Spread the gravel evenly, with a downward slope towards the front to facilitate the removal of sediment. Place the rocks, not too many, into position to present a natural and pleasing aspect. After deciding that they are in the best position, gently ease them down into the gravel – nothing looks worse than a badly placed rock sitting on top of the gravel. The aim is to create a natural-looking underwater scene; for this reason divers and other unnatural ornaments should be excluded.

Cover the gravel with a sheet of newspaper and stand a deep plate upon it. Slowly run water into the plate, as it overflows the newspapers will prevent the gravel being swirled about. However, this will not work if the water enters too fast. As the level of the water rises it may be that the paper will rise with it; nevertheless, it will still disperse any water currents to a large extent. When filled to the required level the plate can be lifted out, and the newspapers carefully pulled up and out of the tank without causing too much disturbance.

If the aquarium is now left for a few days, the water will permeate the gravel and pockets of trapped air will manage to escape. It will be noticed that air-bubbles will form on the interior surfaces; these are excess gases, such as oxygen, which will slowly disperse into the atmosphere. During this time any chlorine, which the water may contain, will also slowly dissipate.

Whilst waiting for the water to settle down the time can be spent in obtaining suitable plants (use the real thing, not plastic imitations).

When buying plants go to a reliable dealer, or water garden centre, and try to be sure that they have been raised in coldwater. As with the rocks, the plants will need cleaning irrespective of where they have come from. First swill the individual plants, and at the same time pick off any strands of Blanket Weed. Remove all snails, their eggs and any other jelly-like substance that is noticed. Gently pull off any yellow leaves, together with any dead roots; try to end up with a perfectly clean plant.

Place the plants in clumps and drifts, as would occur in their natural habitat. Use the taller growing varieties to screen the back and side panels of the aquarium. Do not overplant; allow swimming space for the fish. When the plants have taken root they will begin to grow and, if too many are planted at the start, will require thinning to prevent an underwater jungle forming. Quite possibly some plants will refuse to grow in the aquarium; these can be replaced with the thinnings from the more successful groups. Suitable plants may be chosen from the following.

Vallisneria spiralis– A popular grass-like plant that propogates by means of runners. Suitable for background planting. Do not bury the crown; this may cause the plant to rot. There is a twisted variety that does not grow quite so tall.

Sagittaria– There are several types, of which *natans* is possibly the most common. Another grass-like plant that propogates from runners, and again the crown must not be buried. Not so tall growing as *Vallisneria,* it can be given a more central position.

Myriophyllum types– A tall-growing plant with feathery leaves in whorls around a single branching stem. A contrasting plant suitable for the front corners of an aquarium. The tops can be pinched out and replanted to increase the stock.

Ceratophyllum (Hornwort)– This is similar to the above but does not form roots and tends to be brittle. A favourite of many coldwater fishkeepers.

Elodea– A strong-growing plant with a branched single stem. The reflexed narrow leaves give a tube-like appearance to this plant. Also suitable for screening the corner of a tank.

Eleocharis (Hairgrass)– The common name is very descriptive of this plant, which can be planted in front of rocks. If it takes, it will form dense drifts by means of short runners.

Although there are many more plants suitable for the coldwater aquarium (*see* **Plants**), those named are normally easy to obtain and will provide a contrast to each other. The rooted plants should have their roots covered with gravel, but not the growing crown. Cuttings require holding down by means of a small stone, or strip of lead, until they have rooted.

Before starting to place the plants into position, siphon over the gravel to remove any fine sediment that may have settled. Remove approximately half of the water by means of the siphon tube, which will prevent the water slopping over whilst you are placing the plants in their positions. Step back and consider the effect from the front from time to time. If necessary make slight alterations as you proceed until the desired scene of a natural section of underwater life is achieved. It should not be continually fiddled with, so it is important to get it right in the first place. When you are perfectly happy with the picture that you have created, the tank can be refilled. Lay a sheet of newspaper on the water surface and gently pour water on to this. When full, remove the paper as before, by sliding it slowly out of the water.

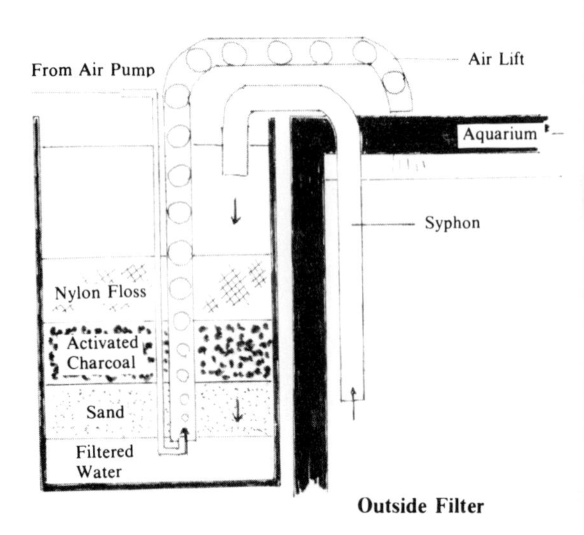

Figure 12 **Airlift Outside Filter**

Cover the tank with a sheet of glass, to keep out dust and prying fingers (or cat's paws), and set the lights in their hood. If the plants are to grow they will need light and electricity provides the most easily controlled source.

There are fluorescent light tubes manufactured specifically for use with aquaria – ordinary household tubes have not proved satisfactory. The length of the tube should match, almost, the length of the tank to provide the correct light intensity. Try to incorporate two 20 watt tungsten bulbs if possible, as these appear to encourage the plants. Initially, observe the results of illuminating the tank for ten hours each day, over a period of a week or so. If the plants start to turn yellow and die it indicates insufficient light. Remedy by either increasing the wattage of the bulbs or extending the hours of artificial light. If, however, algae starts to form too rapidly it is proof that the tank is receiving too much light, the answer is to reduce the period during which the lights are switched on. Observation, and manipulation of the intensity and hours of illumination, will eventually provide the correct combination for the position which the

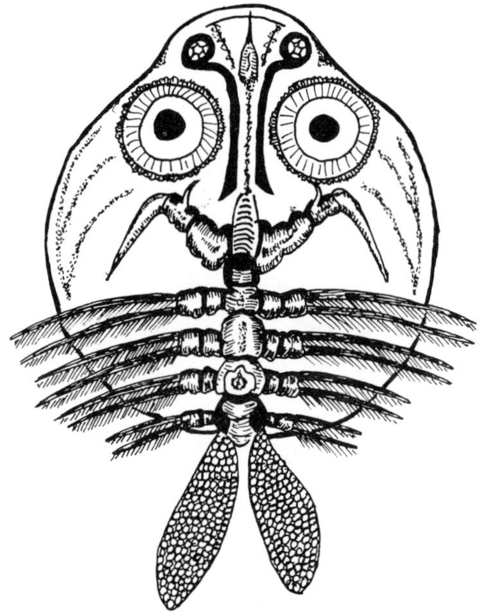

Figure 13 **Fish Louse** *(Argulus)*

aquarium occupies, to the benefit of both fishes and plants.

In order to preserve the healthy state of the aquarium it should have the bottom siphoned over at regular intervals, to remove any sediment. At the same time up to one-third of the water can be replaced – making sure that it is approximately the same temperature as that in the aquarium.

ARENACEOUS. Sandy; sandlike.

ARGULUS. The Fish Louse. This, however, is not a louse despite its common name, it is a copepod. They are disc-shaped, flatish and somewhat oval in outline; perfectly formed for remaining attached to their fish host.

On the underside are large suckers which enable them to take a firm grip on the fish. The compound eyes are very conspicuous. Set between the suckers is a poison spine and there is also a proboscis through which they take the flesh and blood of their victim; There are four pairs of feather-edged limbs for swimming which are constantly in motion. Due to their thin and translucent body they are difficult to see when attached to their host, even though they can grow to about ⅓ inch (8mm) in length. They lay their oval eggs on stones or similar solid surfaces during July and August.

ARGYRONETA AQUATICA. The Water Spider. Usually found in still waters with heavy growth of underwater vegetation.

ARTEMIA SALINA. The Brine Shrimp. The newly hatched nauplii are used extensively as a first food for Goldfish fry. *See* **Brine Shrimp.**

ARTHROPODA. Comprises around 85% of the world's species of animals. It is characterised by having a segmented body with an external skeleton of hard chitinous armour. There are twelve classes which includes the ***CRUSTACAE.***

ASAGI. *See* **Koi.**

ASCHELMINTHES. The phylum which includes rotifers.

ASSIMILATION. The process by which animals and plants convert and absorb nutriment. This activity by aquarium plants is important since these give off oxygen whilst absorbing carbon dioxide. Unless the plants receive sufficient light they will stop assimilating and, instead, will make use of the oxygen that is so essential for the well-being of the fish.

ASTACUS. *See* **Crayfish.**

AURATUS. Golden coloured.

AXILLARY. Pertaining to flowers and leaves, i.e. the axil is the angle where a leaf joins the stem.

AXIS. The main or central line of development of a plant – the stem.

B

BACILLUS. General term for rod-shaped bacteria.

BACK-CROSS. Breeding a hybrid with its parent.

BACKSWIMMER. Another name for the Water-boatman. *See* **Water Bugs.**

BACTERIA. These are the smallest living organisms and are single-celled. Their structure consists of a central protoplasm around which is a membrane. Most bacteria are incapable of voluntary movement and must rely upon wind or water. However, some are capable of self-propulsion through a liquid by means of tiny threads called 'flagella', which they lash vigorously to impart motion.

Bacteria may be **parasitic** and live on live vegetation or animals; **saprophytic** bacteria feed on dead animals and vegetation. In both cases the food is broken down by using ferments, or enzymes, which they produce. They can thus obtain the material they require and convert it into other substances which they release. The food material is absorbed in solution through the membrane. The first stage of breaking down the dead matter is to convert it into carbon dioxide, water, ammonia and various ammonium compounds. Other bacteria then oxidise the ammonia into nitrites whilst others oxidise the nitrites into nitrates, which then become available as plant food.

Most bacteria require oxygen to maintain their life. Under certain conditions the decomposition of the organic matter by anaerobic bacteria will result in the production of sulphurated hydrogen accompanied by the familiar smell of rotten eggs. Methane gas may also be produced, causing bubbles to rise to the surface.

BACTERIOLOGY. The study of bacteria.

BARBEL. Common name for *Barbus barbus,* a member of the ***Cyprinidae*** family. Barbel is derived from the Latin *barbellus* meaning a beard. *See under* ***Cyprinidae.***

BARBELS. Fleshy whiskers, usually appended near the mouth of a fish, which carry taste buds. Barbels are usually a characteristic of bottom-feeding fish, making it easier for them to locate food.

BATRACHIAN. Term at one time used to describe amphibians.

BEETLE. Including some 3,700 species, this is one of the most numerous of insects; it is found in a wide range of habitats.

BIENNIAL. A plant which completes its life cycle in two years.

BIFID. Botanical term meaning deeply divided into two.

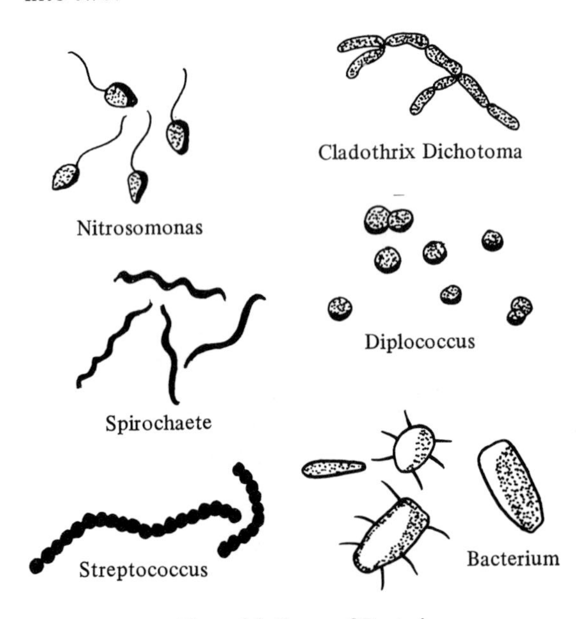

Figure 14 **Types of Bacteria**

BIFURCATED. Forked into two branches.

BIOLOGY. The study of living organisms.

BIOMASS. The total weight of live organisms in a given area.

BIOTA. The fauna and flora of a district.

BIOTYPE. Having equal genetic make-up.

BISEXUAL. Containing both sexes; hermaphrodite.

BITTERLING. *See* ***Rhodeus amarus.***

BIVALVIA. Shell fishes. *See* **Mollusc.**

BLACK-BANDED SUNFISH. Common name for *Mesogonistius. See under* ***Centrarchidae.***

BLADDER SNAIL. (*Physa fontinalis*). Freshwater snail with fragile oval shell. *See* **Mollusc.**

BLADDERWORT (*Utricularia*). Free-floating insectivorous plant furnished with small bladders that capture small creatures.

BLANKET WEED. Common collective name for various filamentous algae that form into masses.

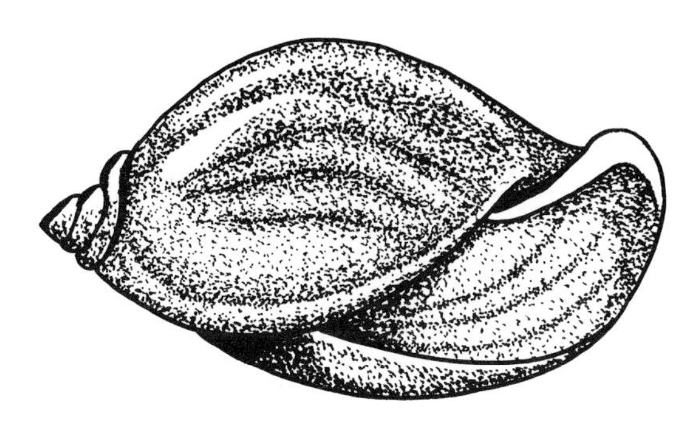

Figure 15 **Bladder Snail** *(Physa fontinalis)*

BLASTOCOELE. The cavity formed within the mass of cells in the egg towards the end of the cleavage period. *See* **Egg, Development of.**

BLASTOMERE. A cell formed during the cleavage period of the fertilized egg. *See* **Egg, Development of.**

BLASTULA. A hollow ball of cells in the embryonic development at the end of cleavage just before gastrulation. *See* **Egg, Development of.**

BLEAK. *Alburnus lucidus. See under* ***Cyprinidae.***

BLOODWORM. Larva of Chironomid midges, bright red in colour, which swims with a figure-of-eight action. Found amongst the debris at the bottom of still-water. *See* **Midges.**

BLUEGILL. Common name for *Lepomis macrachirus. See under* ***Centrarchidae.***

BOG. An area of wet, acid peat-land.

BOGBEAN. Common name for *Menyanthes trifoliata.* An aquatic plant found in acid waters and boggy ground. With trifoliate leaves, it carries conspicuous white flowers. It is a perennial growing from a thick, creeping root-stock. *See* **Plants.**

BRACKISH. Water containing salt.

BRANCHIURA. Class of Crustacean parasites of which *Argulus* is a member.

BRANDYBOTTLE. Common name for *Nymphaea luteum.* This yellow water-lily is so-called because of its flaggon-like seed vessel.

BREAM. *Abramis brama. See under* ***Cryprinidae.***

BRINE SHRIMP. *Artemia salina.* Small crustacean generally present in most of the larger salt lakes of the world. However, the largest proportion of Brine Shrimp eggs which are offered commercially come from the U.S.A. A curious fact is that, despite its need for salt, this creature is not found in any of the oceans.

The adult shrimp grows to a length of about ½ inch (13mm). It has a shortish head and the trunk is made up of fifteen segments. The colour is pale pink to red, being darker according to the strength of the salt concentration in the water. Males are relatively rare. Generally reproduction occurs through parthenogenesis. The eggs are about the size of fine grains of sand and have the ability to remain viable, in a dry state, for many years; they are hard-shelled and do not swell when placed in water.

The very small, newly hatched Brine Shrimps are used extensively in the feeding of small fish fry until the latter reach a size that enables them to accept larger types of food. Hatching should always be carried out in a non-metallic vessel –

glass is most suitable – because the salt will react with the metal. Roughly 2 oz (5.6 g) of cooking or marine salt should be mixed into each quart (1.36 litres) of water. If possible, provide weak aeration to prevent the eggs settling. The rate of hatching depends upon the water temperature; the higher it is the quicker the hatch. The nauplii should be strained through a fine-mesh cloth before feeding to fry, and swilled to remove any salt.

BRISTOL SHUBUNKIN. *See* **Fancy Goldfish.**

BUBBLE-EYE. *See* **Fancy Goldfish.**

BUCKBEAN. Another name for Bogbean.

BULL-HEAD. Common name applied to the *Cottidae.* The Miller's Thumb is the only freshwater representative of these fishes. ***See Cottus gobio.***

BURBOT. *See* ***Lota Vulgaris.***

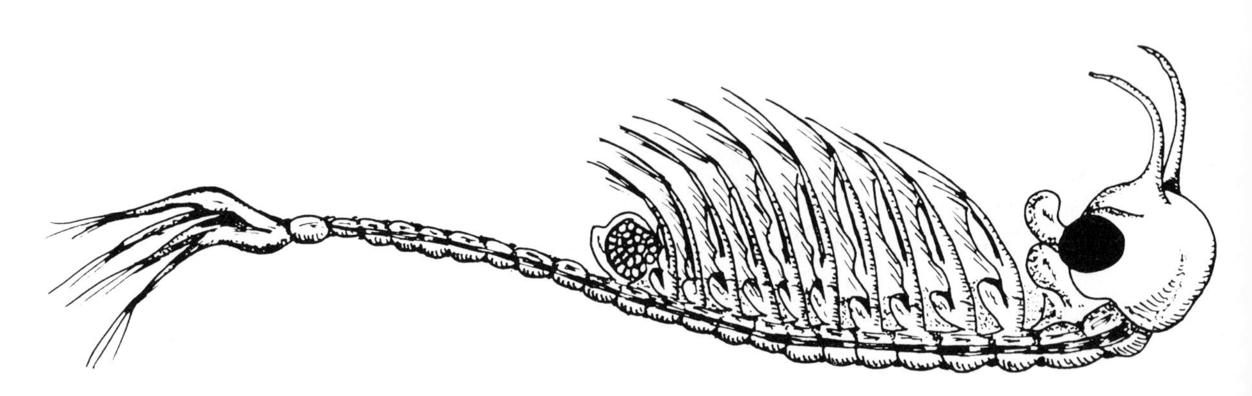

Figure 16 **Brine Shrimp** *(Artemia salina)*

C

C. Often used as an abbreviation for the caudal fin.

CADDIS-FLY. A winged, moth-like insect; there are 188 species in ten families. The larvae are aquatic and attach themselves to plants, stone and such-like, where they conceal themselves in silken tubes for protection. Fish consume both the adult and larval forms.

CAESPITOSE. Botanical term meaning tufted.

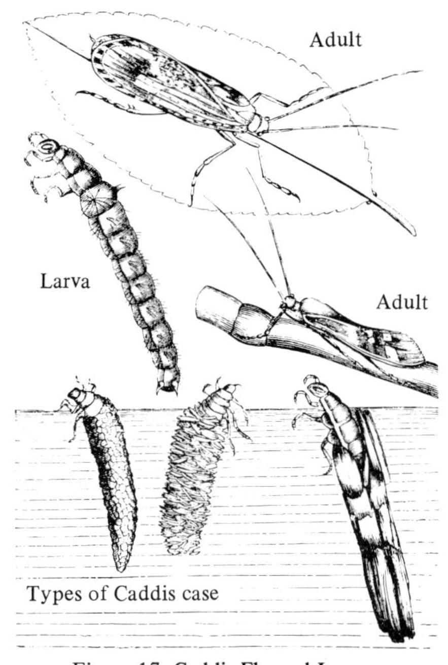

Figure 17 **Caddis-Fly and Larvae**

CALCAREOUS. Containing chalk or lime.

CALLA PALUSTRIS. The Marsh Marigold. With a thick, creeping root-stock, it has buttercup-yellow flowers and broad, heart-shaped leaves. Grows in marshy areas and very shallow water. *See* **Plants.**

CALLITRICHACEAE. Perennial water plants which form dense mats. The delicate light-green, narrowly linear leaves are arranged opposite each other around the stem. Small white flowers are borne above the water surface. *See under* **Plants.**

CALYX. The outer whorl of flower parts, usually green.

CARASSIUS. Pertaining to the Carp-like fishes. *See **Cyprinidae.***

C. auratus– The Goldfish. *See **Cyprinidae** also* **Fancy Goldfish.**

C. carassius– The Crucian Carp. *See **Cyprinidae.***

CARBON DIOXIDE. CO_2. Slightly acid, odourless gas, colourless, and will not ignite. Exhaled by living animals, it serves as a food for plants. However, it is harmful to animal life if inhaled in large quantities.

CARDAMINE LYRATA. An aquatic plant of the family CRUCIFERAE. *See* **Plants.**

CARP. *Cyprinus carpio. See under **Cyprinidae.*** **Carp family**: ***Cyprinidae.*** **Carp-like**: *Cyprinoidae.*

CARPEL. A unit of the pistil, in a flower; it consists of an ovary which is usually surmounted by a stalk, known as the style, and tipped by the stigma. The stigma is fertilized with pollen to produce the seeds.

CATFISH. Two freshwater families that, whilst being of interest to the aquarist, are better kept out of the ornamental pond because of their predacious habits.

Ameiuridae– Family of Catfish from North America. It is fish from this family which are usually available, as young specimens, from pet dealers. Most common of these is the American Catfish (*Ameiurus nebulosus*) which can grow to a length of 18 inches (46cm). It has a broad flattened head and the body is naked, without scales or bony plates. It is cylindrical and laterally compressed towards the rear, with a very slimy skin. The first dorsal fin consists of a strong spiny ray and six to seven soft rays. Set further back is an adipose fin. The first ray of the pectoral fin is a hard spiny ray, which is capable of giving a nasty wound to the unwary handler and usually takes some time to heal. A characteristic of the species are the eight barbels around the mouth: four situated on the upper jaw and four on the lower jaw. The uppermost two barbels stand close behind the nostrils and are as long as those on the lower jaw. The lower two barbels of the upper jaw are

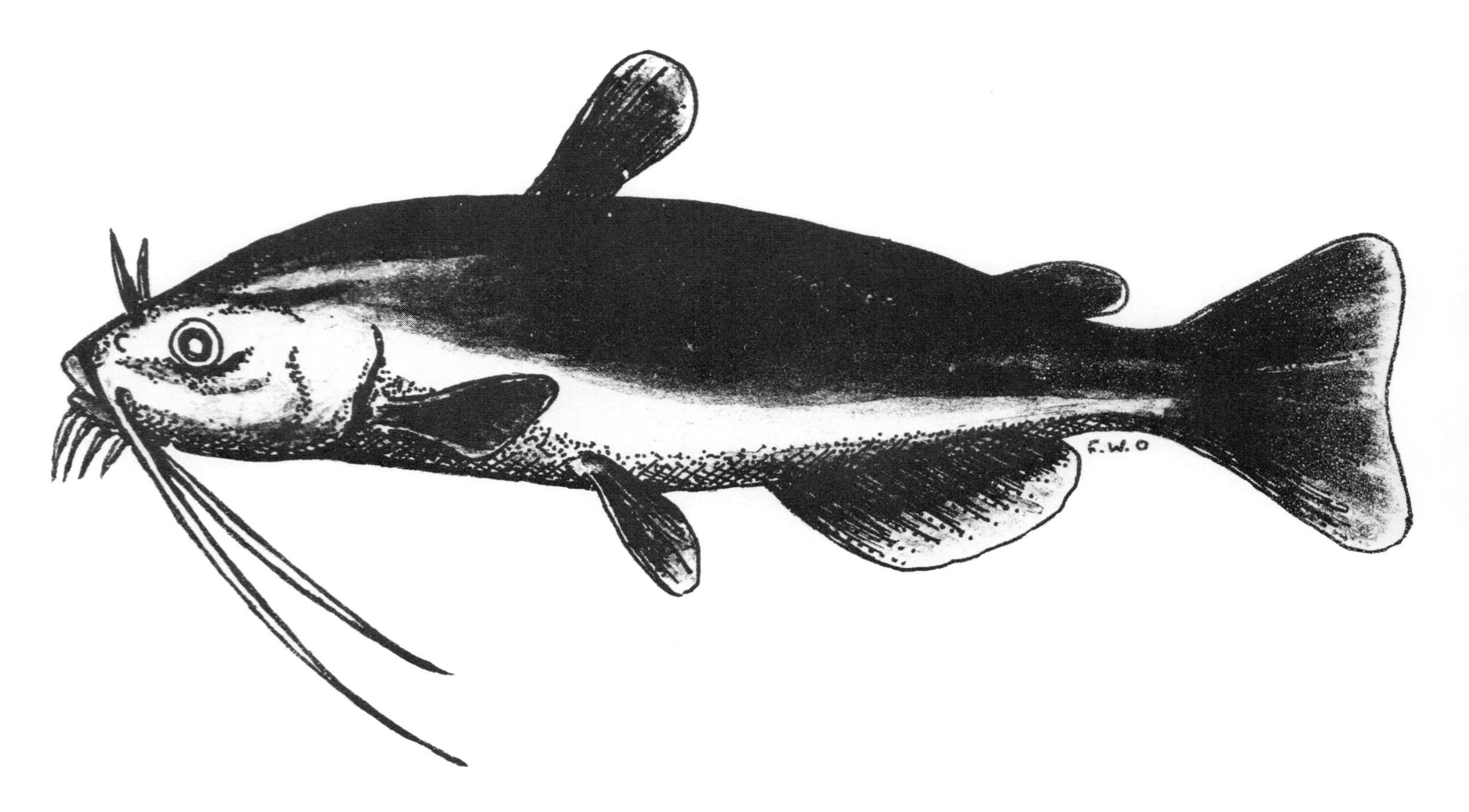

Figure 18 **North American Catfish** *(Ameiurus nebulosus)*

located at the corners of the mouth, they are long and can reach the base of the pectoral fins. The barbels are well equipped with taste buds, which help the fish to find its food. The mouth is terminal and has a wide opening which enables fairly large prey to be swallowed. The jaws are furnished with numerous small teeth.

The colour of the fish varies from greyish-brown to black with a greenish shimmer to the sides. The belly is dirty white to yellowish. The iris of the eye is golden.

Normally a bottom-dwelling fish it does, at times, swim near the surface. It is principally a nocturnal fish, spending much of the daylight hours hidden in holes and similar places of concealment.

These Catfish are very short-sighted, however, they have well developed hearing. They are also capable of intestinal breathing, which allows them to live in waters with a low oxygen content where other fish would die.

Their diet is omnivorous, but they will prey upon any fish smaller than themselves – for this reason they should be kept with fish of their own size, or larger. They will quickly adapt to life in a large aquarium and become quite tame. Feeding presents few problems if they are fed plentifully with solid foods. Earthworms and small fish will satisfy their predatory instincts.

The aquarium should not be too clean, and they like a good layer of mulm over the gravel bed. Plenty of hiding places should be provided into which the fish can retreat. The plants should be capable of withstanding rough treatment; *Sagittarias* and *Vallisneria* are probably the most suitable. It is advisable to employ strong filtration to prevent the water being excessively clouded by their habit of stirring up the mulm. Heating is not necessary and they are not in the least particular about the pH or hardness of the water.

The fish is also known as *Ictalurus nebulosus,* the common name in America being the Brown Bull-head.

Silurus glanis– The European Catfish or Wels. Young specimens may be offered for sale in pet shops during the spring and summer, and appear quite harmless to the unwary. At first glance it resembles the Burbot, but it can be distinguished by its short dorsal fin. The body is rounded, with a small single dorsal fin and a very long anal fin, a broad head and a wide mouth with six long barbels. It is actively predacious and grows to a large size; it is the largest of European freshwater fish.

CAUDAL. The tail fin.

CAUDATA. Order of tailed amphibians which includes newts. *See* **Amphibians.**

CELESTIAL. *See* **Fancy Goldfish.**

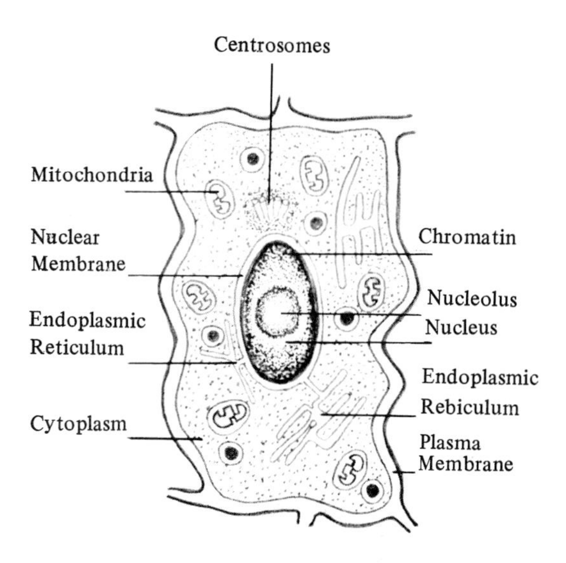

Figure 19 **Typical Animal Cell**

CELL. A live formation made up of a mixture of viscous substances containing protein which is surrounded by a skin, or by a bordering layer of protoplasm. Of especial interest, and importance, is the presence of one or more bubble-shaped bodies, the nuclei, within the cell.

The functions of a cell are manifold, more so in unicellulars than in multicellulars. The functions are, however, characteristic of all cells and consist of reaction to stimuli, metabolism of substances and energies and changes of shape. Also characteristic of cells are certain substances, the so-called nuclear acids, which exert a decisive influence on the development of body substances and reproduction. In the higher forms of life they are found in the nucleus, especially in the chromosomes.

Multicellular organisms grow by the multiplication of cells, which takes place by cellular division. This ingenious process results in an equal distribution of the cellular mass to the newly formed cells. The simplest form of cellular division is that of strangling the cell in two **(amitosis)**.

Figure 20 **Sunfish**

A more complex process **(mitosis)** is preceded by changes in the nucleus. First the chromosomes, which are invisible in the nucleus, becomes visible; this is the **prophasis** stage. The next phase **(prometaphasis)** is when the nuclear plasm gives origin to a nuclear axis, giving an impression that the chromosomes are tied to threads. The chromosomes, which are always composed of two equal parts, then range themselves on the equatorial plain in a nuclear or equatorial plate **(metaphasis)**. After splitting lengthways the chromosomes migrate to the poles in equal parts, in other words one half goes to the upper pole and the other half goes to the lower pole. Each pole now possesses an equal group of chromosomes. These draw together and form new nuclei at the poles, while the nuclear axis dissolves **(telophasis)**. At the same time a new wall develops between the two new nuclei so that the one cell becomes two, both having the same number of chromosomes.

CENTRARCHIDAE. Sunfishes. Perch-like fish of North America, especially abundant in the rivers and ponds of the Eastern U.S.A., with a pugnacious disposition. Although carnivorous they are capable of adapting themselves to life in the aquarium.

Often brilliantly coloured, they are active but quarrelsome. Many of the species will interbreed and this has given rise to a number of hybrids. During breeding, pits are dug and vigorously defended against all intruders. Shallow water that is no deeper than 12 inches (30.5cm) seems to be preferred. After having prepared the pit in the gravelly bed, the male will entice a female by putting on a courting display. His colours become brighter as he shivers and quivers to attract the female. After a time he will escort his partner to the spawning site where, hovering side by side over the pit with abdomens almost touching, they will deposit and fertilize the eggs. After spawning, the eggs will be constantly guarded and the young raised with care. Depending upon the water temperature, hatching can take place in as little as forty-eight hours. The fry will only take small live foods – in the aquarium this can be newly hatched Brine Shrimps followed by screened Daphnia.

In the domestic environment of the aquarium there should be a plentiful supply of plant growth – to provide a refuge for any fish which requires it – and the fish should all be of similar size to avoid any undue bullying; they should also be kept with their own kind. Of those types of sunfish that are known the following are perhaps the most popular:

Elassoma evergladei– The **Pigmy Sunfish**, which is native to the region from North Carolina down to Florida, is an extremely hardy fish that reaches an adult size of 1½ inches (38mm). Two similar species, *E. zonatum* and *E. akefenakee*, are sometimes collected in the same area. The latter is the more colourful of the three.

Lepomis macrachirus– The **Bluegill** of the Eastern States, which reaches a length of around 6 inches (152mm). A hardy fish.

Mesogonistius chaetodon– The **Black-banded Sunfish.** A handsome fish that is found in the New Jersey and Florida areas. The adult reaches a size of around 2½ inches (64mm).

CENTRARCHUS. Spiny anal fin.

CENTROSOME. A minute body, within the cytoplasm, which initiates cell division. *See* **Egg, Development of.**

CERATOPHYLLUM. Genus of perennial aquatic plants belonging to the family of Hornworts. *See* **Plants.**

C. demersum– The most common species of Hornwort. *See* **Plants.**

CESTODA. Tapeworms.

CHAR. *See* **Koi.**

CHAR GOI. *Salvelinus. See under* ***Salmonidae.***

CHILODON(ELLA). Pertaining to the **Ciliates** and causing discoloration of the skin of fishes. The genus consists of a number of unicellular species. The species can be found on all freshwater fish, including tadpoles. Usually it is weakened fish that are infected through transmission from other infected fish.

CHITIN. A hard shell-like armour which contains nitrogen, and is very resistant to acids and alkali. It forms the covering of such creatures as Daphnia and arthropods.

CHLORINE. A pungent smelling greenish-yellow gas, which is added to domestic water supplies for reasons of public health. It acts corrosively upon the mucous tissue of fish. Cold water will retain chlorine longer than warm water, but the gas can be eliminated by allowing the water to stand for a few days. The process is speeded up by continuous artificial agitation of the water, or chemical methods may be used. Much of the chlorine can be removed by forcing the water into a strong jet, when filling an aquarium, which will cause the chlorine gas to separate – as the smell will confirm.

CHLOROPHYCEAE. Green algae.

CHLOROPHYL. The green colour pigment of nearly all plants.

CHLOROPLASTS. Round bodies, usually green, present in vegetable cells. They assist assimilation of carbon dioxide. Their contents consist of chlorophyl, proteins and lipoids.

CHLOROSIS. A condition of plants in which the leaves turn yellowish. Usually due to a lack of iron, magnesium, or other mineral salts.

CHORDATA. The most advanced phylum comprising animals that possess, at least in the embryo stage, a notochord which is the skeletal rod or chord of the early backbone.

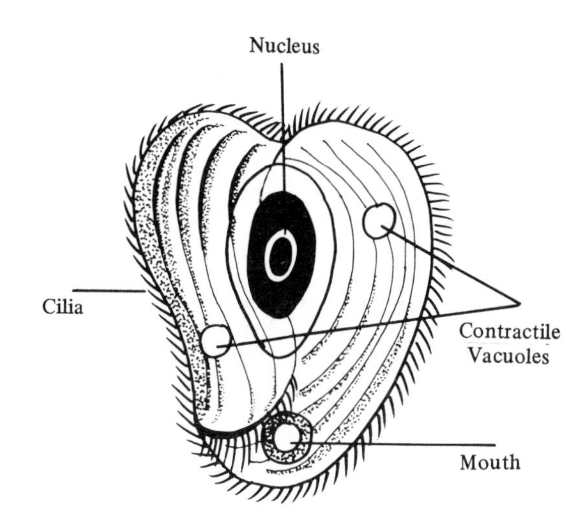

Figure 21 **Chilodon**

CHROMATIN. Constituent of a chromosome.

CHROMATOPHORE. A cell with pigment in its cytoplasm, changing its concentration or dispersion and so altering the colouration of a fish.

CHROMOSOME. The protein thread of the nucleus which carries the **genes.** They are responsible for hereditary characteristics.

CHUB. *Leuciscus cephalus. See under* ***Cyprinidae.***

CILIA. Small, motile hairs which can be used for locomotion or feeding. Common to many organisms, especially unicellulars.

CILIATE. An infusorian which has a body covered with cilia.

CLADOCERAN. Crustaceans that include Daphnia and other water-fleas.

CLASS. A group within the classification.

CLASSIFICATION. All living things, from the lowest to the highest, are scientifically classified into groups of similar kinds. The classification is applied in a descending order, the lowest being the individual specific type, as follows: **Phylum; Class; Order; Family; Genus**; and finally the **Species.**

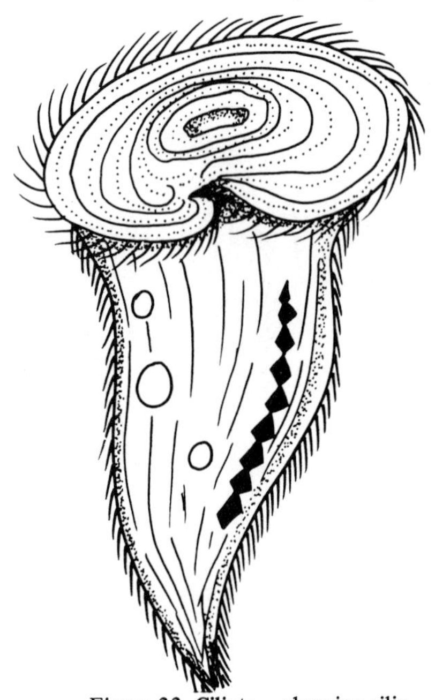

Figure 22 **Ciliate** – showing cilia

CLEAVAGE. Division of the fertilized egg into many cells which become ever smaller as cleavage progresses. *See* **Egg, Development of.**

CLINE. A gradual and continuous change in the character of either animal or plant population over an area, so that the characteristics at the beginning are greatly different to those at the end of the cline.

CLOUDY WATER. Cloudiness of water may be due to several causes. Pollution by industrial, or other sewage, outflows will lead to a proliferation of conditions that are inimical to most forms of life. These evil conditions may result in foul-smelling water of varying colours, a thick silty ooze deposit on the bed and other underwater surfaces – this will often have its colour influenced by the causitive agent, a complete lack of plant and animal life and a super abundance of bacteria.

In the aquarium and decorative pond, when freshly set-up, there may be some clouding during the early days due to the action of bacteria and unicellulars, but this will normally disappear when a state of equilibrium has been established. During the early part of the year, as the hours of daylight lengthen, free-floating algae may turn the water of an outdoor pond green. However, as the submerged plants re-establish themselves the water should begin to clear.

Water which has a slight milky appearance is polluted and is very often the result of over-feeding – although other factors may also give rise to this condition – and can quickly become a dangerous medium for any fishes. To avoid losses the water should be changed and care taken, in future, that any artificial foods are fed sparingly.

Clouding may be due to the fishes stirring the sediment and this will generally re-settle; a filter will help to avoid this situation.

COBITIDAE. The loaches. A small group related to the Carp family, and sharing many of their characteristics, such as the single dorsal fin, toothless mouth and soft fin rays. There are two British species, both similar in habit and appearance. Both are small, with elongated bodies, very small scales which are rather difficult to see, six barbels, smallish eyes, an indistinct lateral line and a mottled body with small fins that are mottled or striped with dark markings. Both frequent the clean bottom bed of small clear streams, although they may also be found in other types of freshwater habitat. They tend to avoid the light, usually lurking under a stone or stick waiting for their prey. They are very hardy and can be kept in an aquarium. They occasionally gulp air as an additional form of respiration.

Cobitis barbatula– The **Stone Loach.** Perhaps the most common of the group, being found almost everywhere in the British Isles. In colour it is brownish or a greyish green, and has a white belly. It has six barbels, two of which are longer than the others. It reaches a length of around 3–4 inches (76–102mm) and spends much of its time hidden under a stone, so justifying its name.

Cobitis taenia– The **Spiny Loach.** Much less common than the preceding fish. It is smaller than the Stone Loach, seldom reaching a length of more than 3 inches (76mm). A rather regular row of darker spots mark the sides of the pale brown body. A double-pointed spine on the snout fits into a little groove below the eyes when it rests. The body is somewhat more flattened than in the previous species, and the six barbels are all of equal length.

Loach feed upon vegetable matter, small larvae, worms and crustacae. Spawning takes place during the late spring.

COLEOPTERA. Pertaining to the sub-phylum HEXAPODA, or insects. They possess fore-wings, usually in the form of hard wing-covers and have freely articulated heads with strong oral organs, often masticatory. They also have well-developed faceted eyes. Water beetles and their larvae are well adopted to life in the aquatic environment.

COLOUR IN FISH. Despite the variety of colours which are exhibited by different species of fish, which make them amongst the most colourful of animals, it is strange that they carry absolutely no green or blue pigments.

The colour pigments are relatively large cells in the dermis, of irregular, ramified shape, containing pigment inside themselves. The **melamines** are of a grainy structure and produce the colours of black, blue-black and blackish-brown. The red and yellow pigments are produced by the **lipochromes**, which are liquid.

The many colours exhibited by fishes are created by an association of the other colours with shiny crystals, showing through the upper layers of the dermis which look yellowish. The delicate metallic colours are the result of mirroring crystals (*see* **Guanin**) bedded in the second layer of the dermis. This explains why some fishes seem to change colour according to the angle of the light which strikes them. The hues are especially vivid when the guanin crystals lie very near to the surface. If they lie beneath the scales, where they form a silver layer, they either produce a silvery glitter or, if overlaid with colour cells, the beautiful luminous colours which are so admired in many freshwater tropical fishes.

Figure 23 **Stone Loach** *(Cobitis barbatula)*

COMET. *See* **Fancy Goldfish.**

COMMON GOLDFISH. *See* **Fancy Goldfish.**

COMPLAINTS OF FISHES. The following lists various maladies which may affect fishes; it also gives suggested treatments. Some of the causitive agents are listed, in greater detail, elsewhere in this book. *See* **Diseases of Fishes.**

Large fish may need to be subdued, to prevent thrashing, before being treated for some complaints. *See* **Anaesthetic.**

Fungus *(Saprolegnia).* A cotton-woolly fungus which attacks weak or wounded fishes. The fungus spores are present in all waters but will not infect a healthy fish. The individual fungus threads grow into the skin like roots. Treat by giving the fish a thirty minute bath in a solution of 5 oz (142g) of salt (not table salt) to each gallon of water. Repeat each day until cured. Alternatively give the fish a long-term bath in water containing **phenoxethol.** First prepare a stock solution of 1cc of phenoxethol well mixed into 9cc of water. Sufficient stock solution should be made to allow 90cc to be stirred into each gallon of water.

Leave the fish in the bath until cured.

Figure 24 **A fish infected with Dropsy**

Cataract of the eye– There are two forms. Firstly *Cataracta traumatica* – characterised by a whitish film covering the lens of the eye. In this case the eye should be painted with a solution of 50-50 iodine and water to which nine parts of glycerine has been added. The second form, *Cataracta parasitica,* appears at first glance to be very similar to the foregoing. However, inspection through a magnifying lens will reveal the film to be composed of tiny white spots. In reality the dots are little worms which feed upon the lens and destroy it. Worm cataracts are due to the larvae of sucking worms. The adult parasite lives in water-birds and the eggs are discharged with droppings into the water. After hatching in the water, the resulting *miracidiae* enter the body of a snail, where they change shape and become *sporocysts.* After a time the larvae leave the snail's liver to move into the water. Upon meeting a fish the larvae enter its body and migrate to the eye. Try curing in the phenoxethol bath, as detailed for fungus.

Argulus (Fish Louse)– A well known parasite, which can be introduced into aquarium or pond with live Daphnia. It is a large creature and can be removed with forceps, or rubbed off.

Flukes– There are two types: the **Gill Fluke** *(Dactylogyrus)* which infests the gills and causes the fish to increase its breathing rate. The gills become pale and tend to be stretched very open. Fish affected by the **Skin Fluke** *(Gyrodactylus)* will tend to lose colour, the fins droop, the skin becomes very slimy and may show blood spots.

Treat against both forms as follows: prepare a solution of 10 parts of ammonia to 90 parts water. Take 45cc of this solution and mix into a gallon of water. Bathe the fish for no more than twenty minutes. It should then be placed into a container of clean water to recuperate. Disinfect the original container or, alternatively, leave it empty of fishes for four weeks. During this time the parasites should die.

Lernea (Anchor Worm)– A thread-like creature which attaches itself to the body of fishes. It should not be pulled off because the head will remain in the fish and fester. Instead, touch the parasite with a fine brush that has been dipped in a strong solution of potassium permanganate. This should kill the creature and it can then be removed. Treat the wound with iodine, as described for cataracts, and place the fish in a clean container. The infected container must be disinfected, or left empty of fish, to ensure that the pests die.

Leeches– Place the fish in a salt bath (*see* **Fungus**). This should make the leech loosen its grip and it can then be removed and killed in boiling water. Treat the wound with iodine solution (*see* **cataracts**). An infested pond must be allowed to dry-out for some time to ensure that

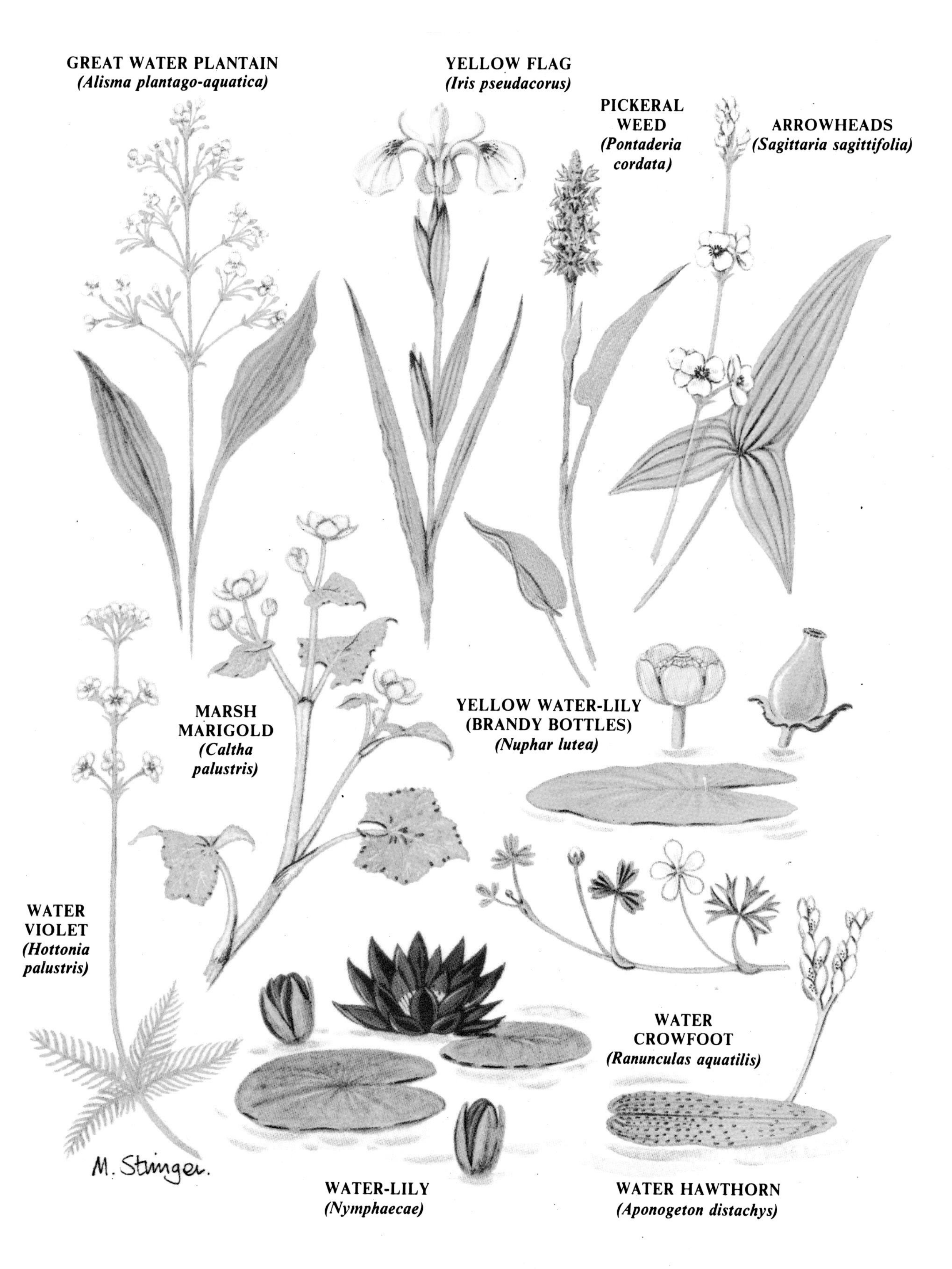

Plate 1 Plants found in or near Ponds

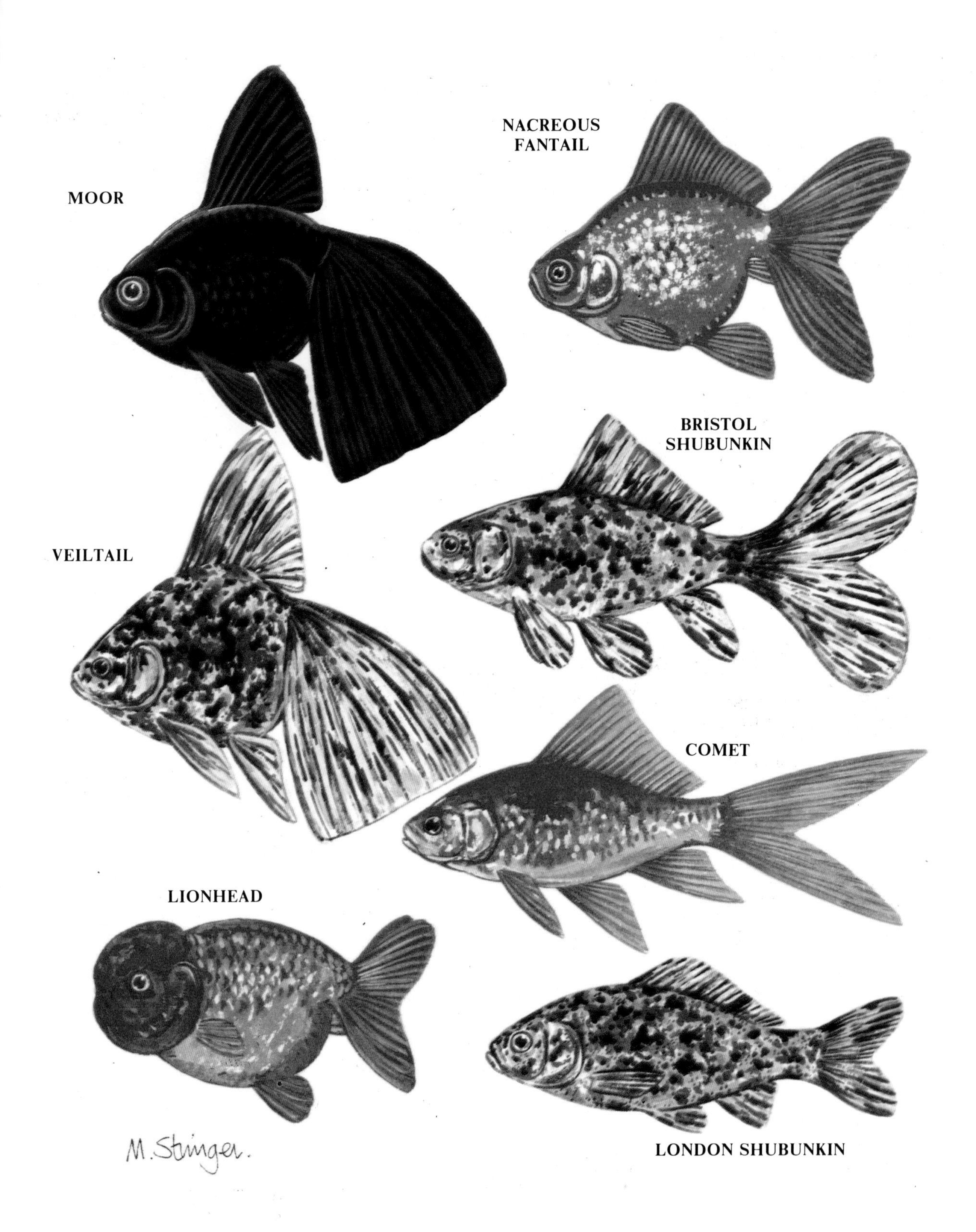

Plate 2 Goldfish

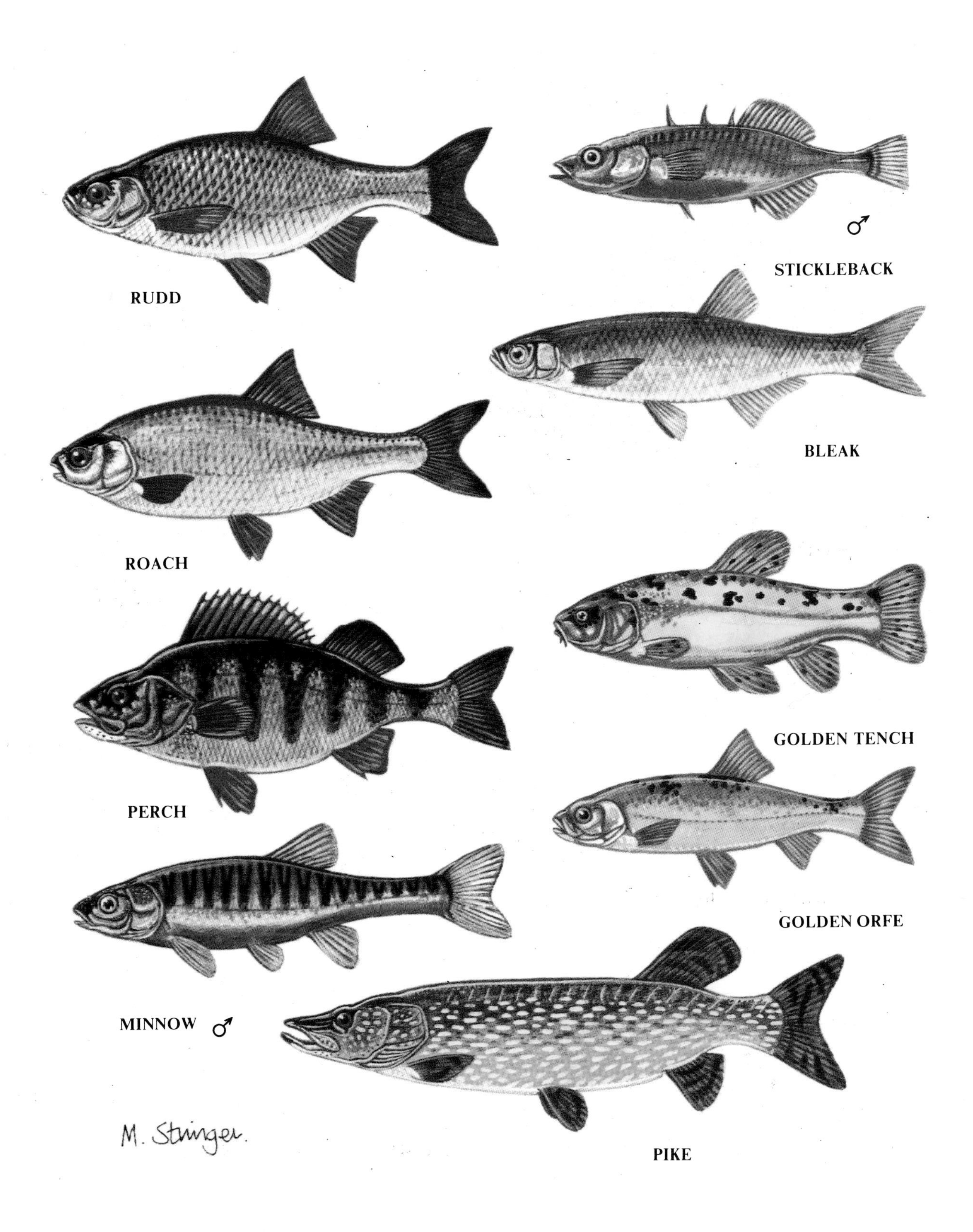

Plate 3 Freshwater Fish

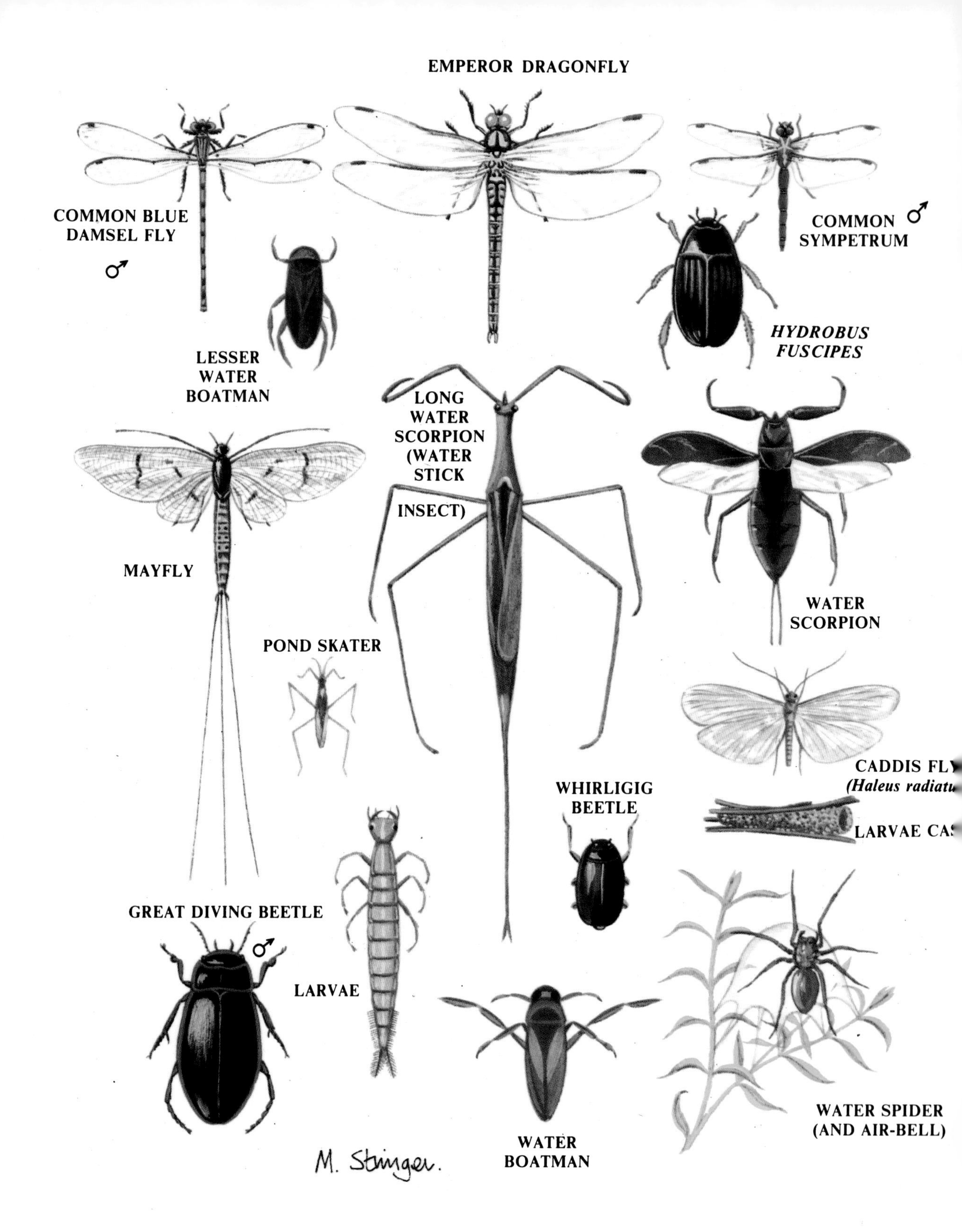

Plate 4 Water Bugs and Insects

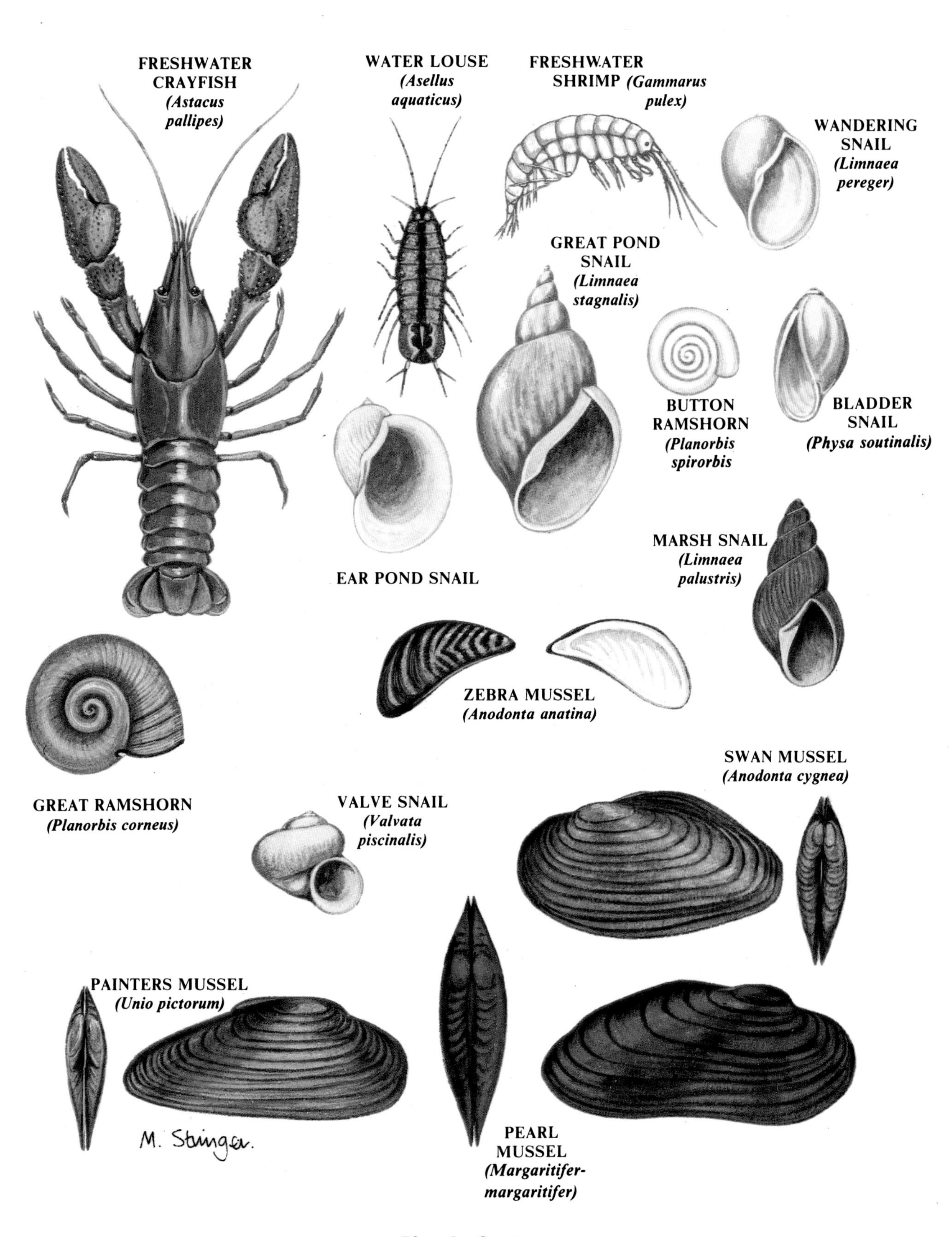

Plate 5 Crustacea

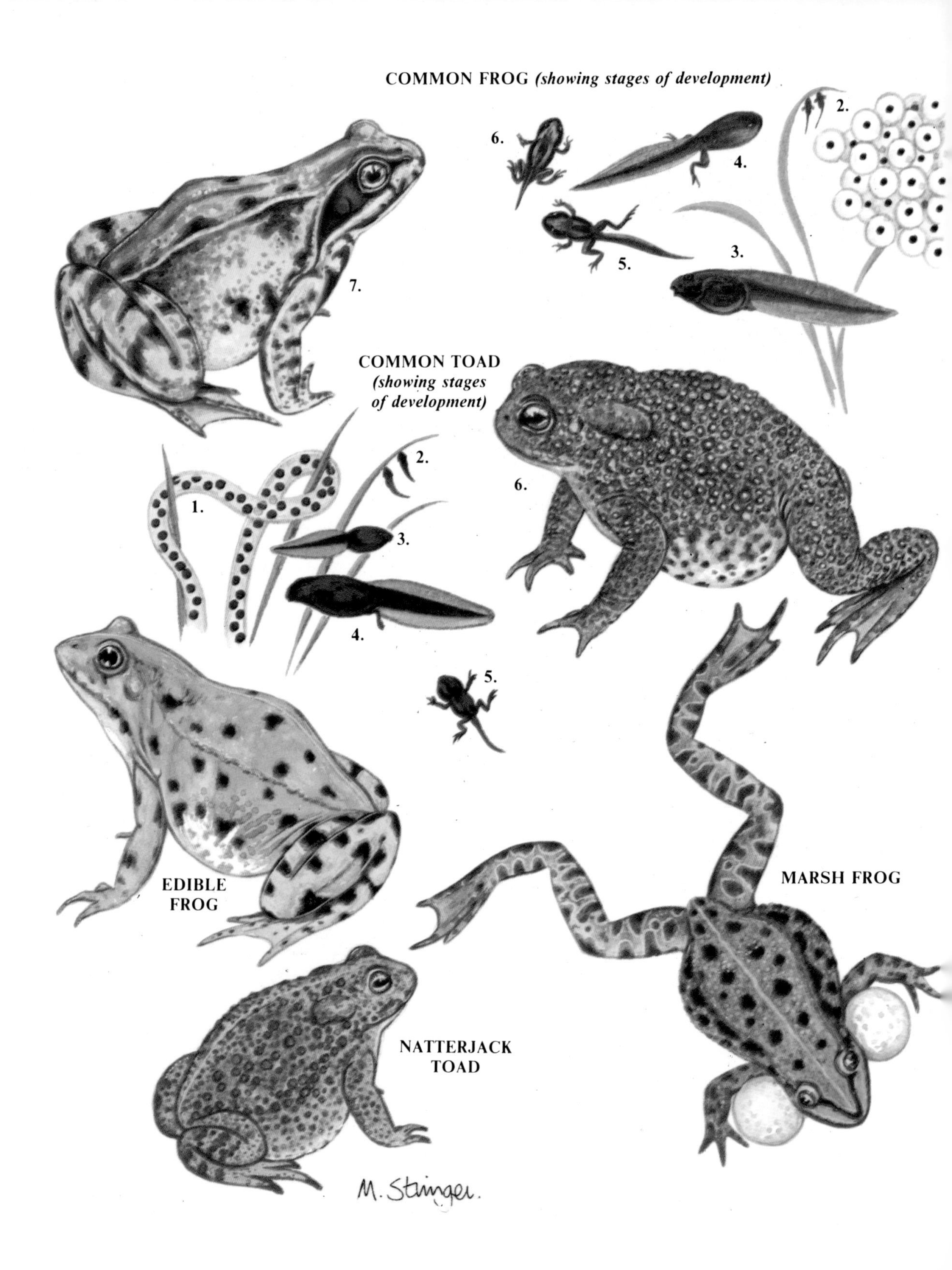

Plate 6 Frogs and Toads

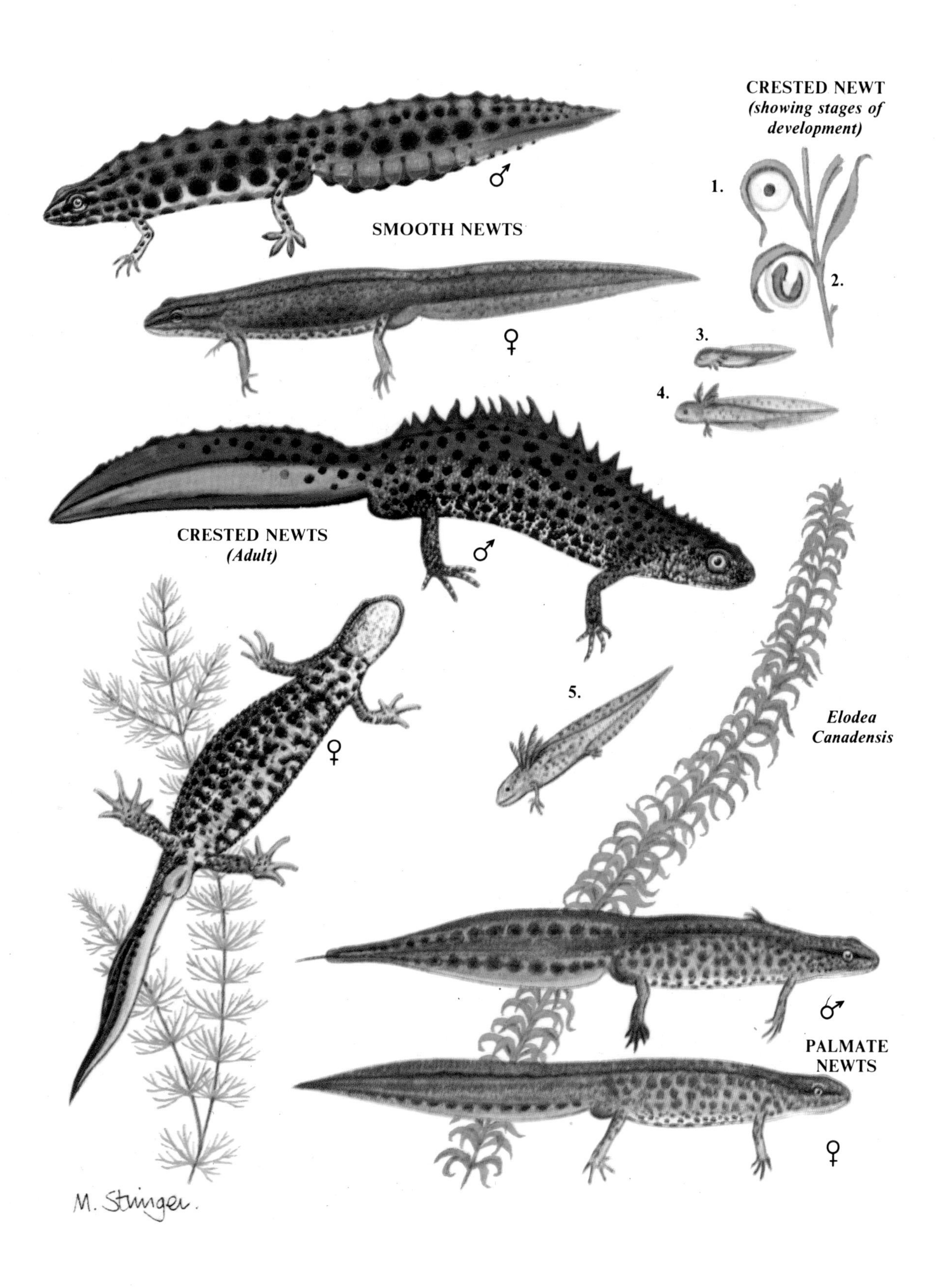

Plate 7 Amphibians

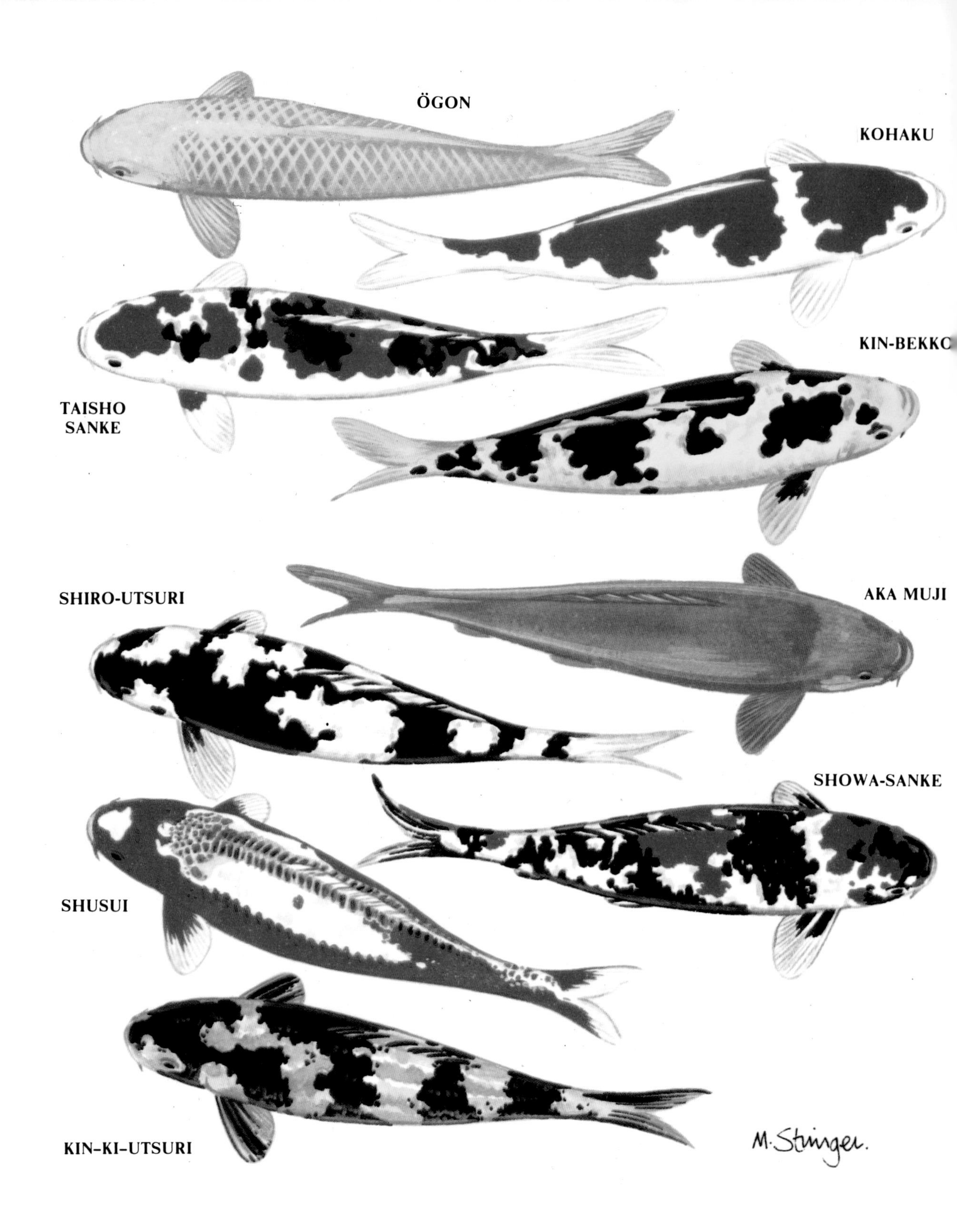
ÖGON
KOHAKU
KIN-BEKKO
TAISHO
SANKE
SHIRO-UTSURI
AKA MUJI
SHOWA-SANKE
SHUSUI
KIN-KI-UTSURI
M. Stringer.

Plate 8 Koi

the parasite and its eggs are killed.

White Spot– *(Ichthyopthiriasis)*. A protozoan parasite which causes small whitish blisters to appear on the body of the fish. If all fishes are removed from the infected water, the parasite will die after about two months through lack of a host. To treat the fishes: prepare a stock solution of 1g of medical quality Methylene Blue mixed into 100cc of hot water. Use 4cc of the stock solution to each gallon of water and mix to disperse the solution evenly. The fishes can be left in the water for a prolonged period if necessary. It is also possible to cure this complaint by moving the fish to clean water every twenty-four hours, making sure that the previous container is thoroughly disinfected, until the fish is cured.

Branchiitis (inflamation of the gills)– Caused by pollution or over-crowding reducing oxygen content of the water. Remedy the cause and give the fish treatment in Methylene Blue (*see* **White Spot**).

Dropsy– A bacterial infection which causes an accumulation of fluid to form within the tissues of one or other of the internal organs. The belly becomes filled with an almost watery liquid, which causes it to swell so greatly that it appears likely to burst, and the scales stand out from the body. In some forms it can be a very infectious disease. Investigation seems to indicate that the disease mainly attacks fish that are poorly fed and have a lowered resistance. It is a difficult problem to cure. Try treating with Chloromycetin at the rate of 60mg to each gallon water, for four days, keeping the water cool. Do not feed whilst treating the fish. If at the end of the treatment period there is no improvement, destroy the fish.

Air Embolism– Due to an excessive amount of dissolved oxygen in the water. The oxygen-saturated water can cause over saturation in the blood of the fish. Visible signs are the appearance of air-bubbles in the fins. Place affected fish in fresh water or, alternatively, apply strong aeration to dispel the excess oxygen from the water.

Fin Rot *(Bacterioses pinnarium)*– As the common name suggests, this is the putrefaction of the caudal and other fins. The fins become torn and ragged and are gradually consumed by the action of the bacteria. Fungus can occur as a secondary complaint. If the disease spreads to the body it may well prove fatal. Treat with phenoxethol (*see* **Fungus**).

Pop-eye *(Exophthalmia)*– In this disease the eye swells and, becoming too large for the orbit, protrudes. Sometimes the swelling is so great that the eye is forced out of its socket completely. It is seldom contagious and the fish may live quite happily despite the affliction. There is no known certain cure, but it can sometimes be remedied by placing the fish in clean, fresh water.

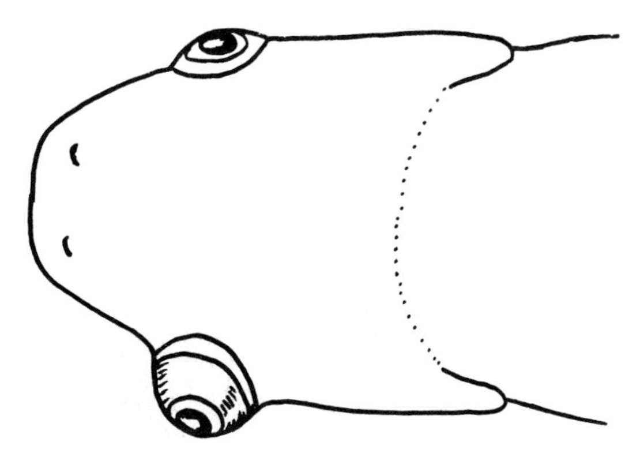

Figure 25 **Head of Fish infected with *Exophthalmus* – "Pop-eye".**

Slime Disease *(Chilodonelliasia)*– Characterised by pale colours under a thin grey film of thickened mucus. The disease can remain latent whilst the fish is healthy, but strike when its resistance is lowered. Affected fish should be given the same treatment as described for fungus.

Mouth Fungus *(Chondrococcus columnaris)*– This is not a fungus infection, but is caused by a slime bacterium. It is both contagious and dangerous. Infected fish become sluggish and lose their appetite. If treatment is delayed the frontal part of the head may be eaten away, and the fish will die. The disease can be cured if early treat-

COMPLAINTS

ment is applied. Treat with Chloromycetin (*see* **Dropsy**) or phenoxethol (*see* **Fungus**).

Gill Rot– Highly dangerous disease. Most prevalent during the warmer months of the year. The malady is furthered by high temperatures and decaying vegetation in the water. The disease is caused by some of the lower fungi which produce branched hyphae that grow into the veins of the gill sheets. This results in a complete stoppage of the blood supply in the affected areas, and sections of the gill sheets start to die, decay and fall off. The fish usually dies from suffocation. By the

Figure 26 **Goldfish with Pox Disease**

time the signs have become very evident it is too late to save the victim. If this disease is suspected treat the fish without delay, first to a salt bath, followed by long term phenoxethol (*see* **Fungus**).

Ulcers– These commence with a small lesion which becomes a pimple-like swelling. The swelling then develops into an open sore. Treat with Chloromycetin, (*see* **Dropsy**); also soak food in the solution before feeding.

'Hole-in-the-body'– An extremely virulent form of the above disease, and is so called because of the very large wounds which it creates. The disease can remain dormant for long periods of time, only to break out in rapid activity. It can infect every fish that has been in contact with the original source of infection, and kill them. Treat as above, but also make a thick paste of the Chloromycetin and place it in the wound. Repeat the treatment every day. Treatment may be required over a longish period, and is not always successful.

Red Pest *(Purpura cyprinorum)*– The skin of the belly becomes a dark red colour. The lower part of the caudal fin, pelvic and anal fins may also be inflamed. The reddening is due partly to an abnormal widening of the blood vessels and also haemorrhages of the skin. The gills may appear blood-shot and have areas of dying tissue. The disease can be very contagious but, if given good conditions and prompt treatment, the chances of recovery are good. Provide strong aeration and run a strong stream of water through the, more than likely, polluted water in which the fish has been living. Treat the affected fish with Chloromycetin (*see* **Dropsy**).

Furunculosis– A very serious freshwater disease which is highly infectious. Infection can occur within a few hours when a healthy fish is placed into infected water and, in bad cases, death may follow within three to four days. It can remain latent in a healthy fish for a long time, but the fish will have acted as a carrier and infected other fishes. It is primarily a disease of the Salmon and Trout species.

First signs of the disease appear in the internal organs. The intestine becomes heavily inflamed and shows a blood-red colour, some fish may die at this stage without showing any external signs of the disease. Fish which survive this stage will develop a diffuse haemorrhagical process in the muscles. These processes penetrate to the body surface and produce swellings or boils, which contain bloody, pus-like matter. These boils or furuncles are the most characteristic feature of the disease, from which it derives its name. They are usually seen as rounded swellings on the sides of the fish. Sometimes the swellings burst and discharge their contents into the water. After eight to fourteen days, after the swellings appear, the fish become lethargic and separate themselves from the others, they are then easily caught by hand.

It is essential that infected fish are separated from the healthy, and dead fish destroyed by burning.

Chloromycetin may effect a cure (*see* **Dropsy**) and, in addition, add 1g of Chloromycetin to each kilogram of food. This treated food should be given to all stock, both healthy and infected, for a sufficiently long period until well after the disease appears to have been cured.

Ichthyosporidium, *(Ichthyophonus)*– A parasitic fungi which attacks a wide variety of fishes; heavy losses amongst continental Trout are often due to this parasite. It is difficult to diagnose this disease in living fish since no distinctive symptoms appear. Affected fishes may become sluggish, while their bellies may become concave and thin. The fish lose their equilibrium and eventually die without showing any external sign of disease. If the parasites penetrate into the brain the fish may make tumbling movements.

It may be that pea-sized ulcerous formations appear in the skin. These ulcers will contain many cysts of Ichthyophonus and these may be accompanied by raw sores or unbroken boils.

An infestation of the liver may cause the belly to be swollen, whereas infection of the eye results in eye protrustion and its destruction.

Occasionally the gills may be attacked, leading to suffocation. If cysts are produced in the vicinity of the swim-bladder, the proper functioning of this organ may be impaired. The pressure of the cysts will prevent the bladder inflating fully and cause the fish to become 'heavy' and lie on the bottom.

Generally, however, the parasites are found in the heart, liver, kidney, spleen, reproductive organs, stomach, intestines and muscles.

The cysts appear as whitish-grey granules lying between the tissues of the organs. Those which are in the organs may vary from yellowish, yellowish-brown to brown or black. Organs containing many cysts will feel hard, like stones, and sandy.

This highly infectious disease takes a very long course which may take months, or even years, before the victim dies as a result of the gradual destruction of the organs.

Infection may take place if a fish eats an infected fish which has died or if it eats the cysts, which have entered the water from the skin or gills of an infected specimen. Ten days after infection occurs, the cysts may be found in the internal organs. The parasites reproduce themselves in the organs of their host and, if the temperature is sufficiently high, can fill the organ with cysts in fourteen days. If it is a vital organ death will quickly follow.

It is almost impossible to cure this disease, although in the early stages it may be possible – try the Chloromycetin bath, as detailed for Dropsy, and pre-soak the food in the solution. Badly infected fish should be destroyed and burnt for safety. A close watch must be kept on all fishes that have been in contact with the victim, or the water in which it has been kept. Great care must be taken to avoid the disease spreading so all equipment must be thoroughly sterilized.

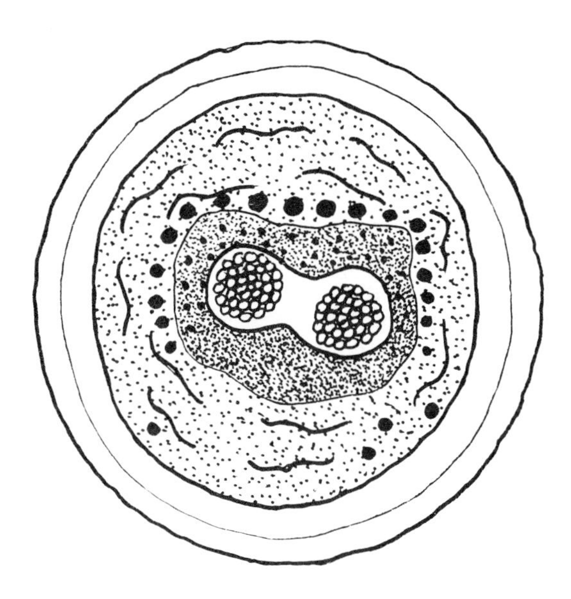

Figure 27 *Ichthyophonus* Cyst

A major epidemic requires drastic treatment: destroy the stock, burn the bodies and all plants, and use very strong disinfection to sterilize the infected areas and sand or gravel.

Pox Disease (*Epithelioma papulosum*)– Mainly a disease of the Carp family, but other fish can be affected. The main signs are small milky-white spots, somewhat tallow-like in appearance, which gradually increase in size. They may grow sufficiently to merge and cover large areas of the fish's skin. The spots are raised above the surface of the skin and are more solid and harder than the surrounding parts. Sometimes the spots may be clouded by the presence of tiny strings of black pigment. Thick growths may assume a reddish-grey lustre.

Generally, the disease is not lethal. Under good conditions, if the water temperature is not too high, the disease will often heal spontaneously. In running water the chances of recovery are better than in standing water.

Figure 28 **Trout infected with *Furunculosis*, showing boils.**

Peduncle Disease– Characterised by swelling, inflammation, discoloration and gradual necrosis of the caudal peduncle. The disease is always fatal, fortunately it is not common.

Whirling Disease (of Trout)– Derives its name from the rapid tail chasing which is often seen when the fish is frightened or trying to feed. The whirling symptom is associated with lesions and disintegration of the cartilaginous skeletal support of the organs of equilibrium. Damage to the head skeleton is evident in older Trout as a depression in the head or as mis-shapen jaws. Pressure on the nerves which control the caudal pigment cells results in **'blacktail'** in many fish. Symptoms may appear as early as two weeks after the fry start feeding. The causitive agent is *Myxosoma cerebralis (Lentospora c.)*, a protozoan which was discovered in Europe in 1903.

It is difficult to eradicate the disease as the spores are resistant to drying and/or freezing. All fish from infected waters should be destroyed and incinerated.

Infectious Pancreatic Necrosis– Commonly called IPN, this is a viral infection of Trout which causes a very high mortality rate in fry and fingerlings and, occasionally, in larger fish. It can be carried and transmitted by apparently healthy fish.

IPN can be transmitted through flowing water which is infected with the virus. Its source is undoubtedly the excreta and intestinal discharges of victims or 'carrier' fish. It is also shed with eggs and sperm, some being inside the egg, and is thereby passed from one generation to another. The disease appears to attack well fed, rapidly growing fish – limited evidence suggesting that less well nourished, slower growing fish are not so vulnerable. High water temperatures accelerate the course of the disease.

Signs of infection are: a sudden increase in the mortality rate amongst the largest and best young fish, fish whirling whereby the victims rotate around their axis – whirling is a terminal sign and death usually follows within an hour or so. Symptoms include overall darkening, protruding eyes, abdominal distention and haemorrhages in the ventral areas, including the bases of fins. Internally the liver and spleen are pale and the digestive tract is empty of food; accordingly the stomach appears whitish. A clear to milky mucus occurs in the stomach and interior intestine.

IPN cannot be treated effectively. Infected stock should be destroyed and burned. Their quarters should be allowed to remain thoroughly dry for a minimum of four weeks to lessen the chances of the virus surviving. Fish which appear to recover from the disease will retain the infection and become 'carriers'.

Swim-bladder disorders– Very often the result of bad management, Incorrect feeding, i.e. too much dried food, rapid temperature fluctuations, chilling or prolonged low temperatures. It is also possible for the swim-bladder to become inflamed, or be attacked by disease. Whether the condition can be relieved depends very much upon the cause of the condition. Try treatment in Chloromycetin (*see* **Dropsy**) and raising the water temperature slightly. If this does not alleviate the condition within a reasonable length of time, destroy the fish.

Evidence of a disorder of the swim-bladder can be seen. The fish may float like a cork to the water surface, or it may have difficulty in rising from the bottom and will do so only with great effort.

Shimmies– This is often due to chilling the fish. The fish tends to remain stationary, making a shivering movement of the body. To remedy the situation: slightly raise the water temperature until the fish is cured, then gradually return it to normal temperatures.

There are many excellent commercial remedies available for some of the foregoing complaints. 'Sterazin' is particularly good for treating against flukes and other ectoparasites of freshwater fishes.

Adequate care, cleanliness, and good management will do much to avoid the incidence of diseases – especially if all newly acquired fish are given a period of quarantine. *See* **Diseases of Fish** *and* **Remedies.**

CONDITIONING. Bringing about that condition of perfect health by providing a fish with first class living conditions, high quality food and ideal temperatures that will encourage the fish to breed.

CONJUNCTIVE TISSUE. Body tissue surrounding, supporting and holding together the internal organs.

CONNATE. Botanical description of two leaves, or other plant parts, which have grown together and become joined.

CONVERGENCE. Similar behaviour patterns and external characteristics exhibited by widely separated living beings, often the result of similar living conditons.

CONVULUTE. Botanical term meaning coiled or rolled up.

COPEPOD. Large sub-class of the ***CRUSTACEA;*** Copepods are small, often microscopic, animals. Included among the freshwater copepods are the well known *Cyclops.* Some copepods are parasitic to fish, *Lernea cyprinacea* is one such.

CORDATA. Botanical term meaning heart-shaped.

COREGONUS. The whitefish: the genus of

Figure 29 **Lochmaben Vendace** *Coregonus vandesius)*

Coregonus, known collectively as whitefish, comprises a number of freshwater species. The general appearance of these fish is very much alike and it would be difficult for anyone who was not an expert to be certain to which species an individual fish belonged. They are not widely distributed, inhabiting only a few lakes. Outwardly these fishes resemble the Herring, but they can be distinguished by the small adipose fin on the back, near the tail, which is typical of the Salmon family (to which they belong), and by the presence of a lateral line.

Coregonus vandesius– The **Lochmaben Vendace.** This is a small species of whitefish that is confined to a few small lakes near Lochmaben in Dumfriesshire. It attains a length of around 9 inches (229mm) and is a silvery-white colour. A gregarious fish, its food is said to consist of small crustaceans. In form it closely resembles the Herring.

Coregonus gracilior– The **Cumberland Vendace.** Although more slender, the size and appearance is very similar to the preceding species. Though rare and seldom caught, it inhabits the English lakes of Derwentwater and Bassenthwaite.

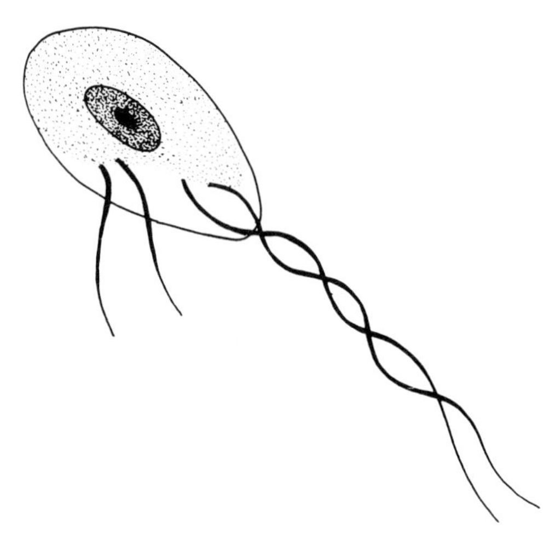

Figure 30 **Costia**

Coregonus pollan– The **Lough Neagh Pollan.** A well known Irish fish; it differs from the Vendace in that the lower jaw does not project above the upper. The Pollan can reach a length of 10 inches (23cm). They spawn during November and December.

Coregonus altior– The **Lough Erne Pollan.** Very similar to the preceding fish, perhaps slightly larger and deeper in the body.

Coregonus elegans– The **Shannon Pollan.** Lives in the Shannon Lakes, but is not a common fish.

Coregonus clupeoides– The **Powan.** Superficially resembling the Herring; it is sometimes known as the Freshwater Herring. Found in Loch Lomond and Loch Esk, they attain an average length of around 1 foot (30cm).

Coregonus stigmaticus– The **Schelly.** With a length up to 16 inches (41cm), it is almost identical to the preceding species, except that it has small black specks on its back and sides. Found in Haweswater and to a lesser degree in Ullswater and Red Tarn in the English Lake District.

Coregonus pennantii– The **Gwyniad** is the Welsh equivalent to Whiting and lives in Lake Bala. In appearance and size this fish is difficult to tell from the previous species.

CORIXIDAE. Water bugs, widespread in still and slow-moving waters. Comprising thirty-three species.

CORM. Enlarged stem base.

COSMOPOLITAN. Found throughout the world.

COSTIA. Genus of Flagellates. Parasitic to the epidermis and gills of fish.

COTTUS GOBIO. The **Miller's Thumb** or **River Bull-head**; this fish is found over much of Europe. A small species of around 4 inches (102mm) long, It is devoid of scales. The head is broad, depressed and rounded in front and the upper surface is covered with a moveable skin. Behind the large pectoral fins the body tapers quickly to the tail. It has two dorsal fins. The anal fin is rather long and the caudal is rounded. Brownish on the back fading to a yellowish-white belly with numerous blotches of brownish-black; the colour changing very quickly to blend in with the background.

A solitary, greedy and carnivorous fish which lurks in the bottom gravel or under stones in clear streams. During March or April eggs are laid in shallow water, usually under a stone in a nest of sorts. During incubation the largish eggs are guarded by the male.

COTYLEDON. The first leaf of a seedling.

CRAYFISH. The largest of the crustaceans, and possibly the most interesting. Of the order *DECAPODA,* the creature resembles the Marine Lobster, although much smaller, and grows to an average length of 4 inches (102mm). The females are smaller than the males. The usual colour is dark brownish, but greenish or yellowish specimens are sometimes found.

Crayfish need well-oxygenated water and are found only in rivers or streams which satisfy this requirement. They thrive best in 'hard' waters and, therefore, they occur most often in limestone or chalky district. Being creatures of nocturnal habits, they hide in burrows under a bank or under large stones during the day. They are mainly carnivorous, capturing almost any kind of smaller creature. In the aquarium they will readily accept worms, but if the food supply is not adequate they may turn cannibal. In captivity they have been observed to eat the moulted cuticles of their fellow inmates, possibly to obtain the lime salts which they contain.

The head and thorax of a Crayfish are fused together and covered by a shield-like carapace. The compound eyes are carried on stalks. In the region of the head are a pair of small antennules which are well supplied with sense organs and a pair of long antennae used as organs of touch which have excretory openings at their base. There are also strong crunching jaws and finally two pairs of accessory jaws, the second of which is used to maintain a current of water over the twenty pairs of feathery blood-gills which are situated at the base of the thoracic limbs – the limbs between the head and abdomen.

The thorax carries three pairs of appendages which help to pass food to the jaws, and five pairs of legs. The first pair of these are the strong pincers which are used for grasping prey and for combat. The remaining four pairs are used for walking. Normally these are used to crawl forwards, but when alarmed a Crayfish can move backwards at a fast speed, using its fan-shaped tail as a paddle.

The segmented abdomen carries a pair of appendages which in the male are deeply grooved and used for passing sperm to the females. Behind these are four pairs of two-bladed **'swimmerets'**, which assist the creature in swimming and are also used by the female for carrying the eggs.

Pairing takes place in late autumn. The male overturns the female and liberates a fertilizing liquid on her abdomen, where it adheres. A little later, in the seclusion of her burrow, the female lays her hundred or more pinkish eggs; these are attached to her swimmerets where they come in contact with the males spermatazoa, and are fertilized. The eggs do not hatch until spring, and the transparent young, which are near minature replicas of the adult, remain attached to the female swimmerets for some time afterwards.

Astacus fluviatilis is not a British native, it is a continental species, and usually the underside of the pincers is a reddish colour. Our native species,

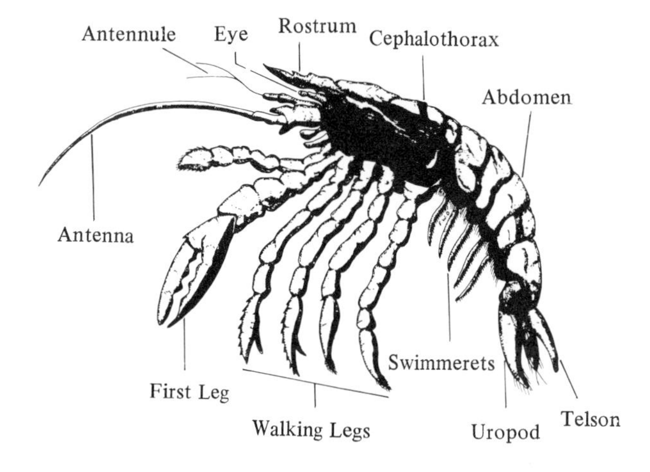

Figure 31 **Crayfish**

Potamobius (*Astacus pallipes*), is somewhat smaller and has whitish pincers.

CRISPATE. With wavy margins.

CRISPUS. Botanical for curly or curled.

CROSS-BREEDING. The breeding, one to the other, of two different live beings of different races, species or genera. The resultant young are 'hybrid' or 'cross-bred',

CROWFOOT or WATERCROWFOOT. *Ranunculus aquatilis. See* **Plants.**

CRUCIAN CARP. *Carassius carassius. See under Cyprinidae.*

CRUSTACAE. The most primitive class of the arthropods. In nearly all cases there are two pairs of antennae in front of the mouth, nearly all have more than four pairs of legs, and the bodies are covered with a chitin shell.

CRYPTOGMAE. Flowerless plants.

CRYSTALWORT. *Riccia fluitans.* A small floating plant.

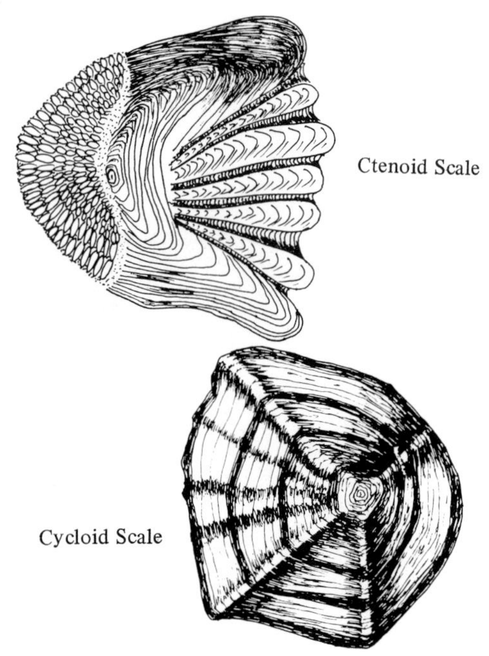

Figure 32 **Ctenoid and Cycloid Scales**

CTENOID SCALES. Scales with a deeply toothed edge.

CULLING. Term applied to sorting out the less desirable specimens of fish and other animals so that only the best are retained, thus improving or maintaining the quality of the stock.

CUMBERLAND VENDACE. *Coregonus gracilior. See under* ***Coregonus.***

CYANOPHYEAE. Blue-green algae. Obnoxious, quickly proliferating algae of the class *SCHIZOPHYTA.* It forms evil-smelling blankets of a blue-green growth.

CYCLOID SCALES. Round scales with a smooth edge.

CYCLOPS. Genus of lower crustacean, often found in the same waters as Daphnia.

CYCLOSTOME. Sub-class of primitive fishes. They have cartilaginous skeletons, no limbs, jaws, ribs or scales. The lampreys belong to this sub-class. *See* ***Petromyzontidae.***

CYME. An inflorescence that forms a forked cluster.

CYPERACEAE. The Sedge family.

CYPRINIDAE. The **Carp family.** Predominantly freshwater fish, they are widely distributed over much of the world. They prefer quiet water with a muddy bottom and, in the winter, will move into deep water where they remain in a quiescent condition, some, such as the Tench, even burrowing into the mud. During the spring and summer breeding season they develop tubercles on the head and/or on the front thickened rays of the pectoral fins.

Cyprinus carpio– **The Common Carp.** This fish has four barbels, an unusually long dorsal fin with from seventeen to twenty-two branched rays, and a strongly serrated third spine of the dorsal and anal fins. The dorsal fin is concave and the caudal fin is deeply forked. The body is deep and thickish, with large scales numbering from thirty-four to forty along the lateral line and five to six and a half from the beginning of the dorsal fin to the lateral line. The back is dark olive-brown, fading to bronze on the sides and to pale yellow on the belly. Under ideal conditions Carp can reach a length of around 40 inches (102cm). They eat both animal and vegetable matter.

Like all creatures which have been domesticated, the Carp is found in several distinct varieties. The variations are of two main types – determined by the body shape and the scale covering. The **Leather Carp** is devoid of scales, whilst the **Mirror Carp** has greatly enlarged scales confined to one or two rows on each side of the body. A highly decorative form of domesticated Carp is the Koi.

Carassius carassius– **The Crucian Carp.** Originating from Asia, in habit it resembles the Common Carp and has been known to grow to a length of 15 inches (38cm), but is usually much smaller. It has a long, rounded and convex dorsal fin, a slightly forked caudal fin, and is very similar in colour to the preceding Carp. Along the lateral line are twenty-eight to thirty-five scales; six and a half to nine from the beginning of the dorsal fin to the lateral line. It has no barbels and a rounded dorsal contour. "Crucian" is derived from the German name for this fish. "Karausche".

Carassius auratus– **The Goldfish.** A well known fish of the pond and aquarium which, like the Crucian Carp, originates from Asia. It has a long, concave to straight dorsal fin with a strong serrated spine. The lateral line scales number twenty-five to thirty, and from the beginning of the dorsal fin to the lateral line, five to six and a half. There are no barbels and the caudal fin is only moderately forked. The young fish have the typical Carp coloration; however, this eventually turns to the well known golden hue, although some may turn yellow or silver and some remain the wild olive-brown colour. There is a tendency for domesticated Goldfish to revert to their wild type, for this reason the uncoloured types are not suitable for breeding purposes.

Starting in China, the ornamental Goldfish can claim recorded history spanning 1,000 years. In China and Japan the breeders of Goldfish have produced many fancy varieties. *See* **Fancy Goldfish.**

Barbus barbus– **The Barbel.** Like the Common Carp this fish has four barbels, from which it derives its name. The dorsal fin is short with only six to nine branched rays, the last being coarsely serrated. The snout is longer than that of the Carp, and it has an overall length of around 3 feet (0.9m) from the top of the snout to the end of the tail. The smallish scales number fifty-two to seventy along the lateral line. Although the colour is variable it is often a dark olive-green on the back, fading on the sides and becoming white on the belly. The body is long and slim, slightly flattened below, with the crescent-shaped mouth set well below the snout and between thick lips. It favours gravelly, swift flowing streams; Barbel are of local distribution, and prefer swimming in shoals near wiers or the buttresses of bridges where they hug the bottom and swim powerfully against the current. For the most part they feed on worms, crustacea and insect larvae.

Tinca tinca– **The Tench** is possibly the most sluggish of the native British coldwater fish and it has the ability to withstand conditions that would even upset the hardy Carp. During the day it keeps to the bottom, in the mud and weeds; if it is a calm and sunny summer day it may approach the surface, to lie motionless beneath a lily pad, but will quickly return to the bottom if alarmed or disturbed. Mostly it forages for food during the night, which consists of crustacea and insect larvae; it is also fond of molluscs.

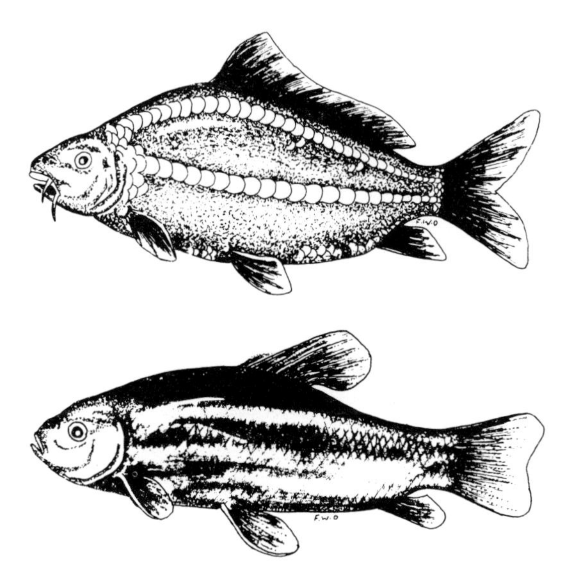

Figure 33 *Top:* **Mirror Carp** *(Cyprinus carpio)*
Bottom: **Tench** *(Tinca tinca)*

The fish has a roundish appearance: the body is rather stout, with a rounded back; all the fins are rounded, including the lobes of the caudal; the snout is short and round, with an oblique mouth. At both corners of the mouth is a small barbel. The scales are very small and numerous, numbering between ninety to one hundred and twenty along the lateral line, and the body is very slimy. The colour varies from deep olive to brownish-black – there is also an ornamental golden coloured variety. It has a small red eye.

The spawning period is between April and August, and is one of the latest of British fresh-water fish to spawn. The numerous small eggs are deposited on under-water plants. Incubation takes about seven days and the young develop quite quickly. On the continent the Tench can reach a length of around 28 inches with a weight of 17lb (7.7kg). In England it can attain a weight of 8 lb (3.6kg).

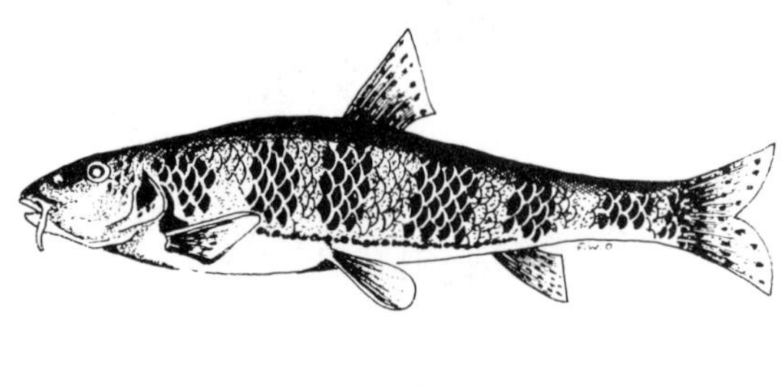

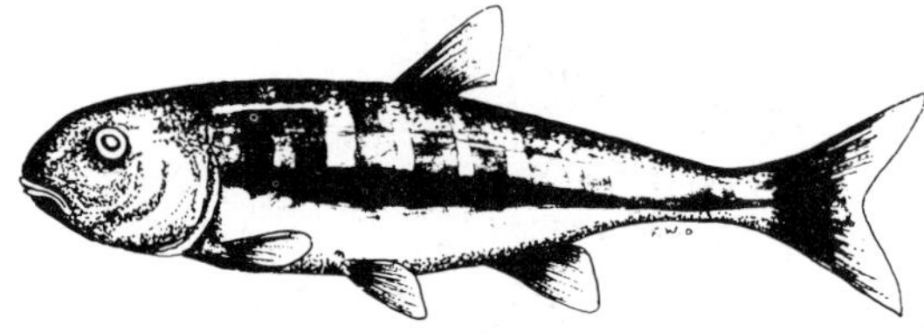

Figure 34 *Top:* Gudgeon *(Gobio gobio)*
Bottom: Minnow *(Phoxinus phoxinus)*

Gobio gobio– **The Gudgeon.** A small member of the Carp family which looks rather like a minature Barbel. It has an elongated and rounded body with a relatively large head and eyes. The large scales number between thirty-nine and forty-five along the lateral line. The colour is variable, being grey or brown, with the silvery or golden tints on the sides being broken by blue-black spots arranged in a line or irregular square; the dorsal and caudal fins are speckled with small grey spots. The mouth carries two barbels at its corners, is crescent-shaped and set well below the snout.

The Gudgeon is gregarious; often forming large shoals near the bottom close to the banks of ponds or rivers. It spawns in running water during May and June, and deposits eggs which are transparent with a clear blue or yellowish shimmer. The eggs are adhesive, and lie on the bottom in small clumps; spawning is gradual, a few eggs only being deposited at one time. Incubation usually takes ten days.

A small species, the average length being 6 inches, it is distributed across Europe from England to the Caspian Sea, except for Greece and the Iberian Peninsular. Although generally distributed in England and Wales, it has not been found in West Wales, Cornwall or the Lake District.

Phoxinus phoxinus– **The Minnow.** A very small fish, seldom exceeding a length of 4 inches (102mm), and found practically everywhere in the British Isles, except in the North Highlands and some parts of the West of Ireland. It inhabits any water that has a sandy or gravelly bottom and is clean. Swimming in shoals between the shallows and deep water, they will quickly dart away if alarmed. However, they have an inquisitive nature and will soon return to explore their former grounds. Their curiosity will attract them to inspect any unusual object.

The body is spindle-shaped with a short snout; there are no barbels. The scales are tiny and number from eighty to one hundred along the lateral line. A series of dark bars descend from the dark green or brown back, marking a silvery-grey background, the sides are bordered with a golden stripe.

Between May and June the fish congregate in large numbers to seek shallow sand or gravel banks to spawn. The eggs are small and adhesive. During the breeding season the male assumes a scarlet colour on the belly.

The Minnow feeds on small animals such as mosquito larvae, small worms and the eggs of fishes, as well as vegetable matter. It is a hardy and lively fish which becomes tame very quickly.

Leuciscus leuciscus– **The Dace.** A small species, the average size being around 10 inches (25cm).

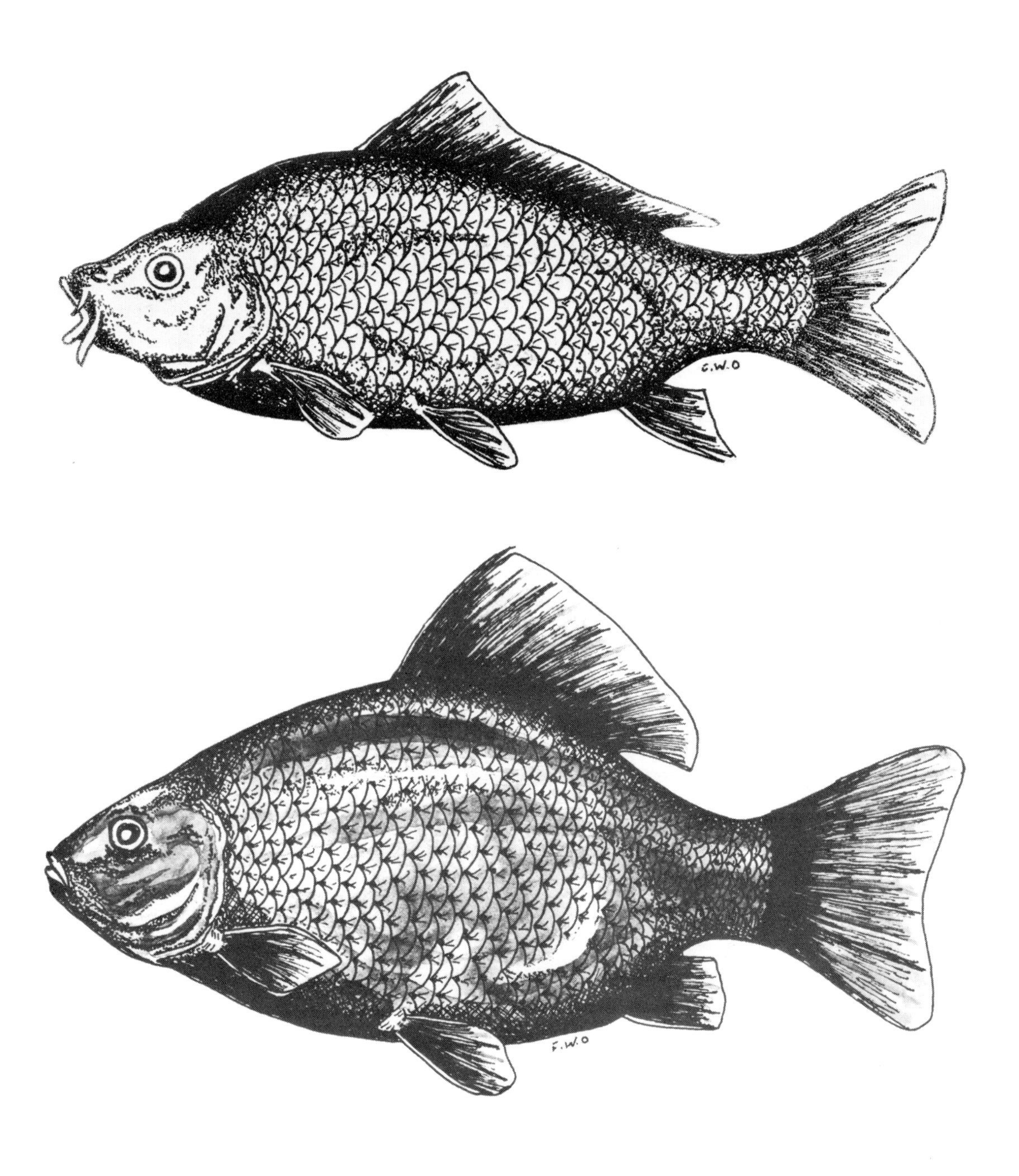

Figure 35 *Top:* **Common Carp** *(Cyprinus carpio)*
Bottom: **Crucian Carp** *(Carassius carassius)*

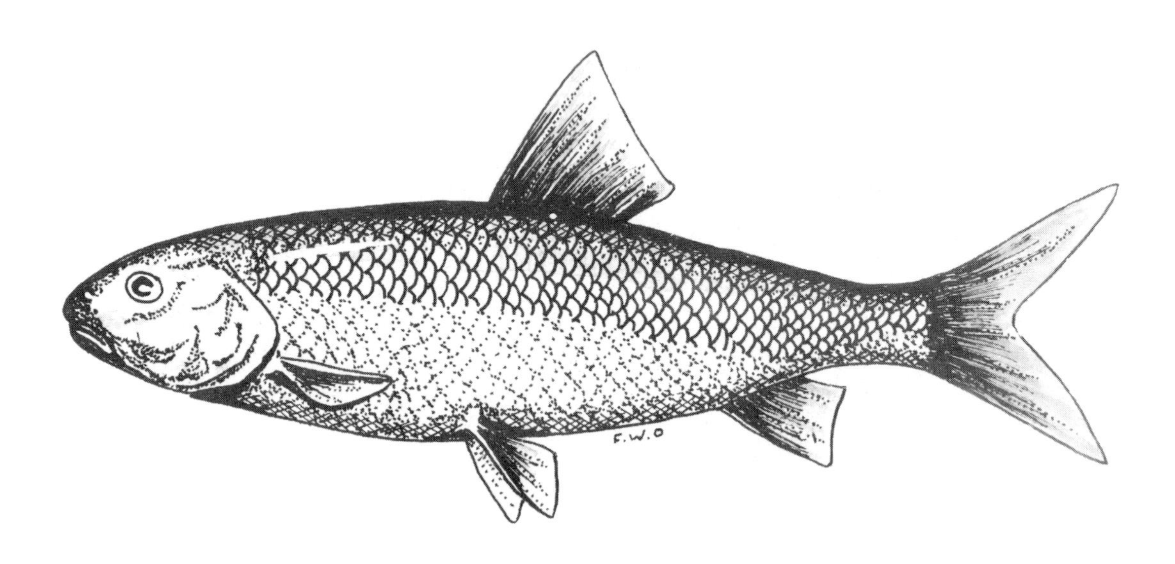

Figure 36 *Top:* **Barbel** *(Barbus barbus)*
Bottom: **Dace** *(Leuciscus leuciscus)*

which prefers clear streams with a fairly rapid water flow. It is common in most English and Welsh rivers and streams, but is not found in Scotland or in Ireland (apart from the Blackwater River). It is a graceful lively fish that prefers a diet of flies, water insects, crustacea and worms. The body is slim, with a back ranging from brownish to bluish green which changes gradually to silver on the sides and the belly. The ventral fins are yellowish or very pale pink; the scales are of medium size and number from forty-seven to fifty-four along the lateral line.

Easily mistaken for small Chub and slender small Roach. It can be distinguished from the Chub by its concave dorsal and anal fins (in the Chub these are convex or rounded and redder), small head and scales. The Roach has concave fins, but they are redder, and the rays in the dorsal and anal fins are more numerous: nine to eleven in the Roach, seven to nine in the Dace.

The Dace spawns in weedy shallows in April and May; the eggs are small and develop quickly.

Leuciscus cephalus– **The Chub.** Looks very much like a bulkier edition of the Dace. It is essentially a surface-living fish. Although preferring running water it can also be found in still waters; it feeds near the bottom but is not fastidious in its diet, being both vegetarian and predatory. It will, at times, take young fish, insects, frogs, insect larvae and worms; at other times it will live on seeds, roots and the buds of water plants and algae. The difference in diet may be due to the age of the fish, the season or the environment. With the onset of winter it devours more animal matter, and also becomes more predatory as its age increases. It has a large powerful mouth set in a large head. The body is rounded and fairly slim, with silvery sides and a dark-green or brownish-green back. The dorsal fin is rounded and convex; whilst the ventral fin and anal fin are red – the latter being rounded and convex. The caudal fin may have a blackish edge. The scales are large and number from forty-two to forty-nine along the lateral line. The Chub can reach a length of around 2 feet (0.6m).

The spawning period is in May and June. The eggs, which are about the size of a poppy seed, are numerous. They adhere to stones and waterplants and hatch out in about one week.

Rutilus (leuciscus) rutilus– **The Roach.** Preferring the quiet waters of pond, lake, canal and the quieter reaches of rivers, the fish is not found in Northern Scotland, in Ireland it is known only in the Blackwater River, and is found only locally in Devon and Cornwall, elsewhere it is common enough. It is a variable species, and though normally the body is moderately deep and compressed, it can be as deep as its near relative the Rudd, or slender like the Dace. The back is dark green, blue, or brown; the sides and belly silvery, with from forty to forty-six scales along the lateral line. The mouth is small with a projecting upper lip, set almost at the end of the snout. All fins are tinged more or less with red; the anal is bright red, concave and short; the dorsal begins almost above the base of the ventral fins.

Figure 37 *Top:* **Chub** *(Leuciscus cephalus)*
Bottom: **Roach** (Rutilus rutilus)

Spawning takes place during April and May; the Roach gathering in large shoals to lay their eggs on the bottom. The numerous eggs are transparent and of a very pale green colour. Incubation lasts for about ten to twelve days, and the resulting fry remain in the shallows for the remainder of the year. At this time they may be seen in dense shoals among the water-weeds near the banks.

Scardinius erythrophthalmus– **The Rudd.** Preferring the slowest and weediest stretches of water, ponds and fens are the favourite home of the Rudd. Its habits are exactly the same as those of the Roach; shoals composed of both species can often be met.

The Rudd has a deeper body than that of the Roach, its depth being from one-third to almost

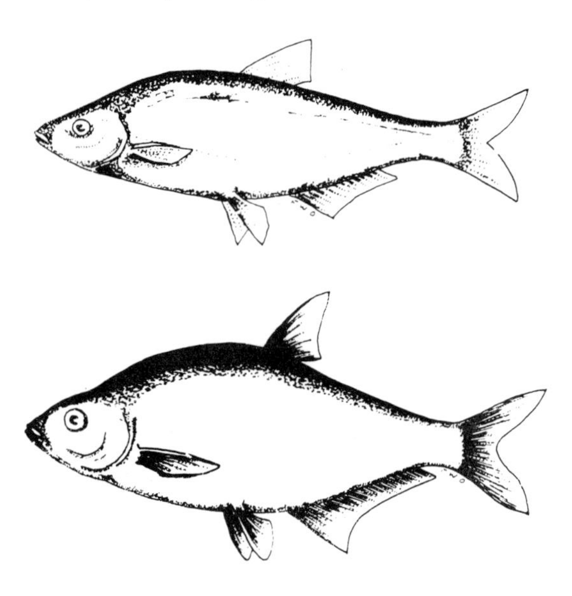

Figure 38 *Top:* **Bleak** *(Alburnus lucidus)*
Bottom: **Bream** *(Abramis brama)*

half the length of the fish. The back is dark blue or brown, the fins and caudal deeply tinged with red; the lips may be outlined in reddish crimson. A yellow shade, which varies from light brass to deep gold, covers the whole body. The scales are large and number from thirty-nine to forty-four along the lateral line. The mouth is oblique with a protruding lower lip. The dorsal fin is placed well after the beginning of the ventral fins, and has a practically straight margin.

The spawning habits, and the development of the egg and fry, are identical to those of the Roach.

Alburnus lucidus– **The Bleak.** A small fish, rarely exceeding a length of 8 inches (203mm). It has a long elongated body, with an oblique mouth and a projecting lower jaw. The long anal fin commences under the base of the dorsal fin. The easily detached scales form a sharp keel between the pelvic and anal fins, and number from forty-six to fifty-four along the lateral line. The colour varies but the fish is generally greenish backed with silvery sides. It lives in shoals and prefers still water and slow running streams. On summer days this lively little fish may be seen at the surface darting about and springing up for flies, feeding on these and worms, crustacea and insect larvae.

The Bleak is widely, but irregularly, distributed in England and Wales but is not found in the Lake District, in Ireland or Scotland. It spawns during April and June, in shallow water, and lays adhesive eggs that stick to stones and water plants. They are delicate fish and die quickly if roughly handled.

Abramis brama– **The Bream.** Seen from the side this is a very portly fish, but when viewed from above it is narrow and flat. It has a very small head and small protruding eyes. It is a large fish, the young adult being at least 10 inches (25cm) long, and is a brownish colour with a bronze sheen; the fins are browny black. The young fish are silvery with pale fins. The deeply forked caudal fin has a much longer lower lobe in comparison to the upper lobe. It has a short dorsal fin and a long anal fin. There are forty-nine to fifty-six scales along the lateral line and it possesses a rather slimy skin.

In Britain, the Bream is found chiefly in the East and South, being absent from the North of Scotland and West of Wales. It prefers quiet waters that are deep with muddy stretches. A gregarious species; it moves slowly around in shoals, grubbing in the mud for anything eatable.

The spawning period is in May and June and at this time the Bream shoals gather in shallow water near the banks, where there is an abundant growth of water plants. There the fish dash about, leaping and splashing at the surface. The adhesive eggs are a light yellowish colour and hatch in from one to three weeks. A female produces up to 300,000 eggs, and they generally spawn in three groups: the oldest first, followed by the others at weekly intervals. After spawning the fish return to the deep water.

Idus idus– **The Orfe.** The Orfe or Ide is a continental fish which closely resembles the Dace. It is a fast growing, streamlined fish which prefers well oxygenated, fast flowing waters or large lakes, with a coolish temperature. Generally, the back is greyish-black, the sides paler, with a silvery belly. With the exception of the greyish dorsal and caudal fins, the fins are reddish. It is a large fish which averages around 20 inches (51cm) in length if well grown; some specimens have reached 30 inches (76cm).

There is a cultivated golden variety which is ideal for ponds. This is a particularly attractive surface-swimming fish. The back is pale gold shading to a pink suffused with silver on the belly. On a warm summer day these fishes will do much to keep down winged insects that approach the water surface, as the fast swimming Orfe leap to capture their prey – which seldom escape.

CYPRINOIDEA. Carp-like fishes. Sub-order of the *OSTARIOPHYSA.* Families of this very wide-spread group will be found throughout the world.

CYPRINUS CARPIO. The Common Carp. *See under **Cyprinidae.***

CYST. A protective covering, often in the form of a raised bladder or membrane, surrounding the dormant larva of a developing parasite, or other small lower animal.

CYTOPLASM. The protoplasm of a cell excluding the nucleus.

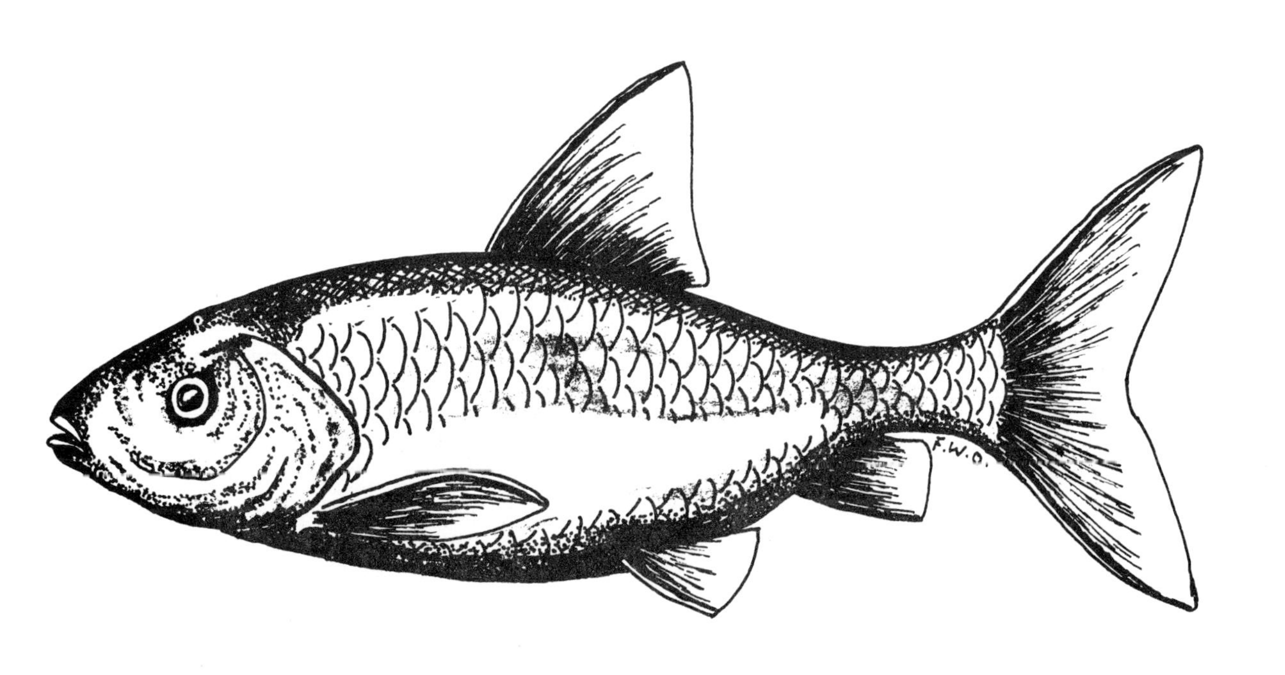

Figure 39 **Orfe** *(Idus idus)*

D

D. Abbreviation for the dorsal fin.

DACE. *Leuciscus leuciscus. See under* ***Cyprinidae.***

DACTYLOGYRUS. Commonly called the **Gill Fluke,** this is a tiny, parasitic, sucking worm that lives on the gills of fishes. It is provided with a disc of powerful hooks with which it anchors itself to its host. It differs from its near relative *Gyrodactylus* by having a four-lobed head with four black eyes. It produces eggs from which the young hatch as larvae. *See* **Fish Flukes.**

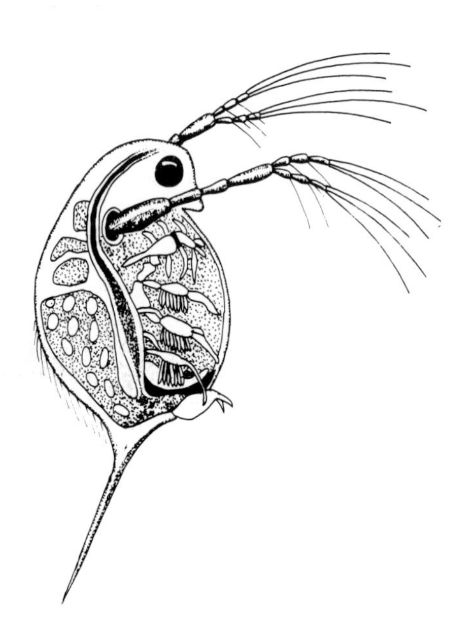

Figure 40 **Daphnia**

DAMSEL FLY. Small dragonfly, of which there are fifteen species, belonging to the *ODONATA.*

DAPHNIA. The Water-flea. This creature is not a flea: it is a freshwater crustacean belonging to the order of the *CLADOCERA.* They are an excellent live food for fishes, with many genera. Being oxygen consumers they should not be used in over large quantities, for to do so may deprive the fishes of oxygen.

Daphnia have a transparent chitinous carapace, and vary in size according to age and genera – up to $^1/_5$ inch (5mm). The colour can also vary from red, green to almost black, depending upon their food source. Food may be algae, bacteria or infusorians. The bright red colour of some Daphnia is due to haemoglobin; as the oxygen content of the water decreases so the haemoglobin increases and thereby causes the blood to become a deeper red.

Daphnia can be found in many aquatic habitats, but mainly where heavy decomposition is taking place. Stagnant ponds, farmyard pools and ponds in city parks are some likely places where Daphnia may be found. In the spring large numbers of females hatch from eggs that have rested over the winter period. (*See* **Parthenogenesis).** These females will produce further living young every ten days or so. With a reduction in food or temperature, or some other adverse condition, the female Daphnia will begin producing eggs that hatch into males. Following this, the two sexes mate, the fertilized eggs then remain dormant during the adverse period, hatching as females when the conditions have improved and start the cycle over again. *See* **Live Foods.**

DAPHNIDAE. Family within the order of *GLADOCERA.* One of the most popular live-foods for fish. *Daphnia magna* can reach a diameter of ¼ inch (6mm). The Common Daphnia (*Daphnia pulex*) is slightly smaller. The two species prefer somewhat stagnant water in smallish ponds that are rich in algae. *Daphnia longispina* and *Daphnia cucullata* (Helmeted Daphnia) both prefer the larger ponds and lakes.

DECAPODA. Characterised by five pairs of legs. An order of crustaceans pertaining to the class of the *MALACOSTRACA,* it contains the larger crustaceans: divided into ***Natantia*** (shrimps and prawns) and ***Reptantia*** (crabs, lobsters, crawfish, crayfish, burrowing shrimps). They possess hard calcified shells and eyes on stalks. *See* **Crayfish.**

DECUMBENT. Botanical term for a prostrate plant whose stems turn upwards towards the tip.

DECUSSATE. Botanical term describing leaves which grow opposite each other, but at right angles to those above and below, as they grow up the stem.

DEFLEXED. Botanical term for leaves, or other organs, which bend downwards.

DEMERSAL. Sinks to the bottom, in water, as do some fish eggs.

DENTATE. *See below.*

DENTICULATE. Botanical term meaning toothed, usually applied to the edge formation of some leaves.

DENTOPLASM. The yolk.

DESMID. Large group of green, freshwater algae, similar to diatoms, quite commonly found as a green film on the water surface of stagnant ponds.

DETRITUS. Organic or plant debris which settles on the bottom.

DEWPOND. A specially prepared depression in the ground usually in a relatively waterless district, made to catch and retain any rainfall. Despite its name, it has little reliance upon dew.

DIAPAUSE. The state of dormancy through which insects and other invertebrates pass.

DIATOM. A class of microscopic one-celled algae. They have hard, siliceous cell-walls and can form a brown scum on stones, or the inside of the aquarium if it does not receive sufficient illumination.

DICOTYLEDON. Plants whose seedlings have two leaves (**cotyledons**). The leaves are usually broad, generally stalked and net-veined and includes: *Nymphaceae, Ceratophyllaceae, Ranunculaceae, Callitrichaceae* and others.

DIFFLUGIA. Shell-bearing amoebae.

DIMORPHIC. Having sharply contrasting forms.

DIMORPHISM. Differences in the form of live beings of the same species.

DIOCECIOUS. Refers to animals and plants that are unisexual; i.e. the male and female reproductive organs are carried, one or the other, by separate individuals.

DIOTIC. Botanical term for plants that carry the male and female flowers on separate plants.

DIPLOID. Organism with the chromosomes paired in the nucleus.

DISEASE OF FISH. Broadly speaking, fish diseases fall into two groups, parasitic and non-parasitic. At times it may be difficult to distinguish between the two, since they may overlap, one being the cause of the other, or several different diseases may show up on the same fish.

Bad management, cross-infection from one fish

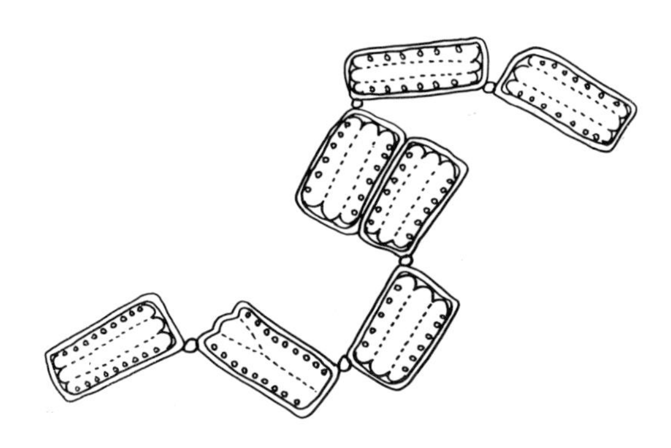

Figure 41 **Chain of Tabellaria Diatoms**

to another, lack of quarantine of new stock, failure to diagnose the early signs of the onset of disease, rough handling and accidents are all possible causitive agents which will aid the insurgence of disease.

Many of the maladies are due to parasites but a healthy fish possesses strong natural defences and, under the correct conditions, will be able to resist the eruption of disease. Under adverse conditions the natural defences are weakened thereby allowing the disease to manifest itself which, if the outbreak is in an environment that is overpopulated, can quickly assume the proportions of an epidemic.

Non-parasitic diseases may be inherited, or due to bad water conditions, incorrect feeding, accidents, and other external causes.

The diagnosis of disease is possible through observation, although it may not be possible to identify the specific disease. Any change in the normal colour or behaviour of a fish, or any anatomical changes – such as swellings – are likely to be signs that a disease has managed to infect the fish. It is a sensible precaution to isolate a suspect fish for closer attention, at the same time closely observing the fishes which have been in contact with it.

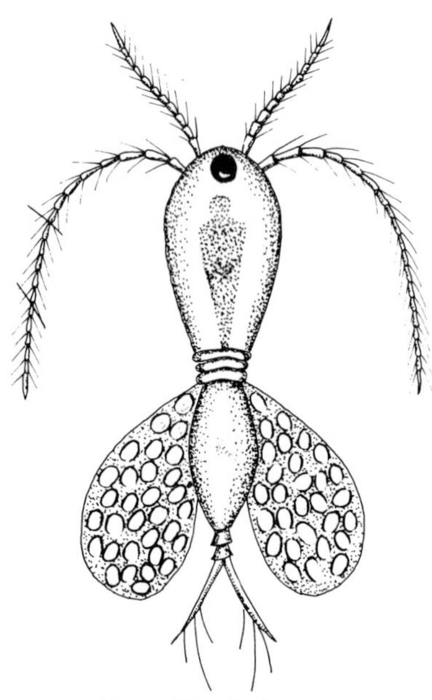

Figure 42 **Cyclops**

A healthy fish will swim with an active, well-balanced action; have its fins held erect most of the time; have bright, clear eyes; the scales will lie flat; the body will be clear of blemishes and the colours of normal intensity and brightness for its particular species.

Signs of disease may be any of the following, and usually are evidence that the problem has taken a firm hold upon the victim: sudden loss of appetite; close folded fins; hiding near the bottom; difficulty in swimming normally; gulping air at the surface; swimming in circles; shimmying movements; an inability to rise from the bottom, or bobbing to the surface like a cork; scratching on firm objects; bloody, inflamed areas on the body or fins; a bloated appearance with the scales protruding; clouding of the eyes or body colours; small white spots, pimples, ulcers, or cotton wool-like tufts of fungus; abnormally fast breathing; swollen gills; protruding eyes. These are a few of the many signs that signal the presence of some form of disease, and require prompt remedial action.

To minimize the incidence of disease the aquarist should apply the following principles of good management:

1. Always quarantine new fish for at least twenty-eight days before allowing them to come into contact with healthy fishes.
2. Avoid overcrowding, and ensure that the aquarium or pond is of adequate size. As a basis, allow 1 inch (25mm) of the fish's body length for every 24 square inches of the water surface area.
3. When transferring a fish always ensure that the temperature of the water equals that of the water from which it has been removed.
4. Feed correctly – do not overfeed. Avoid collecting live-foods from waters inhabited by fishes.
5. Avoid metals contaminating the water. Many metals, especially copper and brass, are exceedingly poisonous to fishes.
6. Immediately remove sick fish before they infect others.
7. Care for the fishes and their environment concientiously. *See* **Complaints of Fish.**

DISSIMILATION. The opposite of assimilation.

DISTICHOUS. Botanical term for leaves, flowers and other organs which are arranged in two exactly opposite rows.

DIVISION. Major grouping in botanical classification, being equivalent to a phylum in zoology.

DOMINANT. Most obvious or noticeable features, which may hide other unsuspected characteristics.

DORSAL. The upper margin, or back of fishes.

DORSAL FIN. The fin that grows from the upper back of a fish.

DRAGON-FLIES. Of the *ODONATA* order. These gaudy insects, with their shining membraneous wings are well known, and comprise forty-three British species – some large, some small. They are both predacious and carnivorous, devouring large numbers of other insects, including their own kind. Their nymphs are equally predacious, they have a so-called 'mask', a moveable structure with strong claws at its end. When at rest the mask is folded back under the head, but as soon as prey comes within reach, the mask is shot forward to seize the victim, after which it is slowly eaten. A sluggish creature, it lurks in wait for potential victims to come within striking distance and can even take small fish. These larvae have the apt title of 'Water-tigers'. *See* **Predators.**

DRIVE. Applied to the chase which takes place during the act of spawning by fishes – spawning drive. At this time the spawning instinct is so strong that fishes often become oblivious to any danger which may threaten them.

DRONE FLY. Common name of *Eristalis tenax:* its larvae is of the 'rat-tailed' type. *See* **Live Foods.**

DROPSOPHILA. Fruit flies.

DROPSY. A disease of fish whereby the scales of infected fish stand out from the bloated body.

DUCKWEED. *(Lemna).* Small, free-floating aquatic plant whose leaf-like fronds carry rootlets. This tiny plant will often grow so quickly that the surface is completely blanketed.

DYSTISCIDAE. The whirligig beetles. Predatory water beetles of the sub-order *ADEPHAGA.*

DYTISCUS. The **Great Diving Beetle.** This is a large, very predacious creature that will readily attack animals larger than itself. It can be found in most natural ponds, and is able to fly from one to another with ease. Olive-brown in colour with a yellow margin around the thorax and wing cases, it can grow to around 1½ inches (38mm). The larvae grow even larger, being up to 2 inches (51mm) long, and carry powerful sickle-shaped mandibles. They are even more vicious than the adult beetle. The victim is seized, and a digestive fluid pumped into it, the dissolved contents are then sucked out, leaving only an empty skin.

A relative of *Dytiscus,* which is very common in most natural ponds, is *Acilius sulcatus.* The adult has a flattish brown body and pronounced black markings on the head and thorax. The larvae is similar to that of *Dytiscus*, but has an exceptionally long first segment of the thorax, so that it appears to have a long neck.

DYSTROPHIC. Suffering from imperfect nutrition.

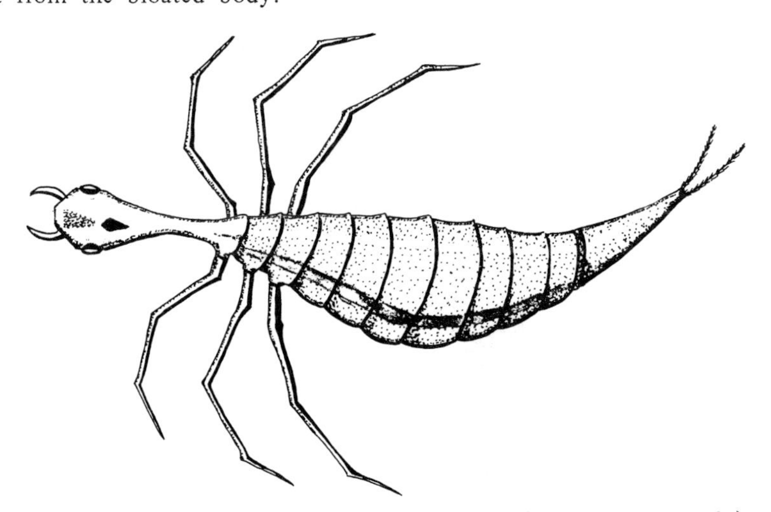

Figure 43 **Larva of *Acilius sulcatus*** (A close relative of *Dytiscus marginalis*)

E

EARTHWORM. Belonging to the order of *OLIGOCHAETA*. They are an excellent food for fish. Soil fertility owes much to the activity of the Earthworm, which also serves an important function by aerating the soil. They prefer a soil with a near neutral pH, which is neither too moist or too dry. The ultra-violet rays of the sun are lethal to the creature; for this reason they usually appear on the soil surface during the hours of darkness.

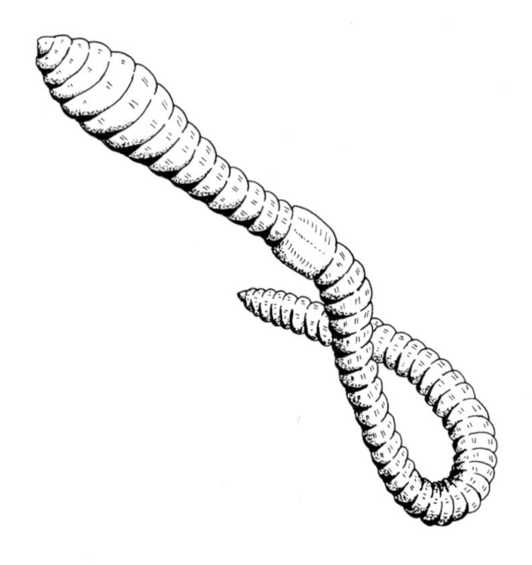

Figure 44 **Earthworm**

ECDYSIS. The periodic sloughing of the skin which commonly takes place in reptiles, amphibians and many insects.

ECOLOGY. The relationship between living creatures and plants and their environment.

ECTOPARASITES. Parasites which live upon the external surfaces of their host.

EEL. *See* ***Anguilla vulgaris.***

EGG. The earliest stage in the development of animals. The egg of an invertebrate is usually referred to as an ovum and is produced by the female. After fertilization, by the male sperm, a complicated process of cell division takes place within the egg to eventually form the embryo.

EGG, DEVELOPMENT OF. The development of a fish egg follows a set pattern. Upon being shed by the female it is fertilized by a male spermatozoon. The outer cover of the egg is pierced by a minute perforation, known as the **micropyle,** which allows only one spermatozoon to enter. Eggs which are not fertilized will become opaque and milky-white; within a short time they will be attacked by a fungal growth. Upon penetration by the spermatozoon, oily droplets contained within the egg fall to the bottom of the egg, leaving the yolk clear. The yolk granules drift to the top of the egg, forming a bump on the surface. In the meantime, the egg shell becomes slightly larger, hardens and lifts away from the egg itself. The surface bump quickly divides into two cells, these two cells divide and double in number again. Each cell so produced continues to divide and double itself, eventually forming two distinct layers of cells. The size of the multiplying cells gets smaller as the numbers increase, until a rounded cap is produced in the area of the **animal pole.** This stage is known as the **blastula,** and becomes flatter as the tiny cells continue to increase and move down over the yolk. As they progress towards the **vegetal pole,** the cells lift slightly to form a gap (the **blastcoele**) between themselves and the yolk.

Before long about one-third of the egg surface becomes covered by the blastoderm, and they begin to build up at the advancing margin. This 'piling-up' at the lateral margins of the **blastoderm** forms the 'egg-ring', and is the start of gastrulation. **Gastrulation** involves the cells in the thickening germ-ring moving underneath the blastoderm. The cells form a band which progressively elongates at the end nearest the vegetal pole, to produce the **embryonic shield.** The gastrula expands to almost cover the surface of the yolk, and a band of cells forms the embryonic **keel** in the centre of the shield.

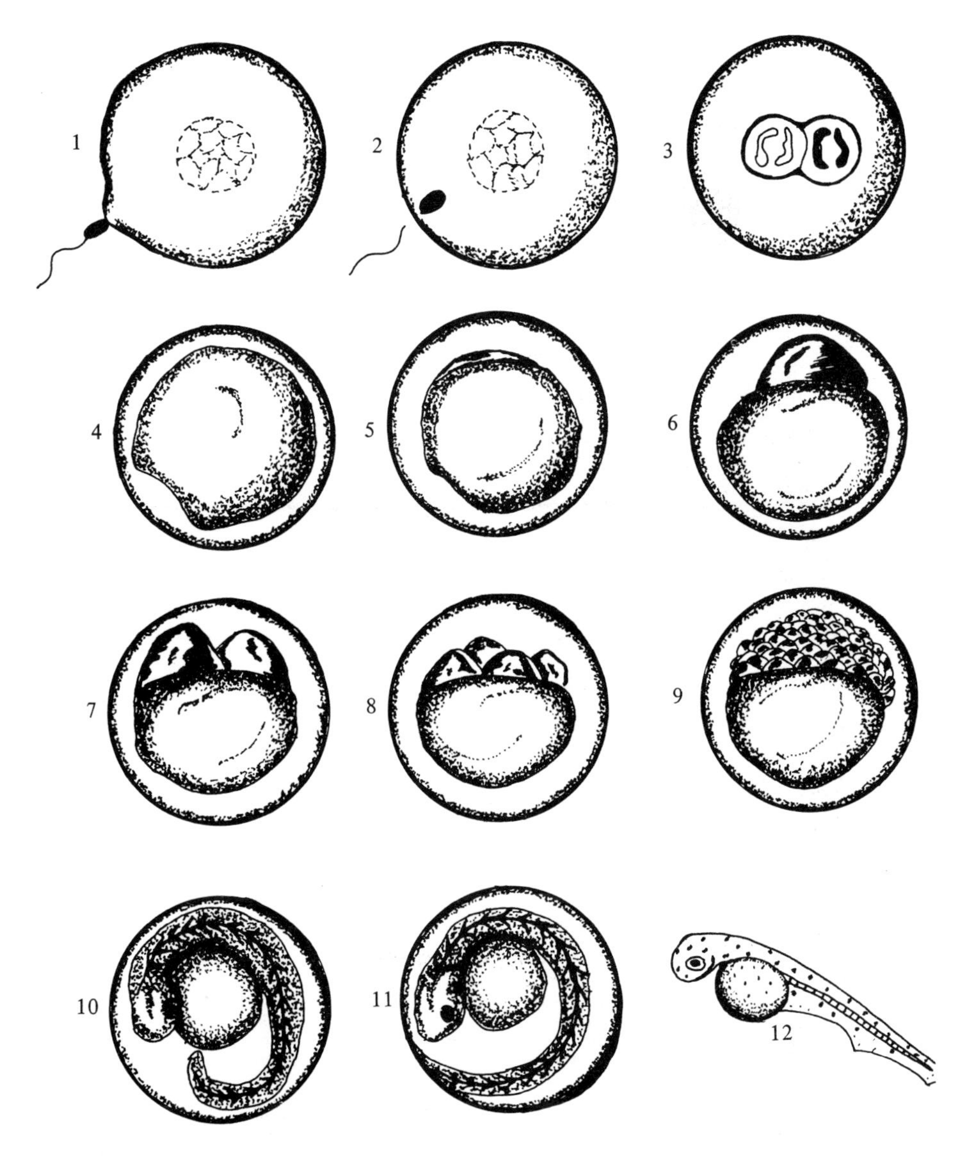

1. The sperm contacts egg, which forms a mound.
2. Sperm enters, through micropyle, and sheds its flagella.
3. The male and female protonucleus each develop two chromosomes, and the first phase of divisional development begins.
4. Shortly after insemination.
5. Perivitelline space is enlarged by admission of water.
6. Immediately before first furrowing of the germinal disc, which has become a cap.
7. The germinal disc furrows and forms two blastomers.
8. Four-cell stage created by further furrowing.
9. The cells continue to increase in number and diminish in size, creating a multi-cell stage – the blastula
10. The tail of the developing embryo lifts away from the yolk, and contracting movements begin.
11. Shortly before hatching. The body is covered in melanospores, the notochord can be seen, and the eye is very obvious – the 'eyed-stage'.
12. Alevin immediately after hatching.

Figure 45 **Development of a Fish Egg**

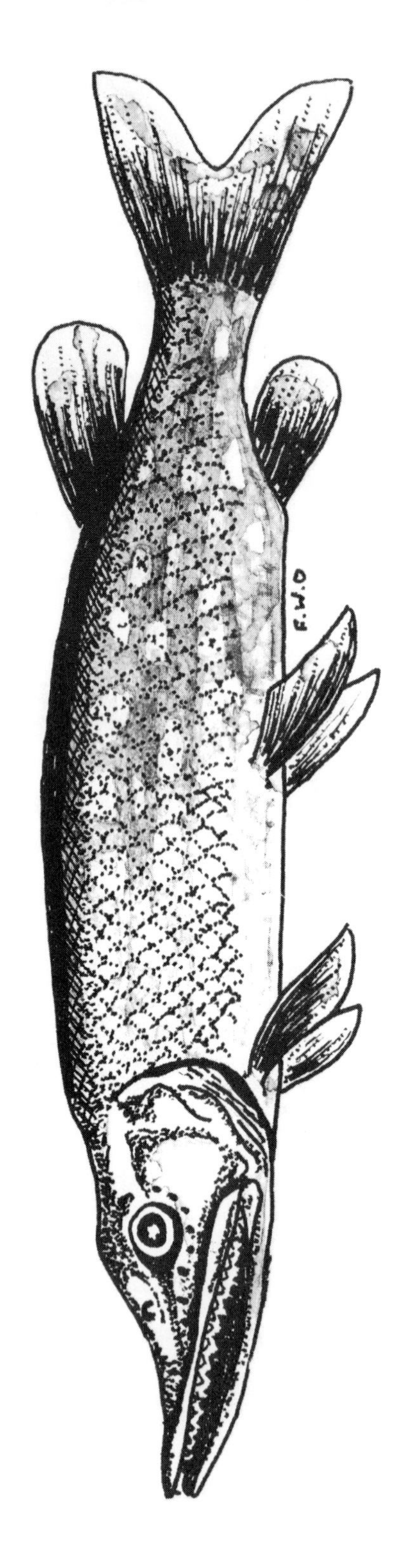

Figure 46 **Pike** *(Esox lucius)*

As development continues, optic vesicles form, which eventually become the eyes, and the main divisions of the brain appear as bulges on the dorsal surface of the keel. The head of the embryo lifts away from the yolk and soon slight contractions of the embryonic heart begin. The embryo grows substantially to cover about half of the circumference of the egg, and the tail lifts off the yolk. The **notochord**, which will become the backbone vertebrae, becomes visible, as do the pigmented eyes.

The pectoral fins form completely, but the only other fin is a combined dorsal/caudal/anal fin. This latter fin will split into the separate fins after hatching. The pelvic fins form after the pectorals.

Shortly before hatching, the embryo makes violent movements inside the egg shell. These movements, aided by an enzyme which softens the shell, enables the fry to break free. The tail emerges first from the egg shell, followed by the head.

The length of time taken for this process to occur, from start to completion, depends upon the species of fish and the prevailing water temperature. Usually, within reason, the warmer the water the shorter the time involved before hatching takes place. Conversely, the cooler the water the longer the process will take. If, however, the water becomes either too warm or too cold the egg may be killed.

EGLANDULAR. Botanical term meaning without glands.

ELASSOMA AKEFENAKEE. *See Elassoma evergladei under **Centrarchidae.***

ELASSOMA EVERGLADEI. The Pigmy Sunfish. *See under **Centrarchidae.***

ELODEA. Genus of sub-aquatic plants. *See* **Plants.**

ELVER. Young Common Eel of three years old, at the time it leaves the sea to enter British rivers. *See **Anguilla.***

EMARGINATE. Botanical term describing a leaf which is notched at its tip.

EMBRYO. Young organism within the egg shell (or mother's body) which will develop into the living animal.

EMERGED. Botanical term for plants which grow totally or partly above the surface of the water.

EMERSED. Growing or standing above the water surface.

ENCHYTRACEUS. Commonly known as the White Worm, a small soil-dwelling worm which is very popular with aquarist's as a live food for fish. It is easily cultivated in wooden boxes filled, not quite three-quarters full, with a mixture of loam and peat. A small depression is made in the surface of the soil and the starter culture of worms placed therein. A sheet of glass is laid upon the surface, to conserve moisture, and the box covered to exclude light. Feeding may be with soaked bread or boiled and mashed potatoes etc. Worms should not be removed until a thriving colony has become established. *See* **Live Foods.**

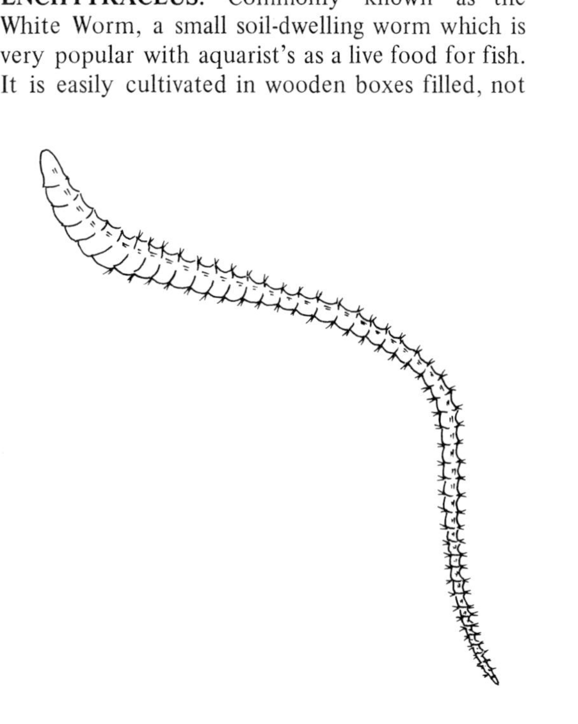

Figure 47 **White-worm** *(Enchytraceus)*

ENDOPARASITE. A parasite which lives inside its host.

ENNEACANTHUS. Genus of the ***Centrarchidae,*** or sunfishes.

ENSIFORM. Botanical term meaning sword-shaped.

ENTIRE. Collective term for all those external factors which influence a living being.

EPHEMEROPTER. Mayflies.

EPHIPPIUM. The hard, brown to blackish, protective cover of the winter eggs of Daphnia. It sits upon the back of the Daphnia like a saddle until shed. *See* **Daphnia.**

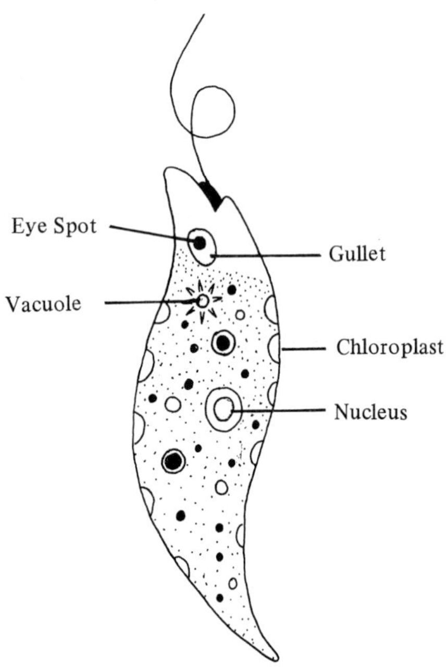

Figure 48 **Euglena**

EPIDERMIS. The outer layer of the skin.

EPIGEAL. Botanical term meaning above the ground.

EPITHELLIUM. Body tissue which is connected and covers the surface of the organs. It can consist of one or more layers.

ESOCIDAE. Pike-like family of fishes belonging to the *HAPLOMI.*

ESOX. Genus belonging to the above family.

ESOX LUCIUS. The Pike. Belonging to the ***Esocidae*** (Pike family) this is the only species found in British waters. The Common Pike has an elongate body covered with small scales. The dorsal fin is set well back, opposite the anal fin. It has no barbels and adipose fin. The gill opening is very wide. Its reputation for ferocity is well deserved for it has a large mouth bristling with sharp teeth, set in a broad flattened head. Of a predatory nature, its diet is normally composed of fish, but it will also take ducklings, small swimming birds, rats and voles, frogs and newts.

A Pike less than 5lb (2.3kg), is often called a **'jack'** and a young one a **pickerel.** They grow to quite a large size – 35 to 45 lb (15.9-20.4kg). Pike are by no means uncommon. Tate Regan recorded that when Whittlesea Mere was drained in 1851 a Pike was taken which weighed 52lb (23.6kg). From the fork of the tail to the end of the snout it measured 4 feet, 4 inches (132cm), of which the head measured a length of 13 inches (33cm).

Spawning takes place between February and May, the eggs being deposited in shallow water. The resulting fry have an insatiable appetite and grow rapidly.

The coloration of the adult Pike makes it well-nigh invisible when lurking in under-water vegetation. It is greenish, has white lower parts with yellow spots or wavy bands on the sides; dorsal, anal and caudal fins have dark spots or stripes

ETHOLOGY. The science which studies the causes and processes of animal behaviour.

EUGLENA. Genus of the FLAGELLATA. It has a spindle-shaped body with a simple flagellum. In large numbers they can turn shallow, stagnant water green. Can be used as a first food for fish alevins.

EUTROPHIC. Rich in dissolved nutrients.

EVOLUTION OF FISHES. Our knowledge of present day forms and their evolution are based upon the study of fossil deposits. From this we know that present day fishes represent only a fraction of the many life-forms which have inhabited our planet during the passing centuries.

The earliest impressions and remains of fishes are found in the Middle and Upper Silurian Age. There are no earlier fossils, possibly because those primitive forms, if there were any, had too few solid parts in their structure for any to remain as evidence of their existence. The first fishes may well have developed from forms closely related to the **Tunicates** and **Lancetfishes.**

In the Silurian Age there are representatives of the **Jawless fishes.** These were primitive fish-like vertebrates with their jaws set in muscular sacs – **Sac-jawed fishes.** They had neither gills nor jawbones, and are possibly the ancestors of today's CYCLOSTOMATA – Round-mouthed fishes. The fossils of these fishes show that they were covered by bony plates.

Other heavily armoured kinds are found in the Devonian and Carbiniferous Ages: the **Armoured fishes** or **Placodermata.** We know that these belong to the true fishes, because they had jawbones; they probably also possessed paired limbs. They were very possibly the ancestors of the sharks. These fishes were of varying sizes, and show a multitude of forms and manner of living. Some were very large and had teeth that were six inches (152mm) in length.

It is in the Triassic Age that we find traces of our present day **Cartilaginous fishes,** their fossils differing very little to those forms which are living today.

Traces of **Bony fishes** can be found in the Devonian Age, and it is quite possible that they share a common ancestor with the Cartilaginous fishes. At the beginning of the Triassic Age we find the forebears of the present-day Sturgeon-like fishes. There were other orders belonging to this group: the *DIPNEUSTI,* or **Lungfishes,** were widely distributed, whilst today only a few representatives remain. Another order was the *NEOPTERYGII,* or **New Fins,** and they alone have developed fully and encompass around 20,000 of todays living species. They are traceable from the Permian Age.

From the Permian Age onwards the modern forms slowly came into being. Herring-like fishes are found in the Jurassic Age; from these the eels developed and beside them numerous orders of Bony fishes, the most recent being the Perch-like fishes. Our present day fishes have evolved over aeons of time in the development of our world and, although not obvious, are continuing to do so.

EXOPHTHALMY. A disease that affects the eyes of fish causing them to become pop-eyed.

EXOSKELETON. A hard external structure which supports the body of an animal, as with the shell of a snail.

EXTERNAL FEATURES OF FISH. Certain features are common to the majority of fishes, although they may vary in form, shape and placement depending upon the particular species.

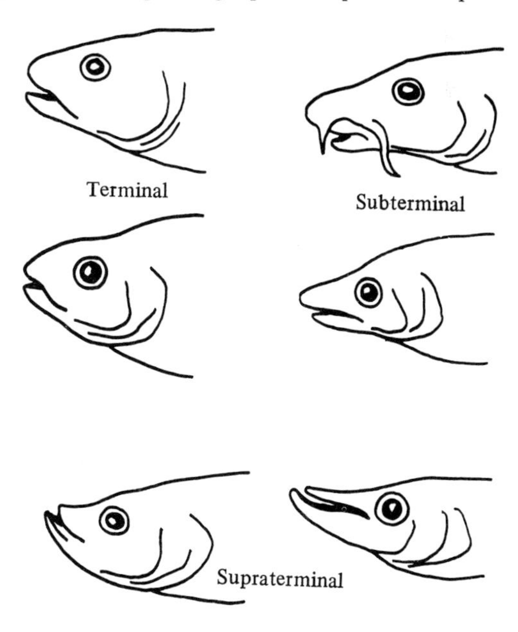

Figure 49 **Fish Mouth Types**

The dorsal fin, for instance, may be in the form of a single fin or it may be more or less divided into two fins, in which case the anterior fin may well be spiny, whilst the rear fin is composed of the more usual flexible rays. Some species carry a small, fleshy adipose fin behind the dorsal fin. The caudal fin may also be of varied shape and size, as may the anal fin; much depends upon the species of fish. The pectoral and pelvic (or ventral) fins are always paired, one of each on the lower of both sides of the fish. *See* **Fins.**

EXTERNAL

Some fish may have a leathery skin, others bony plates. Most, however, have their bodies protected by scales. Often a line of dots can be seen along the sides of the fish, these are the minute pores of the lateral line. *See* **Scales of Fish** *and* **Lateral Line.**

The respiratory organs are the gills which are situated on the side of the head where it joins the body. Bottom feeding fish can often be identified by the fleshy appendages, barbels, attached near the mouth. *See* **Anatomy of Fish, Skeleton of Fish, Skin of Fish** *and also the illustration of the External Features – this shows the different features of the various species incorporated in a single compound drawing of a fish.*

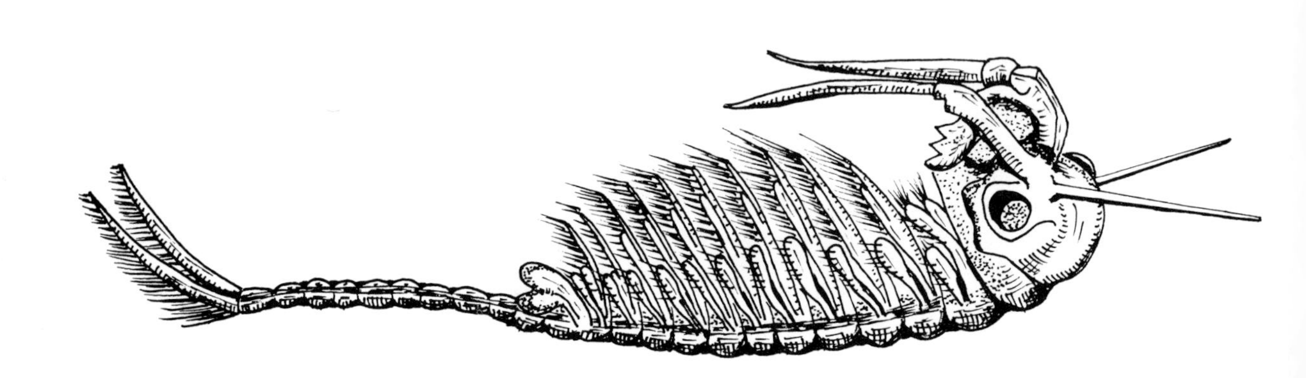

Figure 50 **Fairy Shrimp** *(Chirocephalus diaphanus)*

F

FAIRY SHRIMP *(Chirocephalus diaphanus).* A freshwater crustacean, of the order *ANOSTRACA,* which grows to a length of 1 inch (25mm), is transparent, swims on its back, and occupies temporary pools which dry up during the summer.

FAMILY. A group in the classification of living organisms, consisting of related genera.

FANCY GOLDFISH. All Goldfish are members of the ***Cyprinidae*** – the Carp family – and classified as *Carassius auratus.* This species, however, is very easily interbred and 'moulded' so that many bizarre forms of the one fish have been created. There is some doubt about the earliest date that the Goldfish was first cultivated on a serious scale. However, there is evidence that the fish was being cultivated during the Chinese Sung Dynasty, which was somewhere around 1000AD. During this period Chinese literature contained many references to the Goldfish, thus proving that the species had become well known by that time. Two districts compete for the honour of being the first to produce red Goldfish – the district of Che Chiang Chen, and the district of Chiang Su Chen.

The ancient Chinese segregated those fish which showed mutation in body shape, finnage or colour and, by selective breeding, propogated the new feature. Further variations were created by cross breeding the differing types. Over the following centuries the Chinese developed many different varieties. A number of the Chinese varieties of Goldfish were depicted in the scroll which was sent from Peking to Paris in 1772 – known as the **Peking Scroll** it resides in the Musée Nationale d'Histoire Naturelle, in Paris. By 1500 the Goldfish had become established in Japan, but it appears that they were not bred there until two centuries later. The honour of being the first to breed the Goldfish in Japan is credited to Sata Sanzaemon of Koriyama, during the Hoyei era of 1704-1710. With the passage of time the Japanese created a number of new varieties that differed from those produced by the Chinese breeders.

The Goldfish spread rapidly throughout much of the western world; by the middle of the eighteenth century it was widespread in England; by 1889 America had established its first fish farm in Maryland.

Of the many varieties of fancy Goldfish the following are possibly those best known to western fish keepers.

Common Goldfish– Probably the first deviation from the wild form. A good specimen has a sturdy well-proportioned appearance. The back is moderately curved with a similar curve to the underside of the body. The attractive features of this fish are its colour and brightly shining metallic-like scales. It may be a single colour; i.e. reddish-orange, orange or yellow, but can be variegated by exhibiting combinations of the following colours: reddish-orange, orange, yellow or silvery-white. Black may also be seen, but this is not a permanent colour and will disappear with time. It may also be found that the silver areas will slowly get larger until the fish finally becomes only that one colour.

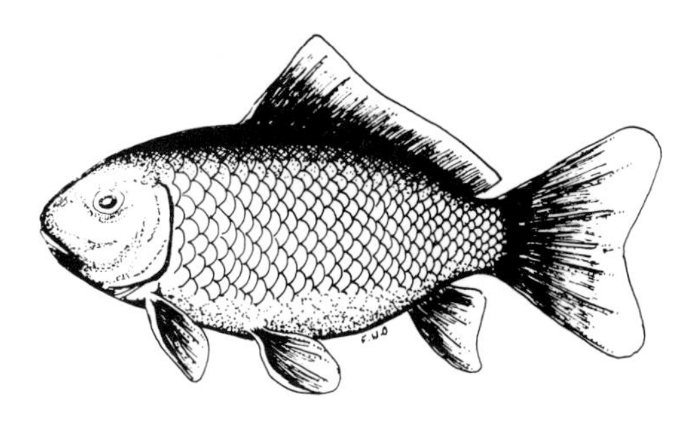

Figure 51 **Common Goldfish**

London Shubunkin– In shape this variety is

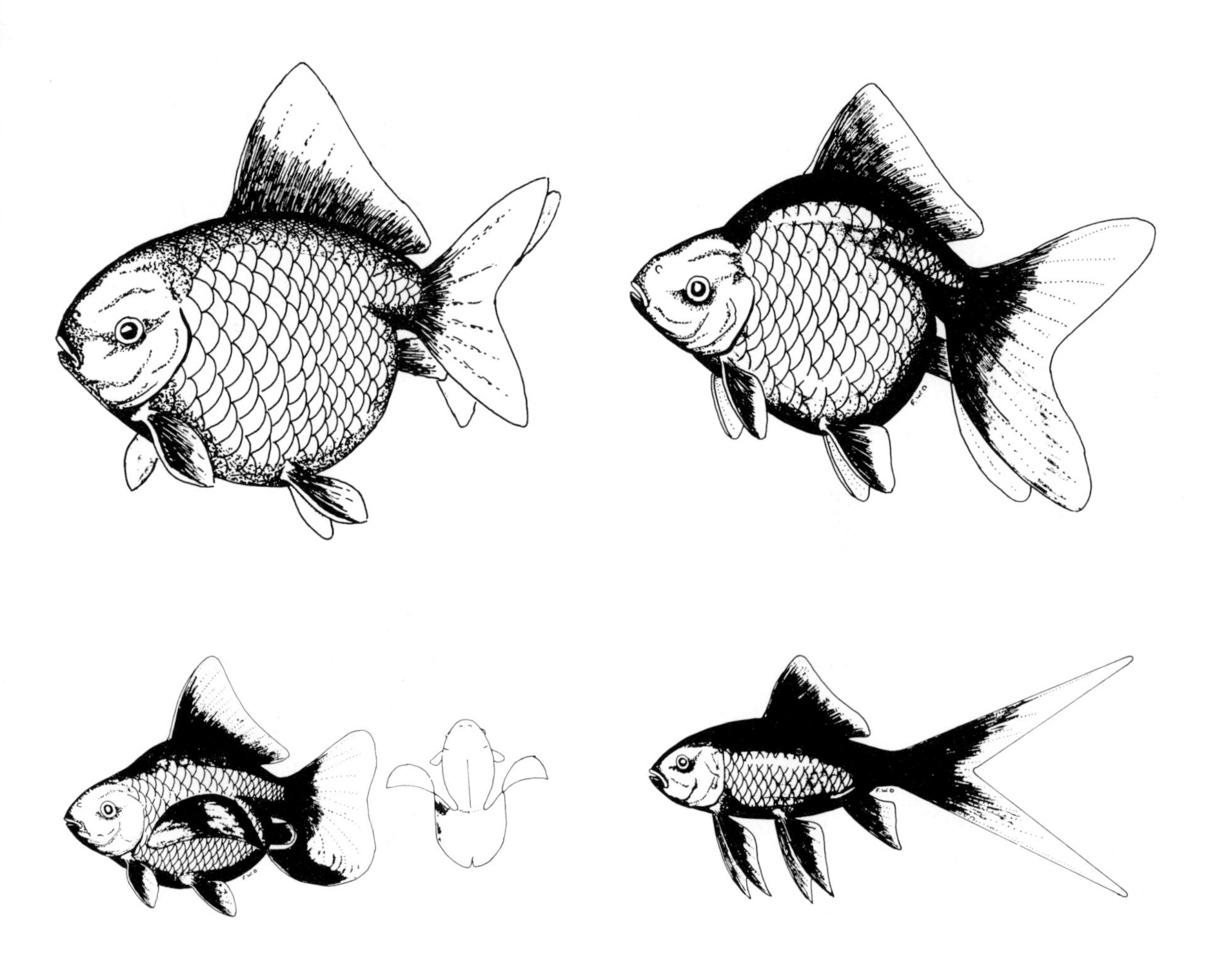

Figure 52 **Fancy Goldfish Varieties – 1**
Top left: Fantail *Top right:* Ryukin
Bottom left: Tosakin *Bottom right:* Comet

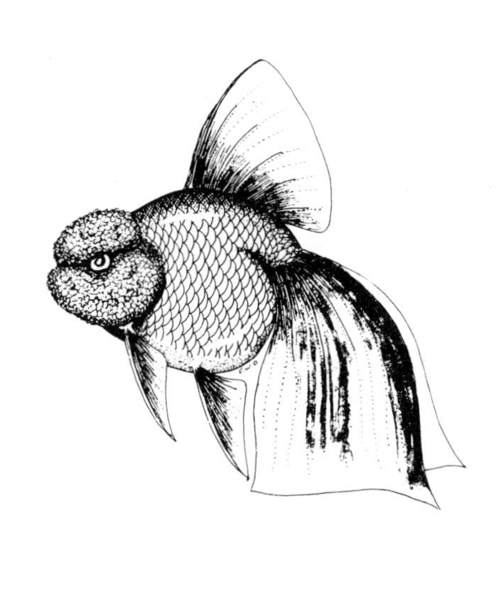

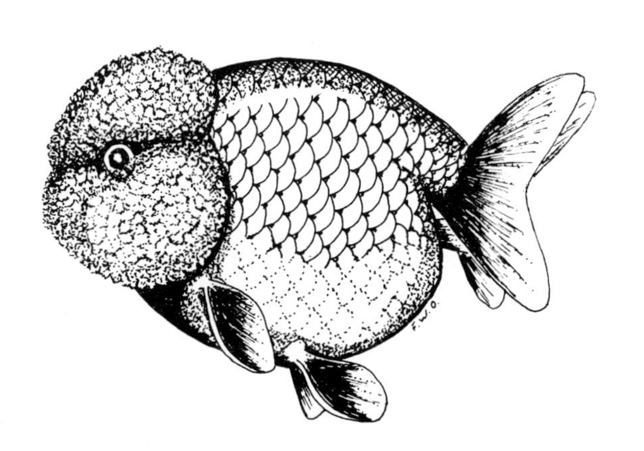

Figure 53 **Fancy Goldfish Varieties – 2**

Top left: Veiltail *Top right:* Oranda
Bottom left: Lionhead *Bottom right:* Phoenix

identical to the Common Goldfish – of which it is a variation. The difference lies in the absence of the metallic shine. The fish is mostly covered with transparent scales and exhibits a patchwork of colours. Ideally the background colour should be a bright forget-me-not blue interspersed with patches of red, yellow, brown, violet and black, over which there is black speckling. The colours should spread into the fin. This non-reflective type of coloration is known as **nacreous** – or the older term of **calico.**

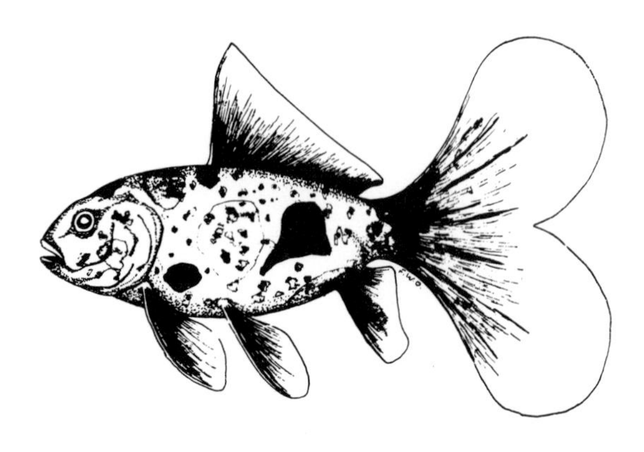

Figure 54 **Bristol Shubunkin**

Bristol Shubunkin– So called because this variety was developed in England by members of the **Bristol Aquarist's Society** – the society produced the first show standard for this fish in 1934. This is another nacreous variety, having the same coloration as the previously described fish. The body is slim and streamlined, with a high dorsal fin. The main feature of this fish is the caudal fin which is much larger than usual and has large rounded lobes; the other fins are equally well developed. A most attractive fish, probably the most colourful of the Goldfish varieties.

Wakin– This is the 'Common Goldfish' of Japan. It has a very similar appearance to the Common Goldfish, except that the caudal fin is double.

Jikin– The Peacock Tail. A very old Japanese variety developed from the Wakin. The body is somewhat thicker in the region of the belly and slightly compressed vertically. The best specimens have a silver body with red lips and fins. The distinguishing feature is the caudal fin. Seen from behind it is shaped like an 'X' and is attached to a broad peduncle. The axis of the caudal fin is almost perpendicular to the axis of the body.

Ryukin– Japan's second most popular variety. In this fish is seen the first real deviation towards the short, deep bodied types. The moderately compressed body is short and deepish, often there is a pronounced hump where the back joins the head. The fins are longer than those of the Wakin; the caudal is forked and divided into two fins, the anal fins are also paired.

Fantail– This is the western version of the Ryukin. It can best be described as an egg-shaped fish with a caudal fin which is deeply forked and divided into two fins. It is not so deep bodied as the Ryukin and should have no trace of a hump. There is a type that has very protuberant eyes. These are known as telescope-eyed.

Tosakin– Probably a sport from the Ryukin, which it resembles. The main differences are a slightly shallower body and shorter fins together with a peculiarity of the caudal fin. The lower lobes are greatly extended with upturned outer edges; the fin has the appearance of being reversed and spread out in the direction of the head.

Comet– Slimmer than the Bristol Shubunkin, it has similar finnage except that the caudal fin is as long as the body, and very deeply forked. Yellow is the most usual colour; however, a deep reddish-orange is preferred. This variety was developed during the early 1800s by Hugo Mullert, an American aquarist living in Philadelphia.

Veiltail– There are both normal and telescope-eyed forms of this variety. The caudal fin is divided into two separate fins, falling gracefully to a broad, square-cut lower edge. The anal fin is also long and paired into two matching fins. All other fins are equally well developed. Created in Philadelphia, during the nineteenth century, by American aquarists.

Moor– A telescope-eyed variety of a deep velvet black colour which extends to the tip of all the fins. The body and finnage is identical to the Veiltail.

Oranda– Identical to the Veiltail, except for the head. The head is covered with a warty growth, which leaves only the eyes, nostrils and mouth exposed. This raspberry-like growth is known as the **'hood'**, (in Japan it is called a 'wen'). The nacreous form of this variety is sometimes given the Japanese name of **Azumanishiki.**

Lionhead– Also known by its Japanese name of **Ranchu**, where it is considered to be the 'King of Goldfish'. This variety has a short, rather deep body that is broad across the back, and a short strong peduncle. The fins are short and sturdy, the anal and caudal fins being paired into matching fins. There is a noticeable lack of a dorsal fin, and the head is covered, like the Oranda, in a raspberry-like hood.

Redcap Oranda and **Redcap Lionhead**– These are simply colour variations of their respective varieties – although the 'hoods' are usually much smaller, tending to be confined to the top of the head. The body is silver and the top of the head red – hence the name.

Phoenix– The body shape is midway between the Common Goldfish and the Lionhead; it also lacks a dorsal fin. The fins are very long, the anal being paired and the double caudal fin deeply forked to give a 'ribbon-tail'.

Pearlscale– Usually silver with large patches of deep reddish-orange. The body is very fat, with a deep belly and flatish back. The fins are very similar to the Fantail, although the caudal fin is not so deeply forked. The main feature of this variety are the scales, which are 'domed', having raised centres. The outer edges have slightly darker margin. The scales lie in even rows along the body and give a distinct 'pearl-like' effect as they reflect the light.

Pompon– Closely resembling the Lionhead in body and finnage but having a normal head. There are two types of this variety: one has the full complement of fins, whereas the other lacks a dorsal fin – British aquarists prefer the latter type. This fish derives its name from the fact that the **narial septa** – the tissue which divides each of the two nostrils – are abnormally enlarged into bundles of fleshy lobes, known as narial bouquets. These ball-like appendages float in front of the eyes.

Celestial– A longish bodied fish with similar finnage to the Ryukin. In this variety the telescope-eyes are turned upwards, so that they gaze heavenwards – hence the name. It has no dorsal fin.

Toadhead– Very similar to the Celestial. The eyes are normal, but below each is a small bladder-like growth which gives a somewhat toad-like aspect to the face.

Figure 55 **Celestial**

Bubble-eye– Similar to the preceding variety. Below the eyes are large fluid-filled sacs, causing the fish to look vaguely like a telescope-eyed fish. Unlike the firm telescope-eye, however, the sacs are soft like water-filled bladders. As the fish swims the bladders move in a most grotesque fashion.

Meteor– A strange egg-shaped fish which has no caudal fin. The lack of a caudal fin is compensated by the over-development of the other fins – especially the pectoral and anal fins.

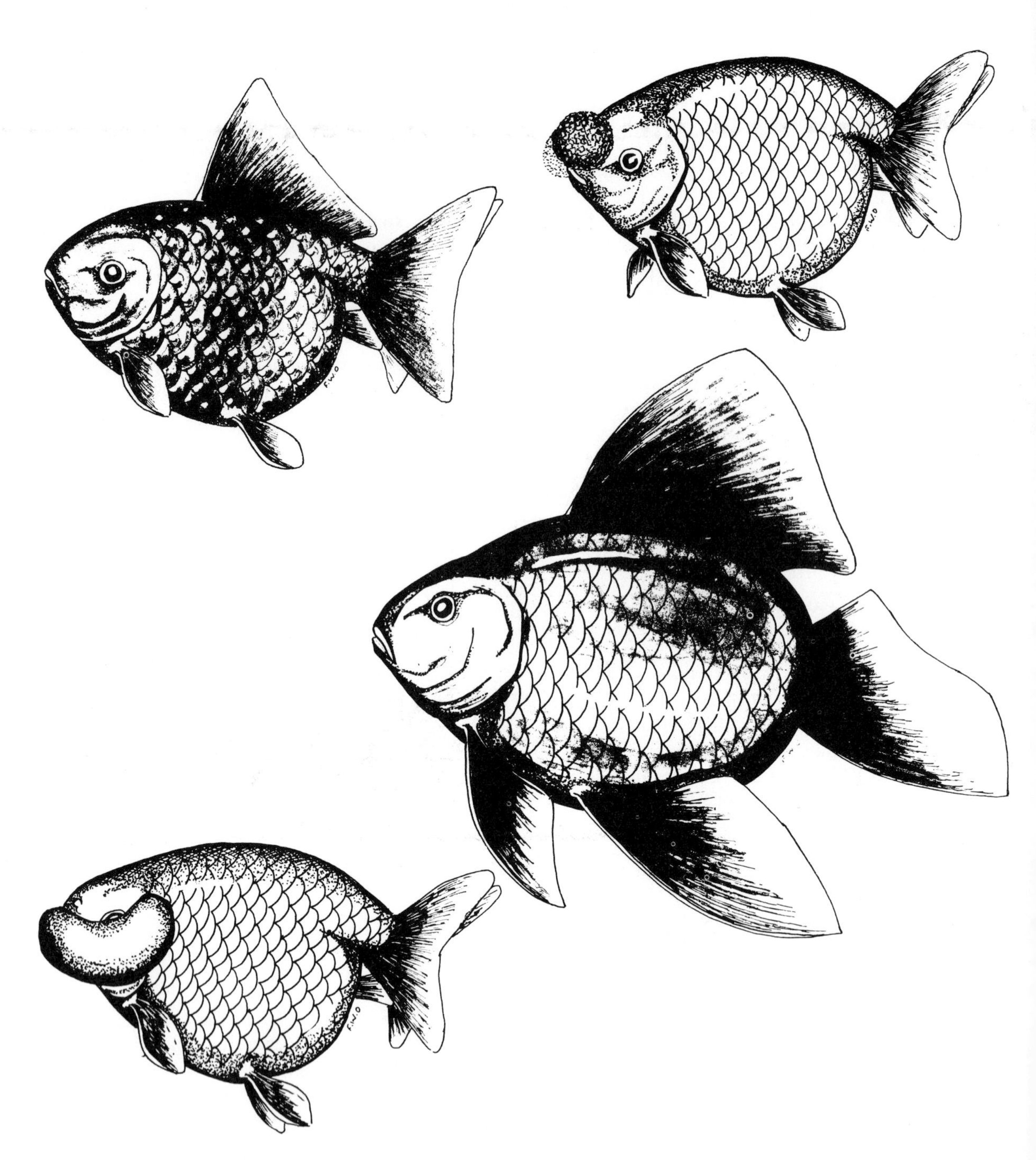

Figure 56 **Fancy Goldfish Varieties – 3**

Top left:	Pearlscale	*Top right:*	Pompon
Bottom left:	Bubble-eye	*Bottom right:*	Meteor

Other varieties– It has been estimated that there are more than 100 different varieties of fancy Goldfish. Many may never be seen in the West, whilst others may be much too grotesque to find acceptance outside their homeland. Many of the varieties may be found in both the bright metallic scaled form and the nacreous multi-coloured form.

Readers wishing to learn more about fancy Goldfish should obtain a copy of the author's book *Fancy Goldfish Culture* which deals comprehensively with all aspects of the Goldfish.

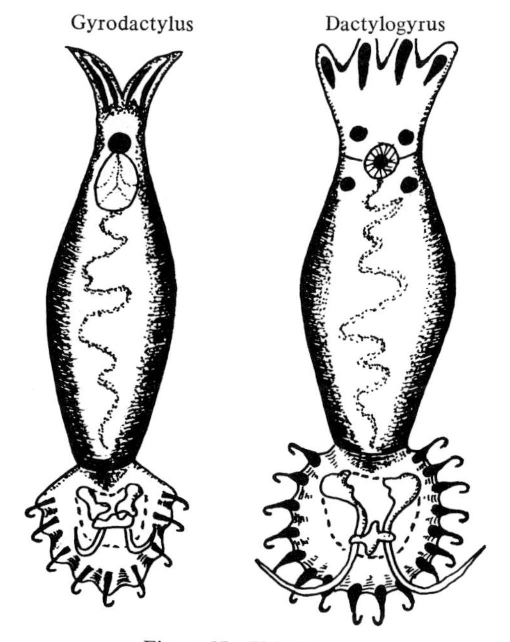

Figure 57 **Fish Flukes**

FANTAIL. *See* **Fancy Goldfish.**

FAUNA. The animal population.

FECUNDATION. The joining together, or union, of two sexually different cells and their nuclei to form a new organism. It serves the purpose, usually, of combining the hereditary characteristics of two individuals and starts the development of the female egg. In animals, fecundation generally takes place during mating.

The male and female cells, or **gametes,** are always of a different shape. The notile male sperm cells search out the female egg. Only the head and so-called intermediate part of the sperm cell penetrates the female egg, the tail, or flagella, being discarded. The head then swells to form a nucleus, with a nuclear structure, and fuses with the female nucleus. When this happens it is proof that fertilization has taken place successfully. *See* **Egg, Development of.**

FERAL. Living in a wild state. Not domesticated.

FILIFORM. Botanical term meaning thread-like.

FILTRATION. The employment of a filter to maintain the water in a state of clarity.

FINS. Organ of a fish composed of very thin, spine-like, flexible bones which are connected to a fine membrane. Depending upon the location of a particular fin it may be used for locomotion, steering, or stability of position. The shape, size, position and number of fins can vary according to the species.

FISH. Cold-blooded, aquatic vertebrate which breathes through gills, the blood temperature varying according to that of the surrounding water. They have fins instead of limbs.

FISH FLUKES. Unsegmented flatworms of the *TREMATODA* class, which infect the skin or gills of fish.

Gryodactylus (the Skin Fluke) is about 1mm long, and bears living young which will immediately attach themselves to the same host when born. *Dactylogyrus,* or the Gill Fluke, attaches itself to the gills. They are egg-bearing, and the young have to find a host after hatching. Flukes attach themselves by driving strong hooks into their host, whilst also secreting a thick, sticky liquid which assists them in clinging firmly. *See* **Complaints of Fish.**

FISH LOUSE. Common name for *Argulus. See Argulus and* **Complaints of Fish.**

FISTULAR. Botanical term for a hollow tubular stem.

FLAGELLATE. Phylum of minute unicellulars or protozoans which move by means of flagellum. They are so primitive that there is some doubt whether they should be classified as animals or plants.

FLAGELLUM. Minute plasm threads which may be found singly or in number, performing similar functions to cilia.

FLATWORMS. Primitive phylum of worms (PLATYHELMINTHES), that have flat, segmented bodies. The classes include planarians, tapeworms and flukes.

FLORA. The world of plants, usually applied to the plants of a region.

FLUKE. Order of small parasitic flatworms which includes both endo- and exoparasitic species. *See* **Fish Flukes.**

FONTINALACEAE. Family of aquatic mosses, commonly known as Willow Mosses.

FONTINALIS ANTIPYRETICA. An aquatic Willow Moss which is distributed throughout the cold and temperate zones of the world. It attaches itself to firm solid surfaces such as rocks by means of ramified threads called rhizoids, it has no true roots. The plant can reach a length of 20 inches (51cm) and forms quite dense bushes.

FORGET-ME-NOT. Common name for *Myosotis.*

FREE-SWIMMING. A stage in the development of fish fry, after hatching, when the yolk has been consumed, the digestive system has fully developed, and the larva, which up to this point has been unable to swim, inflates the air bladder at the water surface, assumes a horizontal position and begins to swim without effort.

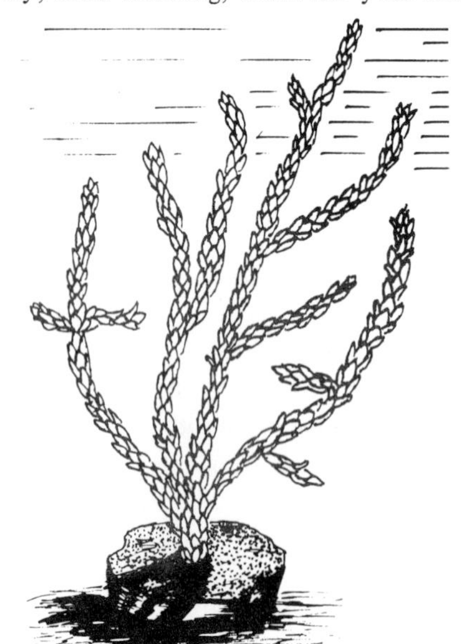

Figure 58 *Fontinalis antipyretica* – **Willow Moss**

FROG. Web-footed and tail-less amphibian of the order *SALIENTIA.* In Britain the early springtime masses of eggs are becoming less common in local waters. Although diminishing in numbers, it is found widespread in many areas. *See* **Amphibians.**

FROG-BIT. Common name for *Hydrocharis morsus ranae.*

FRY. Collective term for very young fish.

FUNGUS. Term given to the disease caused by parasitic fungi. **Saprolegnia** attacks weakened fish and open wounds and is a secondary consequence. **Ichthyophonus** is very dangerous and gives little if any external warning that a fish is affected, confining its attack to the internal organs and nervous system and eventually killing the fish. *See* **Complaints of Fish.**

FURUNCULOSIS. A serious bacterial disease, especially of Salmonids, which is characterized by sores, or 'furuncles'. *See* **Complaints of Fish.**

FUSIFORM. Botanical term meaning spindle-shaped.

Figure 59 **Frog-Bit** *(Hydrocharis morsus ranea)*

G

GAMETES. Sexually different germ cells, such as the female egg cells and male sperm cells.

GAMMARUS. The Freshwater Shrimp of the ***Gammaridae*** family, which belongs to the order *AMPHIPODA*. They can be carriers of parasitic fish worms. Living in clear, slow or still waters, they feed upon decaying animal and vegetable matter.

GASTEROSTEIDAE. Of the order *THORACOSTEIR,* this is the family of Sticklebacks.

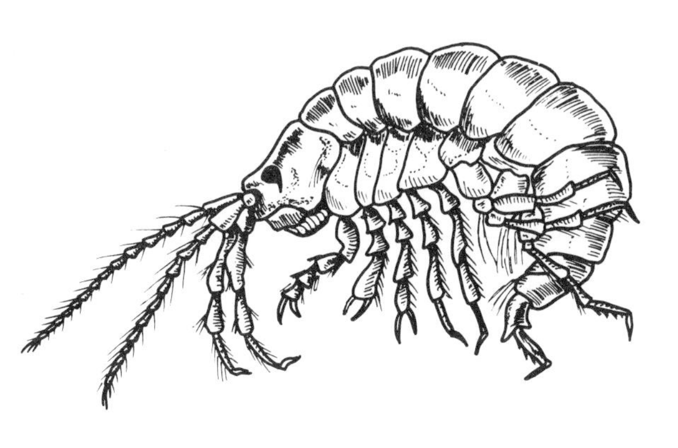

Figure 60 **Freshwater Shrimp** *(Gammarus)*

GASTEROSTEUS. Sticklebacks.

Gasterosteus aculeatus– The **Three-spined Stickleback.** Common everywhere in the British Isles, this is a small, pugnacious, active fish, seldom more than 2 inches (51mm) long. On the back are two strong spines, followed by a smaller one, behind which is the dorsal fin. In place of the pelvic fins are a strong spine and a ray; this soft ray can be used to project the spine outwards as an offensive weapon. The body is more or less covered with little bony shields or scales, taking the place of the more usual fish scales.

It has a greenish back and silvery sides, shot with pale blue and pink. During the breeding season the belly of the female turns yellow, whilst the male assumes a vivid red belly and dark bands on the silvery sides. Predacious in habit, the Stickleback lives in small shoals, preferring water where it hunts insects, worms, fish spawn and small fish fry.

This species constructs a round nest, during the breeding season, by lacing together the leaves of underwater plants along with any other suitable material. These are bound with a sticky thread which is produced from the kidneys of the male who is responsible for building the nest; the female takes no part in the proceedings. Once the nest is completed, the male flaunts his colours in front of a female, until he induces her to enter the nest and lay her eggs. These he fertilizes immediately, then repeats the process with other females. During the hatching period the male guards the nest, forcing a water current over the eggs by fanning his pectoral fins. The eggs take between eight and twelve days to hatch, after which the fry are kept inside the nest until they are big enough to fend for themselves. During this time the male defends the nest against any possible enemy with some ferocity.

Gasterosteus pungitius– The **Ten-spined Stickleback.** Very similar in all respects, apart from the number of dorsal spines, to the Three-spined Stickleback.

Gasterosteus spinachia– The **Fifteen-spined Stickleback** is a salt-water Stickleback.

GASTROPOD. Of the family ***Mollusca*** this class is distinguished by a fleshy foot and a hardly separated head with mouth, eyes and feelers. The flattened underside of the foot affords locomotion by the contraction of muscles. The mantle, a fold in the body-wall, produces a shell-forming substance. The internal organs are protected by a tough sac, the mantle and shell. Most snails are hermaphrodites and lay eggs, but there are some which are live bearing. *See* **Mollusc.**

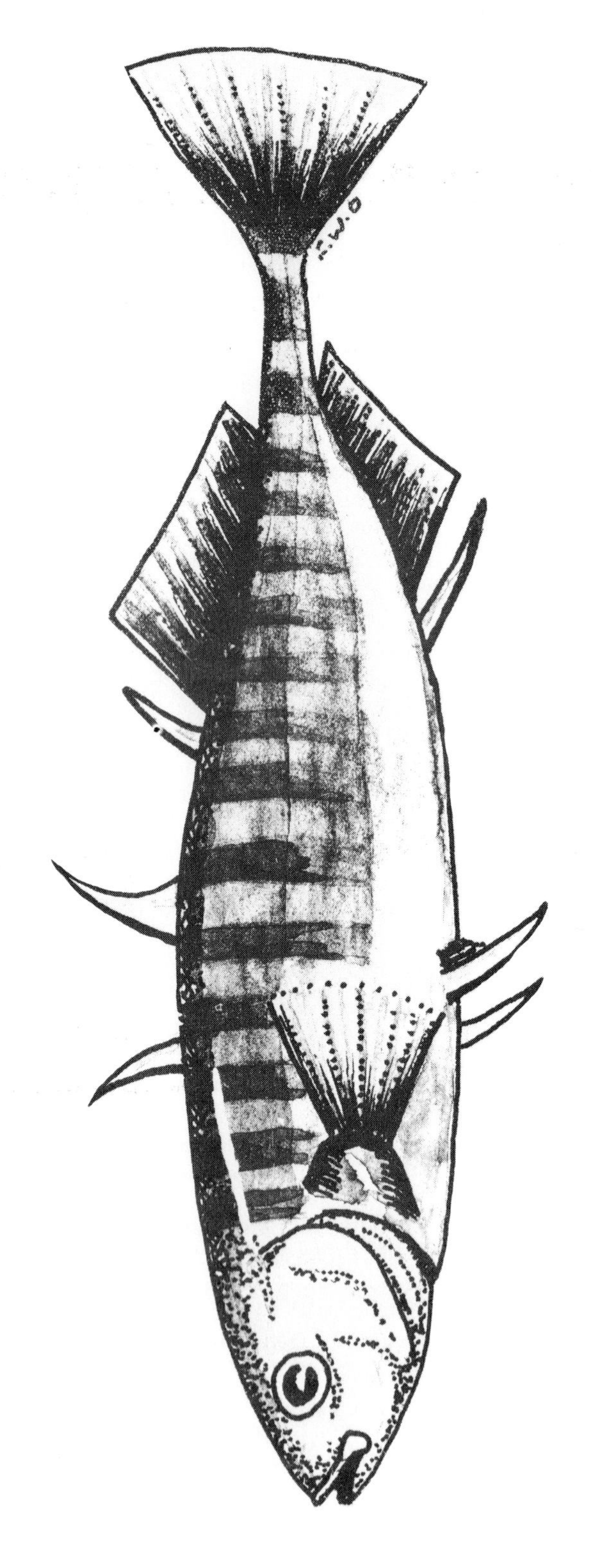

Figure 61 **Stickleback**

GASTRULA. The second stage in the development of an embryo, following the blastula and cleavage. *See* **Egg, Development of.**

GASTRULATION. Complex movements of the cells which occur after cleavage. *See* **Egg, Development of.**

GENE. The basic unit of physical inheritance, genes are pairs of chromosomes, each gene being derived from one or other of the parents.

GENERA. Plural of genus.

GENETICS. The scientific study of heredity and hereditary influences and variations.

GENICULATE. Botanical term meaning bent like a knee.

GENOTYPE. The basic genetic construction of an individual.

GENUS. Next in line to the smallest division in the biological classification of living beings, in which are gathered together a larger or smaller number of species of the same evolutionary origin that resemble each other in body structure and function. Closely related genera are grouped into **families.**

GEOPHYTE. A perennial plant whose buds over-winter in the soil.

GERMINAL CELLS. Cells which are developed within the sexual organs. As a general rule the germ cells are differentiated into female ovum and male sperm.

GERMINATION. To begin to grow.

GHOST LARVA. The transparent aquatic larva of the Phantom Midge. *See* **Phantom Midge.**

GILLS. Respiratory organs of fish.

GLASS WORMS. *See* **Phantom Midge.**

GLAUCOUS. Dull greyish green or blue.

GLOCHIDIUM. The larva of a Freshwater Mussel. which is parasitic on fish during its early life. *See* **Mollusc.**

GLOGER'S RULE. The tendency for the pigmentation of warm-blooded species to become increasingly paler as the mean temperature of their habitat decreases; i.e. the darker colours of tropical species as opposed to the paler colours of species inhabiting colder areas.

GLOSSIPHONIIDAE. Family of small flat leeches, which swim little or not at all, but cling to stones and plants. They suck the blood of cold-blooded vertebrates, sometimes even snails or worms. Their small size makes them easily overlooked.

GNAT. Order of *NEMATOCERA*; a family of delicate, two-winged flies, the larger of which *(Culicinae)* are now usually called Mosquitoes.

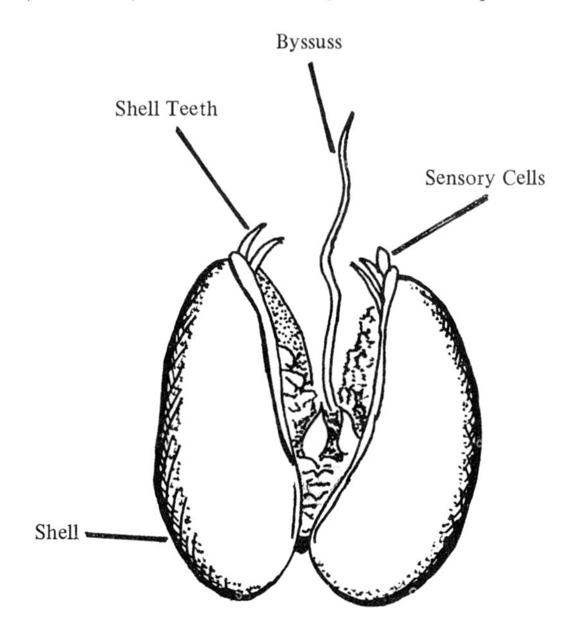

Figure 62 **Glochidium**

These flies pass through an aquatic larval stage, some forms being useful live-food for fish. The Common Mosquito, *Culex pipiens,* is generally known as the **Common Gnat.** The larva of the Phantom Midge, *Chaoborus crystallinus,* is known as **Ghost** or **Glass Larva** and **Glass Worm.**

Winter Gnats have the appearance of small Crane Flies, and are noted for their dancing swarms. They do not bite humans. There are a number of other members of the order throughout the world.

GNATHOBDELLODEA. Another family of leeches which attain a much larger size than the *Glossiphoniidae,* and includes the **Horse Leech** and the **Medicinal Leech.**

GOLDFISH. *Carassius auratus. See* ***Cyprinidae*** *and* **Fancy Goldfish.**

GOLDFISH VARIETIES. *See* **Fancy Goldfish.**

GONAD. Germ cell.

GRAYLING. *Thymallus vulgaris. See under* ***Salmonidae.***

GREGARIOUS. A natural instinct for grouping together – the need of many fish to form into shoals.

GREAT DIVING BEETLE. *Dytiscus marginalis:* the largest and most familiar of the predatory water beetles. *See* ***Dytiscus*** *and* **Predators.**

GRINDAL WORMS. Named after Mrs Grindal of Sweden who brought this easily cutlivated, small White Worm to the notice of fishkeepers – it has since become a popular form of live-food. *See* **Enchytraeus.**

GUANIN. A crystalline secretion produced by fish and deposited as a shiny layer in the skin, iris, swim-bladder and some other parts of the body. The crystals have a strong reflective capacity and produce either a silvery sheen or a number of glowing colours if mixed with pigments, that is exhibited in many fish.

GUDGEON. *Gobio gobio. See under* ***Cyprinidae.***

GWYNIAD. *Coregonus pennantii. See under* *Coregonus.*

GYRODACTYLUS. *See* **Fish Fluke.**

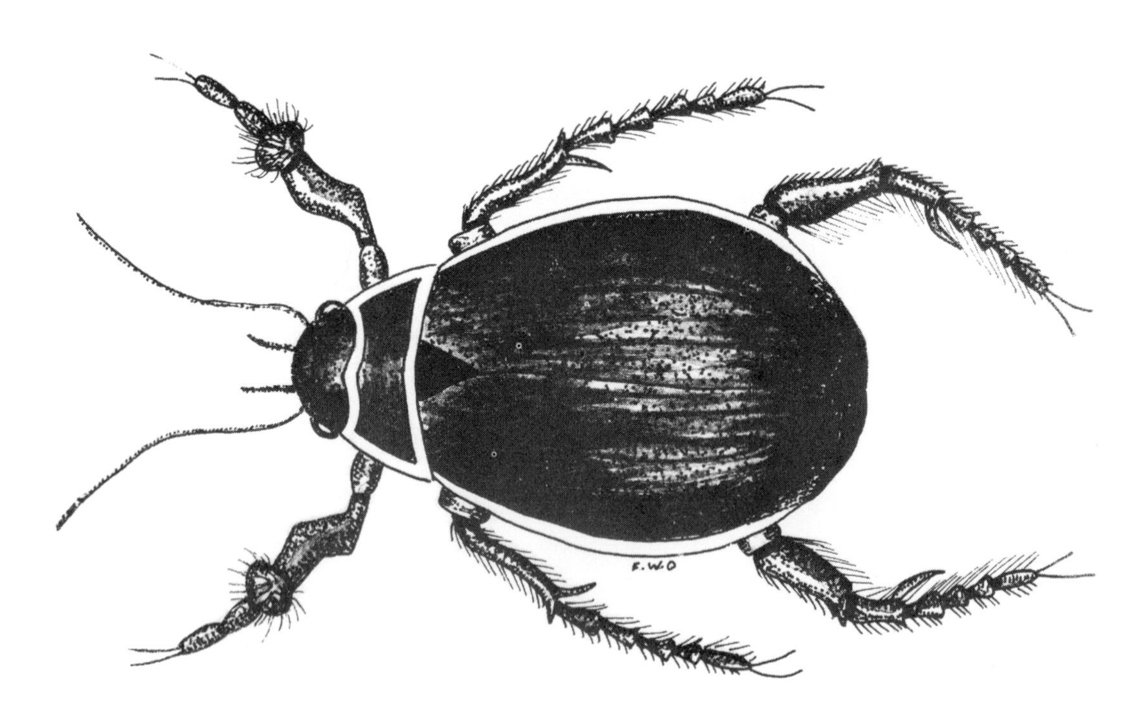

Figure 63 **Great Diving Beetle** *(Dytiscus marginalis)*

H

HAEMOPIS SANGUISUGA. The Horse Leech. This worm can reach a length of 6 inches; its colour is almost black but has yellow edges – it will often leave the water. It is not a blood sucker, but swallows small prey such as worms and insect larvae.

HAPLOID. An organism with a single set of unpaired chromosomes in each cell nucleus.

HARIWAKE OGON. *See* **Koi.**

HELOPHYTE. A marsh plant.

HEREDITY. The transmission of characteristics of an organism to its descendants. It may take place either through vegetative sprouting, through asexual reproductive cells, through simple cellular division, or through the union of differentiated sexual cells. The sum total of all characters which are transmitted from generation to generation are called the **hereditary dispositions.** The hereditary dispositions, which are typical for a species as well as for its individuals, are termed the **hereditary picture.**

The hereditary picture comprises all dispositions, both of the body design as well as the functions and manner of behaviour, often down to the smallest particulars.

Generally the hereditary picture of a species is not completely uniform, it may fluctuate within certain limits. Among the descendants of a pair of fishes which have grown up under identical conditions we find specimens that may differ in shape or colour, both quick and slow growing ones, some that are prone to disease and others which are resistant. The breeder of fishes must include these facts in any breeding calculations. By making use of these factors, fishes kept in captivity can be improved or changed into more desirable types.

Fishes which have been bred under completely natural conditions, without interference by man, must be considered to be of mixed hereditary, that is they are linked to a mother and father whose characters do not completely coincide. Pure hereditary can only be obtained by a process of inbreeding and continuous selection for the desired characters. In this way the favoured characters are strengthened and those of less desirable quality are weakened.

HERMAPHRODITE. A being in which both sexes are combined in a single individual.

HETEROPTERA. Sub-order of bugs comprising over 500 British species. Characterized by the wings being closed flat over the back.

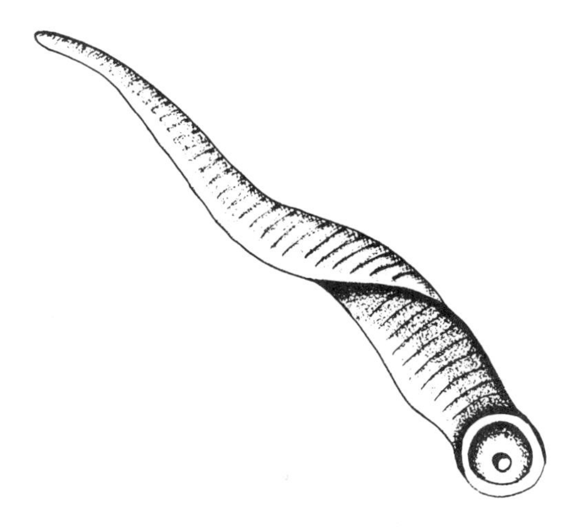

Figure 64 **Horse Leech**

HETEROPHTOIDEA. Order belonging to HEXAPODA; the phylum of insects whose lower lip is developed into a beak with stinging or sucking bristles, for the purpose of sucking blood or plant juices.

HETERZYGOTIC. Uneven heredity, due to combining of different paternal and maternal heredity characteristics.

HEXAPODA. The phylum of invertebrate animals which comprises the insects, and forms the largest group in the animal kingdom.

HIBERNATION. Passing the winter in a lethargic or torpid state.

HIKARI MONO. *See* **Koi.**

HIRUDINEA. *See* **Leeches.**

HIRUDO MEDICINALIS. The Medicinal Leech. Can reach a length of 6 inches (152mm). It is a greenish-black with lighter longitudinal stripes on its back, and a black spotted pale-green underside. Their supply of nutrition is derived from the blood of vertebrates. It has become rare in the wild.

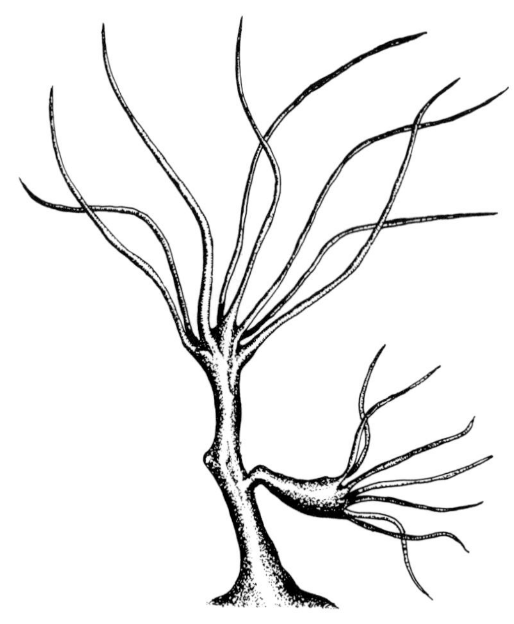

Figure 65 **Hydra**

HISPID. Botanical term for plants with large and coarse hairs.

HI UTSURI. *See* **Koi.**

HOLOTYPE. An individual specimen chosen as a representative to describe a whole species.

HOMOIOTHERMIC. Warm-blooded, the body temperature being maintained at a higher level than that of its surroundings.

HOMOLOGOUS. Similar in origin, structure, or development.

HOMOMORPHOUS. Having the same external appearance or form.

HORMONES. The product of glands within a being's body, which are released into the blood stream and lymph and quickly set into motion responses from other organs. Each hormone is responsible for one given effect only, they trigger and direct certain functions of the organism. Amongst other things, hormones are responsible for the intensified colours of a fish during the breeding period.

HORNWORT. Common name for *Ceratophyllum. See under* **Plants.**

HYBRID. The product of cross-breeding between different species, genera or sub-species which have divergent hereditary characteristics. As a general rule hybridization is possibly only between related species or sub-species, the hybrid which results often being infertile.

HYDRA. This is the only common representative, found in freshwater, of the phylum COELENTERATA which includes such marine types as sea-anemones and jellyfish. They can grow to a length of almost 1 inch (25mm), and have a longish tube-like body crowned with up to ten tentacles. Hydra eat only small animal food; in the main this consists of Daphnia, other small crustaceans and sometimes even small fish will be taken. The food is captured by coming into contact with the tentacles and being paralysed, it is then drawn into the body of the Hydra and digested. When food is plentiful an amazing amount will be eaten.

At times one or more buds will develop on the side of the body, these grow rapidly and soon resemble miniature versions of the parent. Although their gut cavity communicates with that of the adult it, nevertheless, captures its own food. After a time the bud attachment will constrict, the young Hydra breaking free to lead an independent existence. These creatures also reproduce sexually, generally during the autumn. Both male and female cells develop on the same adult individual, the male sperms escape into the water to make their way to the female egg-cells – which are contained in a swelling at the base of the adult's body. The fertilized eggs are released into the water, some becoming attached to plants, others falling to the bottom. During the following spring the larvae hatch out and quickly grow into adult Hydras.

Hydra attach themselves to underwater plants, submerged stones and similar firm supports to which they remain firmly attached, by means of a sticky secretion, for long periods. However, they can move when necessary. Sometimes they glide over their support for a short distance. They can also indulge in a form of swimming by writhing about in the water until they find a new location. Another, more usual, method of moving residence is to lean over and grip the support with the tentacles, release the base, and move the body to a new position, repeating this process as many times as need be. *See* **Hydroidea.**

HYDROCHARIS. Genus of floating plants belonging to the family of Frog-bits.

HYDROIDEA. The fresh water polyps order, belonging to the class of hollow animals or *CEOLENTERATA,* which has several genera. Of interest, in particular, are *Cholorohydra, Hydra* and *Pelmatohydra.* These lead sedentary lives, often attached to plants and stones, and are carnivorous – capturing their prey in similar fashion to the Marine Anemone, which they resemble in a minature form. Reproduction is by budding off new individuals or by a sexual process.

HYDROLOGY. The scientific study of water in its natural state.

HYDROPHYTE. A plant that grows in water in very wet places.

HYGROPHILOUS. Inhabiting a wet or damp place.

HYPHA. A tubular thread of the fungal mycelium.

HYPOGEAL. Botanical term meaning underground.

HYPOLIMNION. The cold lower layer of water in a lake.

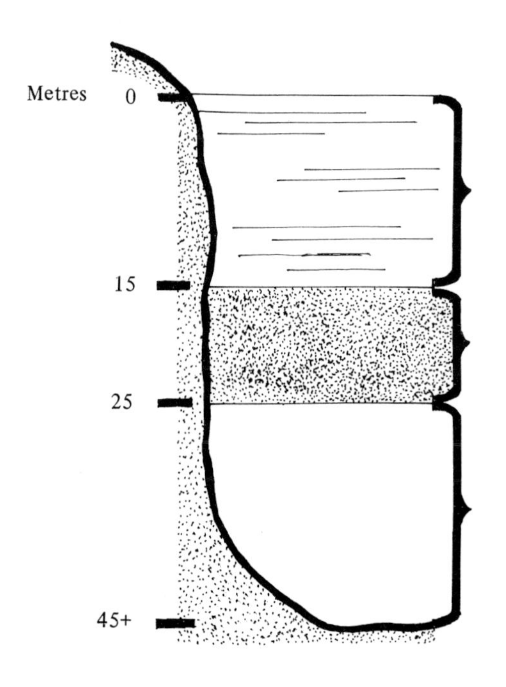

Epilimion
Warm and light.
Most photosynthesis.
Water able to circulate freely at this level.

Thermocline
At this level the temperature changes rapidly.

Hypolimnion
Cold and dark.
Possibly very little oxygen available.

Figure 66 **Water Temperature Zones**

I

ICHTHYOLOGY. The scientific study of fishes.

ICHTHYOPHONUS. (Ichthyoporidium). *See* **Complaints of Fish.**

ICHTHYOPHTHIRIASIS. *See* **White Spot.**

ICHTHYOPHTHIRIUS. A widely distributed disease of fishes. It manifests itself as small white spots, or knots, on the external surfaces of the fish. It is caused by a ciliate and, if allowed to

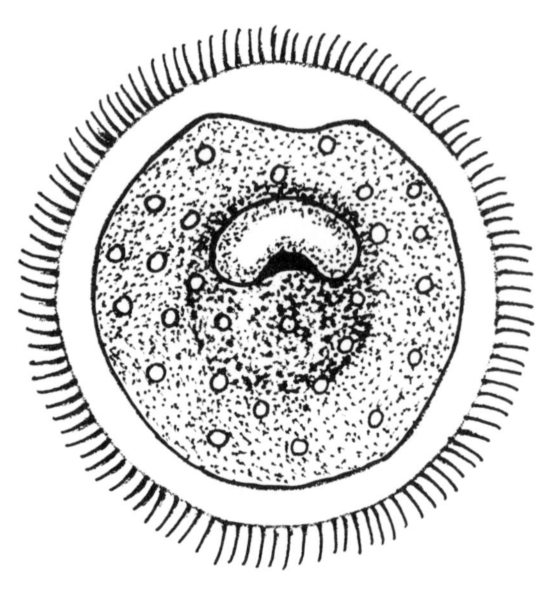

Figure 67 *Ichthyophthirius multifilis.* **The organism which causes White Spot.**

proliferate without treatment, will prove fatal. *See* **White Spot.**

ICHTHYOSPORIDIUM. *See* **Complaints of Fish.**

IDE. *Idus idus,* **the Orfe.** Belonging to the ***Cyprinidae,*** this is a genus of school fishes. The Ide is essentially a central European fish of fast flowing waters and large lakes, it is not found naturally wild in British waters.

The sturdy streamlined body is elongated and only slightly compressed laterally. A fairly large fish, it can reach a length of 30 inches (76cm) under ideal conditions and is variable in colour. The dorsal and caudal fins are darkish, with the other fins being a reddish colour. There is a golden variety, known as the **Golden Orfe,** which is a more attractive fish. These fish are mid-water and surface swimmers, ideal for cool, well oxygenated ornamental waters. *See under* ***Cyprinidae.***

IMAGO. The fourth and final stage in the metamorphosis of some insects, when the mature form is assumed.

IMBRICATE. Meaning to overlap, like tiles on a roof.

IMMUNITY. An acquired resistance to a specific complaint, generally due to having conquered a disease, whereby the body develops sufficient antibodies to resist further attacks by the disease. It is possible to inherit an immunity.

INBREEDING. The mating of blood-related individuals. An essential in the creation of pure breeding lines requires not only inbreeding but, also, incest breeding. Only in this way is it possible to fix desirable characteristics in the stock. Inbreeding must be strictly controlled by careful selection to avoid inherited faults developing. Several generations are required before a true assessment can be obtained of the results of inbreeding a line. *See* **Heredity.**

INCUBATION. The period of time required for a disease to manifest itself after initial infection. Also the time taken for an egg to hatch.

INDIVIDUAL. A single being.

INDUMENTUM. The down or hairs on a plant.

INFECTION. The penetration of the body by germs causing a disease.

INFLORESCENCE. The complete flower of a plant, which can exist in a variety of shapes.

INFUSORIA. A name once applied, erroneously, to all protozoans and other minute organisms, but which should correctly only be applied to the ciliates. The best known are *Paramecium,* the Slipper Animalcules, *Vorticells,* Bell Animalcules, and *Euglena.* These can be cultured in infusions of hay or other vegetable matter; i.e. the material is left in water for a few days.

INSECT. The most numerous class of arthropods. The adult body is divided into a head, thorax and abdomen; the head bearing a pair of antennae, and the thorax three pairs of legs and usually wings. Insects generally pass through the stages of egg, larva and pupa before reaching the fourth stage of an adult.

INSECTIVORE. An animal or plant that feeds on insects.

INSTINCT. An inherited natural impulse or action, as distinct from learned behaviour. Instinct promotes actions necessary to the survival of the individual, its offspring and thus the species, without recourse to previous experience. Very young animals have an innate instinct for feeding and another for reflex safety action when alarmed.

INTERMEDIATE HOST. The host upon which a parasite spends only a part of its time during development. A further change of hosts is required for the parasite to reach adulthood.

INTERNODE. The stem between leaf joints or nodes.

INTROGRESSION. The acquisition of genetic characters by one species from another closely related species in which the character originated, usually by hybridization.

INTRORSE. Botanical term for anthers which open towards the centre of the flower.

INVERTEBRATE. Animals with no backbone; i.e. all animals with the exception of CHORDATA.

IRIDACEAE. Iris. *See under* **Plants.**

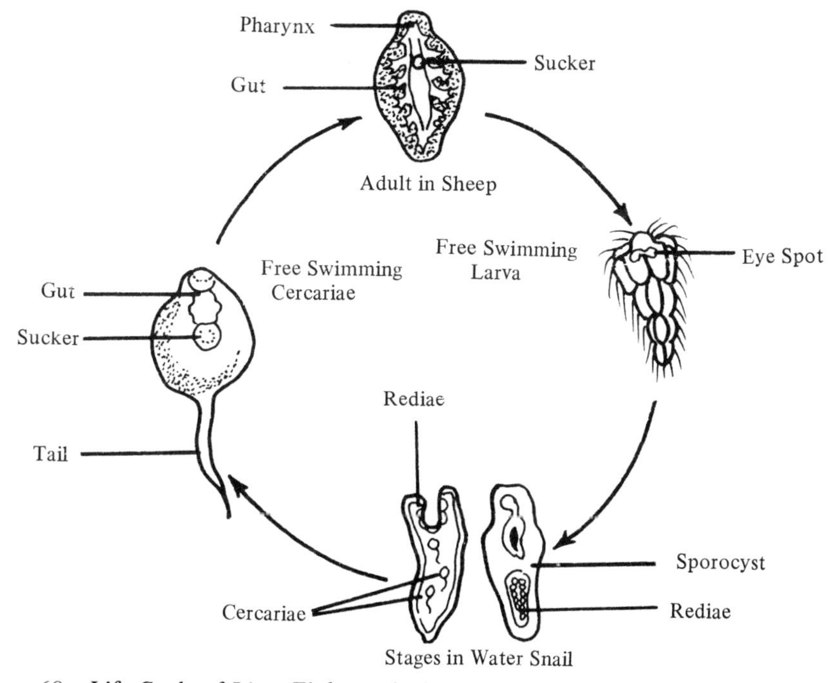

Figure 68 **Life-Cycle of Liver Fluke** – the Water Snail being the intermediate host.

J

JIKIN. *See* **Fancy Goldfish.**

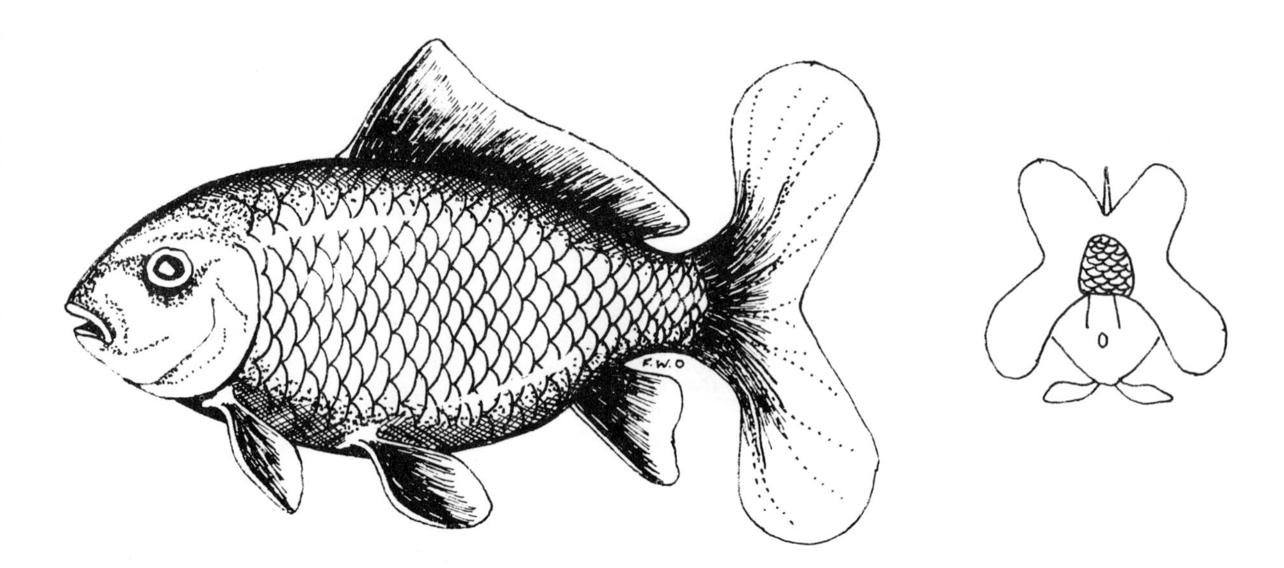

Figure 69 **Jikin**

K

KAEMPFER. Engelbert: 1651-1716. German physician who served with the Dutch East India Company. One of the first Occidentals to describe the cultivation of Goldfish in the Far East.

KELT. Spent Salmon after spawning. Kelt normally return to the sea where they may either die or survive to spawn again.

KI GOI. *See* **Koi.**

KINGCUP. Marsh Marigold. *See* **Plants.**

KIN KABUTO. *See* **Koi.**

KIN UTSURI. *See* **Koi.**

KI UTSURI. *See* **Koi.**

KOHAKU. *See* **Koi.**

KOI. The coloured Carp of Japan. To be correct it should be known as **Nishiki Goi,** or **Brocaded Carp,** to differentiate it from the **Ma Goi,** or **Wild Carp** – Nishiki is Japanese for brocaded and Goi means Carp. However, the western pronunciation and spelling now commonly accepted is Koi.

The Koi is a variation of *Cyprinus carpio* (the Common Carp) and differs from the wild form in colour only. This fish symbolizes Japan more than any other fish: on the 5th May (Children's Day) cloth Carp banners are hung on poles to celebrate the recent birth of a male child.

The first Common Carp were introduced into Japan hundreds of years ago as food fish, and though destined to be eaten were also treated as pets – they were believed to be omens of good luck. It was only natural that colour mutations were noted, segregated, and attempts made to propogate and enhance the colours further by breeding. Soon coloured Carp were being kept, for their ornamental qualities, in the gardens of the wealthy in and around Kyoto, the ancient Japanese capital. In 1868, after the Meiji Restoration, farmers began to keep and cultivate these Carp. In the Niigata Prefecture ponds were built, parts of which extended into the house to provide winter protection for the fish. Year by year the strains were improved, and soon the breeding of these colourful Carp became a major part of the occupation of the Niigata farmers. In 1914, the third year of Taishō, the Carp attracted large crowds when they were exhibited at the Grand Exhibition in Tokyo's Ueno Park. At this time they were given the name Nishiki Goi.

So great was the demand that professional breeders began to raise these fish in areas such as Kōriyama in Nara, Hiroshima, Yamaguchi and, of course, Niigata. Niigata continues to lead in the production of Koi, and breeders are continuously striving to improve their strains by producing ever more colourful fish.

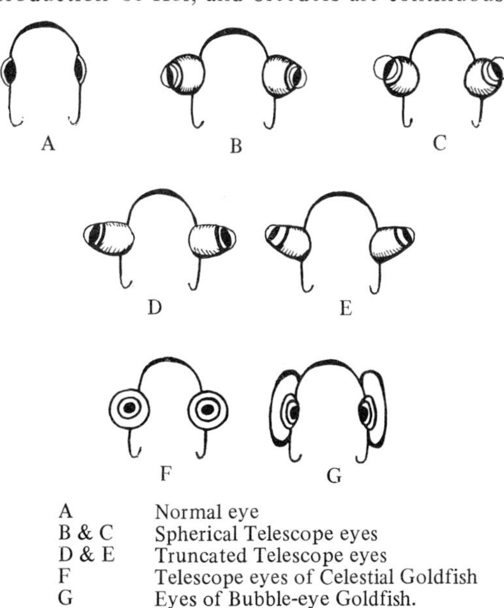

A	Normal eye
B & C	Spherical Telescope eyes
D & E	Truncated Telescope eyes
F	Telescope eyes of Celestial Goldfish
G	Eyes of Bubble-eye Goldfish.

Figure 70 **Eye Types of Fancy Goldfish**

From Japan these colourful fish have spread to many parts of the world, where they have found many admirers and devotees. Koi are the largest growing of domesticated ornamental fish, reaching a length of 24 inches (61cm) or more when kept under ideal conditions; it has also been claimed that examination of scales has proved some to be capable of living to an age of over 100 years.

Whilst all Koi are of the same species, *Cyprinus carpio,* they are, nevertheless, arranged into various varieties which are given Japanese names. These different names are given to fish with certain colour patterns. Although, for the most part, these varieties do not breed true; they are divided into two groups. The monotone group are those of only one colour, the patterned group having two or more colours. Commonly used terms in relation to these Carp, are as follows:

Akame meaning red-eyed, this indicates albino or semi-albino fish which lack melanophores; **Doitsu** meaning German, indicating **Mirror Carp** and **Leather Carp** both of which are considered to

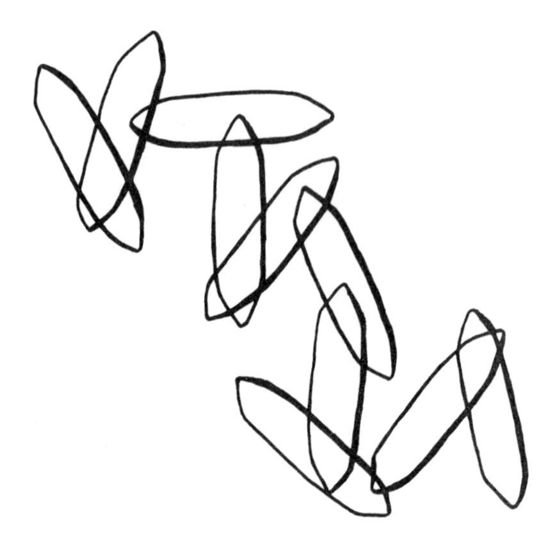

Figure 71 **Guanin Crystals**

have originated in Germany; Koi is often changed into **Goi** if it is preceded by a modifying word, as in Hi Goi and Doitsu Goi; **Ma Goi** is the Wild Carp; **Moyō Goi**, the Patterned Carp, is a fish with a colour additional to the main colour; **Nishiki Goi** (Brocaded Carp), is the name given to good specimens of **Hi Goi**. Hi means red, thus Hi Goi translates into Red Carp; **Gin** indicates silver, as in Gin Rin or silver scales; **Kabuto** was the name of the helmet worn by the ancient samurai, it is used to describe a contrasting colour on the head when it is thought to resemble a helmet.

The various varieties are as follows:

Kōhaku – This is the most popular variety. Kō means red, haku is white – therefore, Kōhaku is a white fish overlaid with a red pattern. If the fish also has red lips it is known as a Kōhaku Kuchibeni, or rouged Kōhaku. If it has silvery scales it is a Kōhaku Gin Rin. The pattern should be extensive, especially on the back, deep-red in colour with sharp outlines.

Tanchō– A name taken from Tanchō Zuru, a Japanese white bodied crane with a red head. This is a sub-variety of the Kōhaku, the red colour appearing only upon the head. The ideal is a round red mark in the centre of the top of the head, the rest of the fish is white.

Shiro Muji– Shiro means white, muji means nothing else. Thus this a pure white fish.

Aka Muji– Aka means red, thus this is an all red fish. The deeper the red the better the quality. When there are reflective scales it is known as Kin Rin. Reflective scales on the white fish give it the name of Gin Rin.

Shiro Bekko– This means turtle shell. This is a white fish with velvety-black spots on it.

Aka Bekko– A red bodied fish with black spots. The ideal fish carries the clear black spots upon the back only, whilst the lower part of the fish is clear.

Taishō Sanke– A variety produced during the era of Emperor Taishō, after which it is named, between 1912-1926. Sanke means three-coloured. This fish has a white body over which is a patterned area of red and black. The red and black areas should not overlap, each must be distinct with edges that are sharp, they should be well proportioned and symetrical, confined mainly to the dorsal region. Specimens with Gin Rin or Kuchibeni features are greatly admired, good specimens commanding small fortunes from would-be buyers.

Ki Goi– Ki means yellow. Ki Goi is, therefore, a yellow carp.

Shōwa Sanke– Shōwa refers to the Emperor Shōwa era (1916-19–) during which this variety was produced. It carries three colours: the back-ground is black upon which there are red and white patterns.

Utsuri Mono– The basic colour is black, over

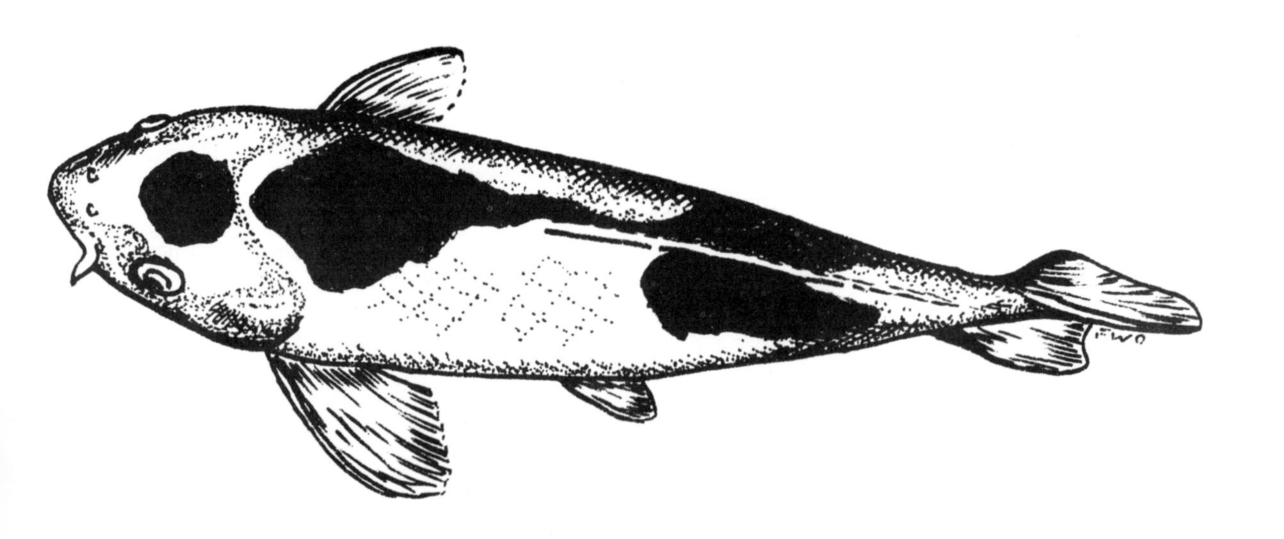

Figure 72 **Koi**

Figure 73 **Moor**

which other colours are scattered. Utsuri means changing colour.

Shiro Utsuri– A white pattern on a black body.

Hi Utsuri– Red patterns on a black body.

Ki Utsuri– Black body with yellow patterns.

Kin Utsuri– Kin means gold. This fish has a black body with gold scales scattered over the background.

Cha Goi– A brown fish, Cha meaning brown or chocolate colour.

Asagi– This means blue, and this fish has a light blue or blue back with a reticulated scale pattern.

Marsuba– Meaning 'leaf of the pine tree', this word is applied to this variety because the brownish colours are thought to resemble the withered needles of a pine tree. The scales are reticulated.

Shūsui– An old variety that was developed by Kichigorō Akiyama Sr., between 1868 and 1926. It has mirror type scales, the back is sky blue becoming lighter on the sides, and the ventral side is red.

Ōgon– A golden fish covered with glittering scales, first developed by Sawata Awoki and his son in the Niigata Prefecture.

Oreng ji Ōgon– Orange-coloured Ōgon.

Yamabuki Ogon– A bright yellow fish with the glittering scales of the Ōgon group. Yamabuki is the name of a yellow flowered Japanese plant.

Kujyaku Ōgon– Kujyaku means peacock. This is a gaudy fish of varied colours and with glittering scales.

Hariwake Ōgon– A fish resembling the ordinary Ōgon, but with areas of a greyish colour.

Purachina Ōgon– Purachina, meaning platinum, indicates that this is a platinum coloured fish.

Kin Kabuto– Means golden helmet. It has gold on the head only, the rest of the fish is devoid of the glittering gold scales.

Koi are pond fish, and are viewed from above, for this reason the colours tend to be concentrated upon the upper part of the body of the fish. Due to their large size they require much larger ponds than those of the Goldfish, and may need some form of protection during the coldest months of the year.

L

LACINIATE. Botanical term describing leaves with ragged edges and very narrow lobes.

LAGAROSIPHON. *See* **Plants.**

LAGG. The vegetation on the edge of a raised bog.

LAGOON. A longish sheet of fresh or brackish water near the sea, often running parallel to the coast, usually only separated from the sea by a bar of sand or shingle.

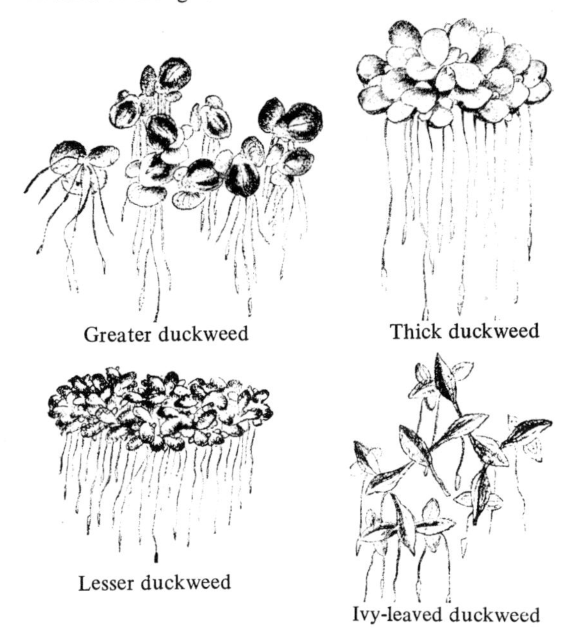

Figure 74 **Lemna – Duckweed**

LAKE. A large sheet of inland freshwater. There is no recognised quantitive distinction between a lake and a pond, although it is generally understood that a lake is the larger of the two.

LAMINA. A thin piece of plant tissue.

LAMPREY. *See under* ***Petromyzontidae.***

LANCEOLATE. Lance-shaped. Usually applied to leaves that are several times longer than their width, broad at the base and narrow at the apex.

LARVA. The active second stage of animals which do not assume an adult form directly from the egg but pass through stages of metamorphosis. The larval form usually differs greatly from the completed adult animal. In insects, the stage between the ovum and the pupa.

LASHER. An artificial waterfall that takes the water that has by-passed a lock on a river or stream.

LATERAL LINE. A sense organ of fishes. Along the side of the body are a series of perforated scales known as the lateral line. These scales cover a canal which runs along both sides of the body under the skin, extending from the head to the root of the caudal fin. It branches into three, over and under the eye and along the lower jaw. This canal is filled with mucus. With this sensory organ the fish can determine changes in water pressure, and the direction and strength of currents. It is thought that fish can also detect vibrations through the lateral line.

LEAF. That part of a plant which usually acts as an organ of assimilation. The amount of assimilation determines the vividness of the green colour and the extent of its surface.

LECTOTYPE. Specimen used as a substitute for a missing holotype, when this is missing, and no paratype is available.

LEECH. *HIRUDINAE.* Aquatic worm-like animals, with a sucker at both ends, which enable them to grip their victim. Mostly they are blood-sucking and secrete hirudin, which is an anti-coagulant, resulting in a wound which takes a long time to heal and often allows a secondary infection of fungus (*Saprolegnia*) to occur.

LEMNA. Genus of small floating plants belonging to the Duckweed family.

L.gibba Linne– A species of the temperate zones of Europe. The plants measure around ⅛ inch (3mm), are rounded and a shiny dark green colour. Reproduction is by budding, the plant often forming dense mats.

L. minor Linne– Although smaller than the previous species it is similar in all other aspects.

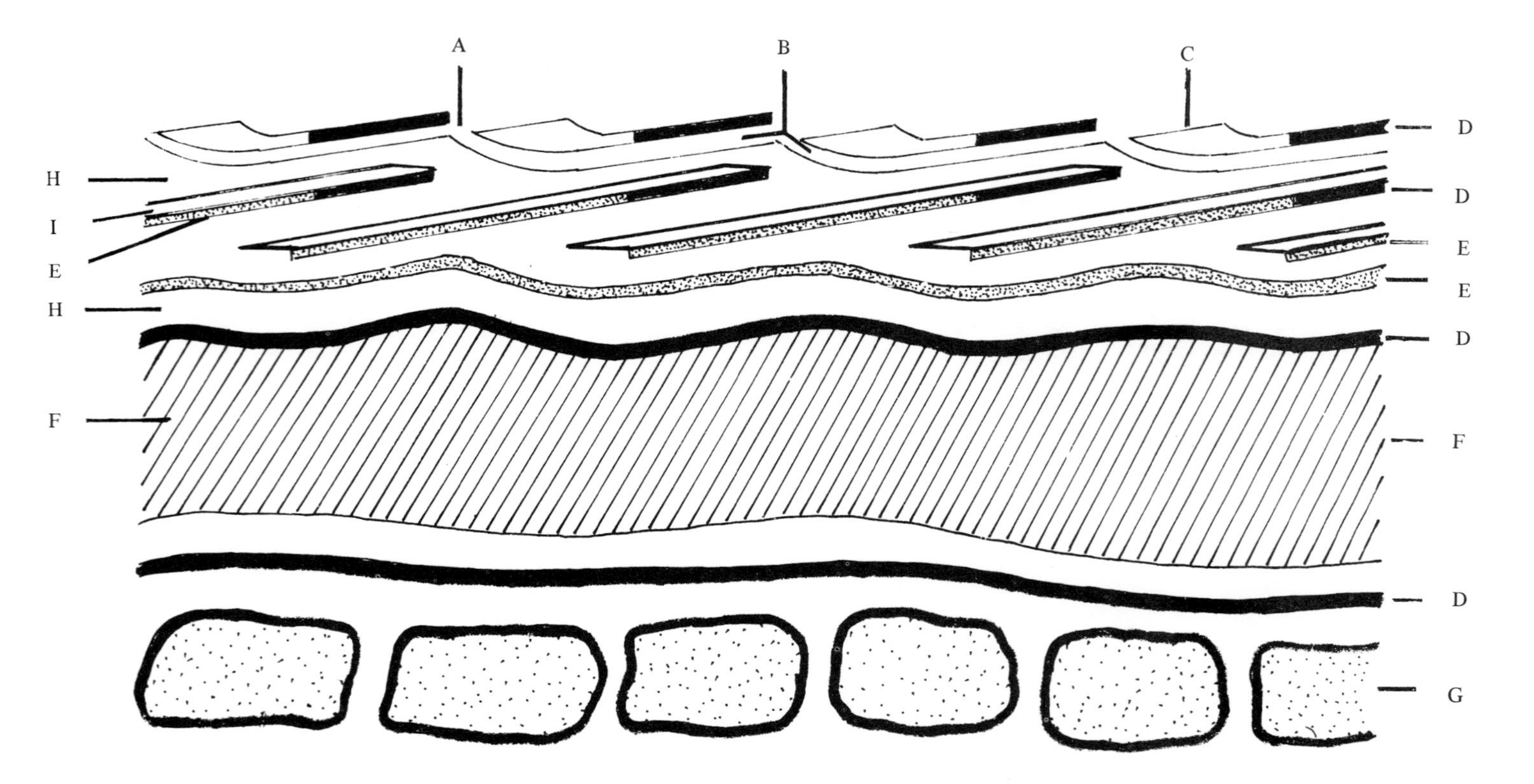

A. Lateral Line Pore
B. Lateral Line Canal
C. Epidermis
D. Chromatophore Levels
E Reflective Tissue (Iridocytes)
F. Adipose Tissue
G. Muscular Tissue (Myotomes)
H. Cutis
I. Scale

Figure 75 **Section through Lateral Line of Fish**

L. trisulca Linne– This species is found in Europe, Asia, North America and Australia. The triangular leaves are light-green and are connected in branched colonies which float at the water surface.

LEMNACEAE. The Duckweeds. Family of perennial aquatic plants of the class ***MONOCOTYLEDONEAE,*** which generally float free at the water surface. Genera are *Lemna, Wolffia. Spirodela.*

LENATIC WATER. Non-flowing, standing water.

LENTICULAR. Botanical term meaning shaped like a lentil.

LEPOMIS MACRACHIRUS. The Blue Gill. *See under Centrarchidae.*

LEPTOCEPHALID. Transparent elliptical larva of the Common and Conger Eels.

LERNAEA CYPRINACEA. The Anchor Worm. This is not a worm but a copepod. It reaches a length of ¾ inch (19mm), and the female is a parasite of fish. It is somewhat worm-like in shape with appendages that resemble an anchor; by means of these anchor-like appendages an adult female is able to firmly adhere to her host. The anchors penetrate the body of the fish and seat themselves into muscles, this deep penetration causes the fish to be badly injured. The male is rather different in shape and does not attack fish.

Reproduction takes place during May. Two egg sacs are formed at the end of the female's body, from the eggs nauplis larvae hatch which resemble those of Cyclops. Whilst growing, the larvae spend their time swimming freely in the water, until they meet a fish. After reaching a fish, the young Anchor Worms burrow into their host. They remain within the muscles, feeding on the victim and growing. The end of their body becomes visible outside the skin of the fish by the beginning of September. At the end of May those adults still preying on their host die, leaving large holes with round openings in the body of the fish.

LIGULATE. Botanical term meaning strap-like.

LIMNOLOGY. The study of the freshwater environment, including the flora and fauna.

LINGULATE. Botanical term meaning tongue-shaped.

LINNE, CHARLES de. 1707-1778. The Swedish botanist and physician who founded modern systematics. He created the first comprehensive system for classifying animals and plants.

LINNEAN. In honour of, or pertaining to, Charles de Linne (Linnaeus) who established the binominal system of naming plants and animals. *See preceding entry.*

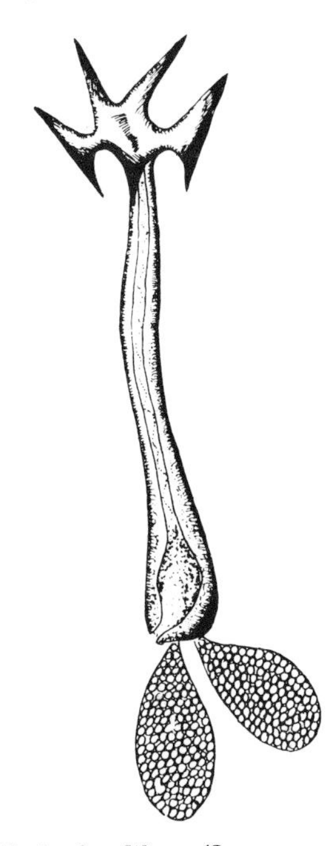

Figure 76 **Anchor Worm** *(Lernaea cyprinacea)*

LIONHEAD. *See* **Fancy Goldfish.**

LIPOIDS. Vitally important chemical compounds, located in chloroplasts of plants and near the surface of the cell plasma. They are soluble in the same manner as fats, and play a role in the selection of food substances taken in by cells.

LIVE FOODS. Most aquarists regard live food, of one sort or another, as the best form of food for their fish. They are one of the natural foods that would form part of the fish's diet in the wild. Many species will, in fact, only eat live foods.

Earthworm– Small red or pink worms are best; large worms tend to be tough and hard to digest. The worms should be swilled before feeding to the fish and, if necessary, be chopped into suitable sized length. Worms can be brought to the surface by watering an area with 2 gallons (9 litres) of water in which ½ oz (14g) of potassium permanganate has been dissolved. A sheet of black polythene, spread flat upon the ground, will encourage worms to gather beneath it after a few weeks.

White Worms– An easily cultivated small creamy-white worm which reaches a length of up to ¾ inch (19mm). A shallowish, lidless box is half filled with a mixture of sterilized loam and peat. The mixture should be slightly moist. A slight hollow is made in the surface, into which the worms are placed, and a small amount of food placed on top. Moisture is conserved by placing a sheet of glass upon the surface of the peat/loam mixture. The box is then covered to exclude light, and placed in a fairly cool position. Replenish the food, whenever it is consumed, by using soaked brown bread, mashed saltless potatoes, or any other food which can be made into a stiff pulp. The colony should be allowed to become well established before any worms are removed.

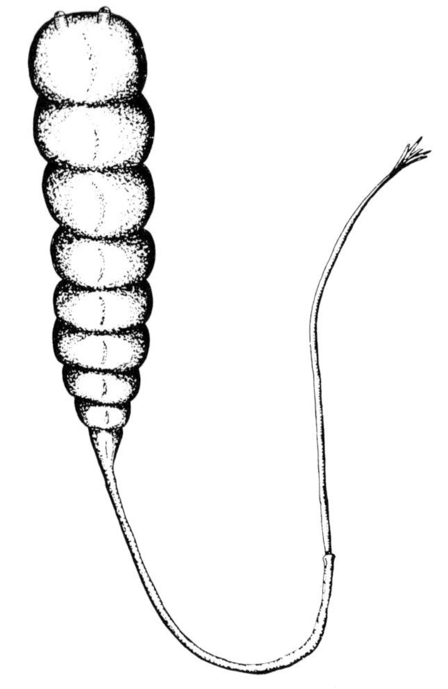

Figure 77 **Rat-Tailed Maggot** – the larva of the Drone-Fly

Grindal Worms– Very similar to the White Worm, but slightly smaller. They can be cultured in the same way, although they prefer just a little more warmth – up to 70°F (21°C) is ideal.

Daphnia– This small crustacean is eaten readily by most fishes. It is inadvisable to collect it from waters which also contain fish, and water taken should always be screened to remove any undesirable creatures. *See* **Daphnia.**

Cyclops– An even smaller crustacean, often found in the same waters as Daphnia. It will also be eaten by many fishes, although large fish may ignore it.

Tubifex– Considered by many to be one of the finest of live foods; viewed with great suspicion by others. They are a reddish, thread-like aquatic worm inhabiting areas that are grossly polluted. Often large colonies are found near sewage outfalls, transforming human waste products into the characteristic black homogenous substance that marks sludge banks. Before being fed to fishes they must be thoroughly cleaned. The usual method is to keep them, for several days, in slowly running water. At frequent intervals the balls of worms is broken up, to free any dead worms or other unwanted matter. They are considered safe when all internal secretions have been excreted.

Rat-tailed Maggot– The larva of a Drone-fly, found in the soft bottom mud of polluted waters, just a few inches below the water surface. The body is a dirty white to yellow colour, slightly transparent. They have a prehensile segmented tail which acts as a telescopic breathing device. This snorkel-type appendage can be extended to several times the length of the creatures body, to reach the water surface. It has a somewhat thick, tough skin but will be eaten by many fishes.

Bloodworms– Not worms, they are the larvae of the *Chironomidae,* or midges, and are easily recognised by their blood-red colour and figure-of-eight swimming motion. A highly satisfactory food that can be found in most natural fresh-waters, they may even be found in rainwater barrels. *See* **Midges.**

Glassworm– The predacious larva of the Phantom Midge, which is not a worm despite its common name. These transparent creatures, which allow their air-sacs to be seen, are often found in waters that have a low oxygen content and do not receive a high intensity of light. They are an excellent food, but can be a danger in a tank of fish fry. *See* **Phantom Midge.**

Mosquito larva– A smallish creature which hangs head down from the water surface, unless disturbed. They are almost black in colour, and swim with a whipping movement when leaving the surface for deeper water. They feed upon microscopic food. Mosquito larvae are good food, and are found in most still waters. *See* **Mosquitoes.**

Asellus– Related to the well known Wood Louse, it is not an exceptionally good food because of the very hard shell – although it may be accepted by some fish.

Gammarus– The Freshwater Shrimp. Frequents beds of submerged vegetation in slow moving waters. Beware of any which are spotted with red; they are probably infected with a parasitic worm that will harm fish. Often shrimps will be found carrying another on its back. As a food it is only suitable for the larger, hard mouthed species of fishes because of its hard shell.

Frog tadpoles– Often eaten by fishes.

Maggots– Such as sold by stores dealing in anglers' supplies, will be readily eaten by most fishes.

LOACH. *See* ***Cobitidae.***

LOCHMABEN VENDANCE. *C. vandesius. See under* ***Coregonus.***

LONDON SHUBUNKIN. *See* **Fancy Goldfish.**

LOTA VULGARIS. The Burbot. This is the only freshwater member of the Cod family. It resembles a rather thick, portly Eel, with a dark mottled skin which varies from yellowish to brown, and possesses a pale yellow or white belly. The skin is thick and slimy, with small scales. Upon the back is a very short dorsal fin and, behind it, another that is very long; the tail is small and rounded; the small ventral fins are placed on the throat; the anal fin is as long as the second dorsal. It has a large mouth, with bands of pointed teeth; the lower jaw bearing a central barbel whilst two smaller barbels are found near the nostrils. A good specimen can reach a length of about 2 feet (0.6m).

Spawning takes place during January to March, when shoals gather in shallow water to deposit numerous very small eggs; the eggs are a yellowish colour and contain an oil drop. The young hatch out within roughly four weeks, with down-bent heads, and then make rapid growth. At the end of the first year they will reach a length of approximately 4 inches (102mm); they reach sexual maturity in their third or fourth year.

LOTIC WATER. Flowing water.

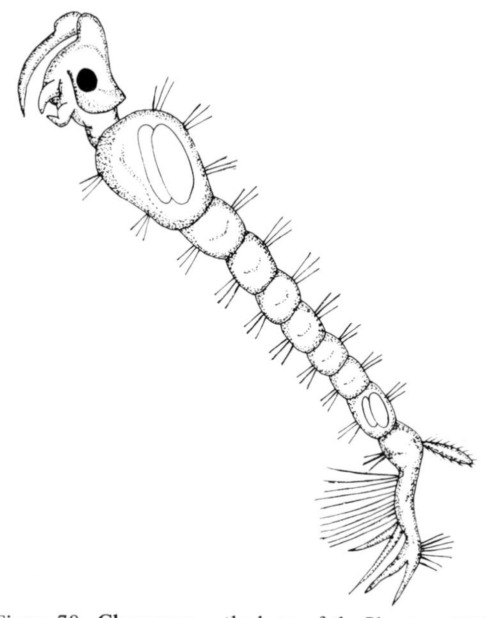

Figure 78 **Glassworm** – the larva of the Phantom Midge.

LOUGH ERNE POLLAN. *Coregonus altior. See under* ***Coregonus.***

LOUGH NEAGH POLLAN. *Coregonus pollan. See under* ***Coregonus.***

LUMBRICIDAE. The Earthworms. Belonging to the order of *OLIGOCHAETA* and much used by fishkeepers as a form of live food for conditioning their fishes. Before feeding to the fishes they should be swilled to remove any exterior matter and are then cut into pieces of a suitable size. Most useful are the red coloured worms, whereas those with a greenish or yellowish colour found in manure heaps, should be avoided.

M

MAGGOT. Larva of many two-winged flies; it is legless and progresses by wriggling; often used as a live fish food.

MALACOLOGY. The study of molluscs.

MARSH. Waterlogged ground in which the water level, during summer, is at, or near, the surface.

MARSUBA. *See* **Koi.**

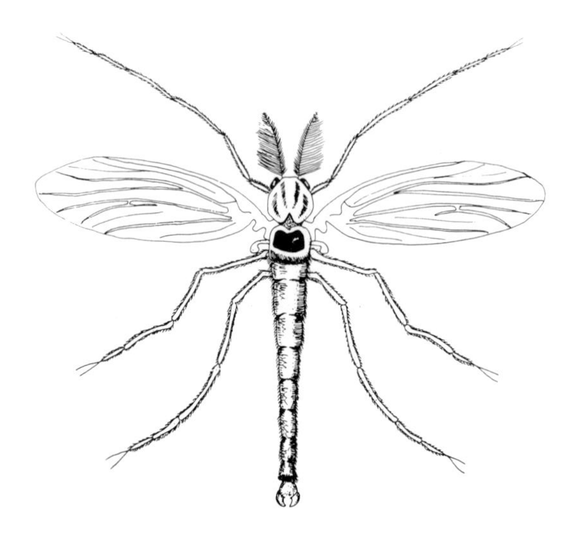

Figure 79 **Midge** *(Chironomus)*

MAYFLIES. Of the order *EPHEMEROPTERA,* they are well known aquatic insects. There are forty-seven species in Britain, the nymphs varying greatly in both their form and mode of life. However, they are easily distinguished from those of other insects by their three long tail-like appendages. Their food consists mainly of vegetable matter. The adults can be recognised by their long, slender tail filaments and the manner in which they hold their wings erect when resting.

MEAL WORM. Sometimes used to feed the larger fishes. It is the larvae of the Hard-backed Meal Beetle and has a hard skin.

MEDICINAL LEECH. *See* ***Hirudo medicinalis.***

MEDUSA. In freshwater, the free-swimming stage of the Hydras, correctly known as *Limnomedusae.*

MEIOSIS. The maturity division of a germinating cell, which precedes insemination, in order to reduce the chromosomes down to the needed half in number and quality.

MELANIN. The black pigment found in the chromatophores of cells, formed from a protein substance.

MELANISM. A colour variation due to excessive melanin pigments, causing a fish to look very dark or black.

MENDELISM. An early name for genetics based upon the researches of Abbé Gregor Mendal of Brno in Moravia which were published in 1865.

MERE. A shallow lake or pond.

MESOGONISTIUS CHAETODON. Black-banded Sunfish. *See under Centrarchidae.*

METAMORPHIS. The change in form and structure when the larval form changes into the adult.

METAZOA. The sub-kingdom of multicellular animals.

METEOR. *See* **Fancy Goldfish.**

MICROPYLE. The minute opening in the membrane of the ovum, through which the male gamete effects fertilization, and closes immediately after impregnation. *See* **Egg, Development of. Development of.**

MICRO-WORMS. Small thread-like worms belonging to the genus *Turbatrix.* Easily cultured livefood suitable for baby fishes. *See* **Live Foods.**

MIDGES. ***Chironomidae.*** The true Midges comprise some 400 species. However, contrary to popular belief they are not biting insects. There is hardly a freshwater habitat that does not contain the larvae of one or more of the species. The adult males may often be seen 'dancing' in vast clouds over water and elsewhere.

The familiar 'Bloodworms' are one of the Chironomus larvae, and occur in a wide variety of aquatic environments. Their burrows, which are often tube-like, are often found attached to the sides of water butts and similar containers of standing water. At times, the larvae leave their shelter and swim rapidly through the water by means of vigorous, figure-of-eight contortions of the body. *See* **Live Foods.**

The red body colour is due to the presence of haemoglobin in their blood. This substance combines with oxygen to form oxyhaemoglobin, which rapidly gives up its oxygen to any tissue which requires it. This gives the larvae the ability to live in waters which are low in oxygen content but high in decaying organic matter.

The food of chironomids consists mainly of particles of organic matter, generally obtained from the bottom detritus.

The larvae can take up to two years to complete their development, the pupae looking somewhat like a comma as they swim to the water surface. The eggs are laid in gelatinous ropes near the water surface, usually attached to a plant or other firm attachment.

MILFOIL. *See Myriophyllum, and under* **Plants.**

MILLER'S THUMB. The only freshwater Bullhead. *See* ***Cottus Gobio.***

MINNOW. *Phoxinus phoxinus.* The smallest member of the Carp family. *See* ***Cyprinidae.***

MIRE. A marsh.

MITOSIS. Division of cells or nuclei under the development of chromosomes.

MOLECULE. The smallest unit into which a chemical combination may be split without interferring with its properties.

MOLLUSC (MOLLUSCA). Second largest phylum of higher animals, after the ARTHROPODA.

Although a large phylum only two classes are found in freshwater – ***GASTROPODA*** and ***BIVALVIA.*** Of the gastropods there are thirty-six species found in Britain, in a wide variety of water environments. Appearing slow in movement they are, nevertheless, very active creatures in their search for algae and other matter upon which they feed. Despite there being no distinct head, the front part of the body, which carries the sensory tentacles and mouth, is referred to as such. The major part of the body is contained within a shell, into which the head and foot can also be withdrawn. The shell is spiral-shaped, due to the body twisting one way or the other – depending upon the species, and this contains the massed internal organs, known as the **visceral hump.** As the body grows the shell is gradually enlarged by additional whorls, so that the first and smallest whorl is, in fact, the original shell of the small snail. The mouth has a rasping tongue or **radula**

Figure 80 **Miller's Thumb or Bull-Head**

and bears many rows of fine teeth, enabling algae and other material to be scraped away for consumption.

The gastropods are divided into two subclasses – ***PROSOBRANCHIA*** and ***PULMONATA.*** The first are gill-breathers, who also possess either a chalky or horny plate (**operculm**) which is used to seal the shell opening after the foot and head have withdrawn into it. This feature, which is a protective device, gives these creatures the title of **operculates.**

The **pulmonates** have no operculm, nor do they have gills. Their main supply of air is obtained from the water surface, where it is drawn into a cavity, the lung, which lies between the mantle and the dorsal wall of the body. The opening to this cavity is situated on the right-hand side of the snail and is a small, round, tubular structure.

When a pulmonate renews its air supply at the surface, the breathing structure is pushed into the atmospheric air and then, by muscular movements, air is taken into the body cavity. The aperture is then closed before the snail descends.

Figure 81 **Great Pond Snail** *(Lymnaea stagnalis)*

Although both male and female organs are possessed by each pulmonate, and both are, therefore, capable of laying eggs, it is usual for cross fertilization between two individuals to take place.

Amongst the snails contained in this class (***GASTROPODA***) are the following:

Lymnaea stagnalis– The **Great Pond Snail,** which is found in many ponds and slow-moving waters and can reach a shell height of around 2 inches (51mm) or more. Like all *Lymnaea* they have thin, brownish shells which are conical in shape and sharply pointed, and possess non-retractible tentacles which are flat and triangular. Eggs are laid in sausage-shaped, jelly-like masses on the underwater surfaces of plants. Unlike most of its kind, this snail is not a pure vegetarian, but will also eat decaying animal matter – it has been known to attack newts and small fish if given the chance.

L. palustris– The **Marsh Snail,** can be found in ponds and other watery situations, but not in marshy areas.

L. peregra– The **Wandering Snail,** is without doubt the commonest of the British pond snails, being found in all types of freshwater habitat. Variable in form and size, the shell is normally a little under ¾ inch (9mm).

L. trunkata– Seldom lives in water, preferring flooded and swampy areas. This snail is the intermediate host of the Sheep Liver Fluke.

Physa fontinalis– The **Bladder Snail,** has a thin oval shell that has a height of a little under ½ inch (3mm). Often the lobes of the mantle are wrapped around the shell to act as gills. It is a common species, frequenting streams and clear watery ditches.

The Planorbis species– of which there are fourteen, are commonly referred to as **Ram's-horn Snails** because of the flat, spiral coiled shell. The head carries a pair of long, thin, tapering tentacles. The small foot is rounded at each end. The species range in size from the tiny *Planorbis crista,* with a shell breadth of ⅛ inch (3mm), up to the 1 inch (25mm) or so of *P. corneus.* The latter, commonly known as the **Great Ram's Horn,** is often found in aquariums. The blood of these snails contains haemoglobin, which is unusual in molluscs, and is, therefore, red. The red specimens so popular with some aquarists are, in fact, albinos which lack the normal brown pigmentation in body and shell, thus the blood shows through making the snail appear a vivid red colour.

Freshwater limpets are also pulmonates, only two species being found in British waters – *Ancylastrum fluviatile* and *Ancylus lacustris.*

The second class of molluscs is the ***BIVALVIA,*** which comprises the freshwater cockles and mussels. The characteristic feature of the bivalve is the shell which consists of two equal halves, which are hinged together at the top by an elastic

MOLLUSC

ligament. Inside the two valves are strong muscles which can tightly close the shell. In front of the hinge is the **umbo**, a raised hump – this is the oldest part of the shell.

The bivalve has no head, and the foot is the only part to protrude through the front section of the shell. This is sunk into the mud, whilst the two valves are held slightly apart – usually two thirds of the front of the mussel is buried in the muddy bottom. At the rear there are two siphon tubes, the uppermost is the **exhalant siphon** whilst below, fringed with finger-like growths, is the **inhalant siphon.** Inside the shell, alongside the foot, are two pairs of spongy gills which bear cilia. By lashing these cilia a current is created that draws food-bearing water through the mantle-cavity which is then expelled. Oxygen, for breathing, is extracted from this water whilst food particles are trapped by the gills, whence it is transferred in a sticky mass to the mouth at the front of the foot.

The smaller bivalves are dual sexed, the larger ones are usually individually sexed, although occasionally some are found to be hermaphroditic. During the summer months the female produces thousands of eggs; these are passed from ovaries and stored in brood-pouches in the outer gills. The eggs are fertilized when sperm from a male mussel enters through the inhalant siphon. However, development is not completed until the following spring, when peculiar larvae, known as **glochidium,** are expelled into the water. The glochidia have a minature bivalve shell, triangular in shape, at the free apex of which is a sharp tooth. Within the minutely perforated valves there is a coiled, sticky thread attached to the muscle which opens and closes the valves, this is the **byssus.** After ejection from the female, the larvae swim for a time by snapping their valves together, until they either sink to the bottom or become entangled in water plants by the byssal threads. At this stage they are parasitic and must find a fish to act as a host if their development is to continue. Those which are fortunate and find a host, by attaching themselves by means of the byssus, will embed themselves in the skin of the fish with the aid of their sharp teeth, this causes a cyst to form around the larva. The encysted larva will live in this state for about three months, feeding on the blood of its host in true parasitic fashion. During this time a new shell is developed, under the old one, and after development is complete the now perfectly formed minature will depart to lead an independant existence.

The larger mussels belong to the super-family ***Unionacea;***

Anodonta anatina– The **Duck Mussel**, and *Anodonta cygnea,* the **Swan Mussel,** are very similar and often found together. The Swan Mussel has an oval, greenish-yellow shell that grows to a size of around 5 inches (127mm) or

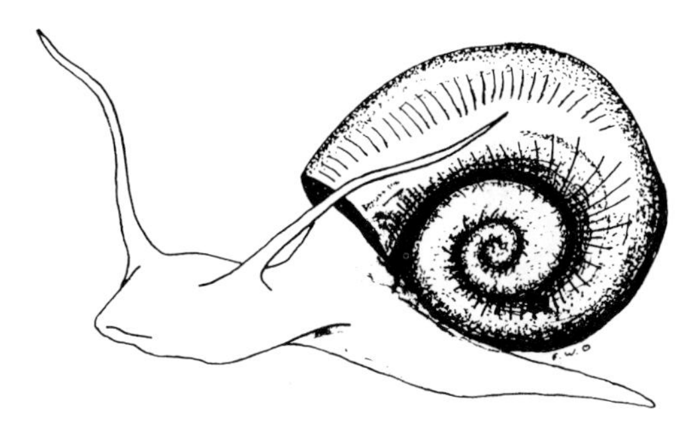

Figure 82 **Ram's Horn Snail** *(Planorbis corneus)*

more. The Duck Mussel is generally smaller, thicker and darker in colour.

Unio pictorum– The **Painter's Mussel,** has a long thin shell, between 3-4 inches (76-101mm) in length, with straight upper and lower margins.

Margaritifer margaritifer– The **Pearl Mussel,** has a blackish coloured shell that is long and oval and can reach a size of about 6 inches (152mm).

Dreissena polymorpha– The **Zebra Mussel,** has the marine habit of attaching itself in groups to submerged objects. It was first noticed in Britain in 1824, and is thought to have been brought here from the Baltic – possibly in timber-ships. The shell grows to about 2 inches (51mm) in length, and is yellow or brownish in colour with wavy transverse markings of brown or yellow bands.

MONOCOTYLEDON. Class of plants characterised by having one germinating leaf.

MONOECIOUS. A plant that has separate male and female organs on the same individual. In animals, a hermaphrodite.

MONOGENEA. Order of leeches with one sucking disc.

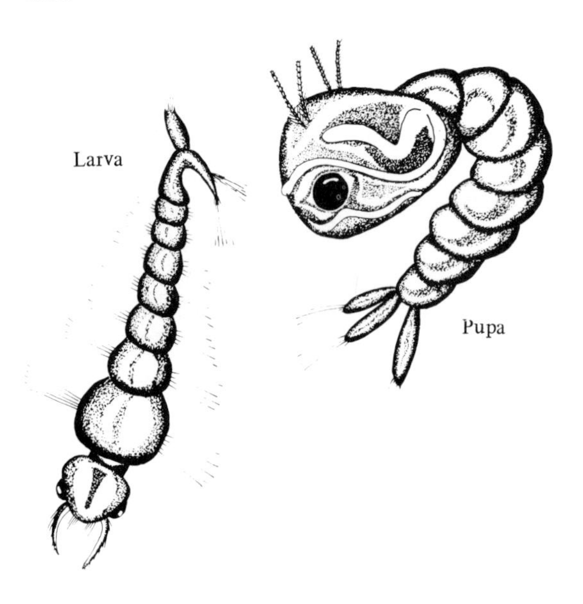

Figure 83 **Immature Mosquitoes** *(Culex pipiens)*

MONOMORPHIC. An organism which is not polymorphic.

MOOR. Often called the **Blackmoor,** which is incorrect because it states the obvious, a Moor is only a Moor if it is black and has telescope-eyes. *See* **Fancy Goldfish.**

MORPHOLOGY. The study of the construction shape and form of live beings.

MOSQUITOES. Blood-sucking gnat, the two best known genera being *Culex* and *Anopheles,* the latter capable of transmitting malaria. It is possible to differentiate between the two: *Anopheles* adults incline their body when settled, so that their heads almost touch the surface upon which they are resting whilst the larvae rest with their body level with the water surface. In comparison *Culex* adults hold their bodies roughly level with the surface upon which they have settled; the larvae hang downwards in the water, the tail just touching the surface film. All Mosquitoes spend their larval and pupal stages in water.

Culex pipiens– Possibly the commonest species, breeding in almost any open area of water, including water-butts and even old tin cans. They lay blackish, canoe-shaped egg rafts of cigar-shaped eggs, numbering about 300, which float on the surface of the water and are unsinkable. The larvae spend most of their time near the surface, feeding upon microscopic size foods. The pupae are shaped like a comma, and do not feed until, eventually, their skin splits and the perfect insect emerges.

Anopheles maculipennis– Has a similar life-style to *C. pipiens* apart from its eggs which are laid singly, with a small float on each side to make them buoyant. *See* **Live Foods.**

MUSSEL. Large freshwater bivalves with more or less oval shells. Includes the Swan Mussel *(Anodonta cygnea)* and Duck Mussel *(A. anatina),* which grow to around 6 inches (152mm) long – occasionally the Swan Mussel can reach a length of 9 inches (229mm). These are the mussels of most interest to the breeder of Bitterling (see separate entry). Mussel larvae are known as glochidia and are parasitic on fishes. *See* **Mollusc.**

MUTANT. An organism in which one or more genes have undergone a change so that it carries some abnormal characteristic.

MUTATION. A change in the genes of a chromosome.

MYRIOPHYLLUM. *See under* **Plants.**

N

NACRE. Mother-of-pearl.

NACREOUS. Describes a mother-of-pearl appearance

NAIAD. Dragon-fly larva or nymph.

NAUPLIUS LARVA. The free-swimming early stage of the simplest crustaceans.

NECROPHAGY. The eating of dead matter such as carrion.

NECROSIS. Putrification or death of bone and/or tissue, corresponding to gangrene of the flesh.

NECTON. Minute animals which swim in the water, unlike plankton which merely floats.

NEMATODA. The great class of worms consisting largely of endoparasites. Mostly very small with unsegmented cylindrical bodies.

NERVOUS SYSTEM OF FISH. System of nerves by which a fish co-ordinates its responses to the environment. The brain of a fish is relatively small and somewhat elongated. Twelve nerves are connected to the brain, of which the most important are the following: the paired nerves of smell which originate in the olfactory lobes of the fore-brain, the sight nerve from the intermediate brain, the accoustic nerve connecting the hearing and sense organs of the skin, the taste nerve and nerves operating the muscles, gills, the heart and the intestine.

The spinal column encloses the spinal medulla, which transmits stimuli from the brain. Paired nerves branch out from it, forming the unspontaneous, sympathetic nerve system.

NEUSTON. Microscopically small organisms, forming a community and living upon, or very close to, the water surface. Under the right conditions the live organisms will form a fatty skin over the water surface.

NEWT. Small lizard-like amphibian. *See* **Amphibians.**

NEZU OGŌN. *See* **Koi.**

NITELLA. Genus of algae.

NITRATES. Salts or esters of nitric acid, formed through the action of certain bacteria, in the water, being the final result of the metabolism of protein (nitrification).

NODE. The junction of one or more leaves with the stem.

NOMENCLATURE. The conferring of scientific names. Whilst common names may have local meaning, only scientific names have an international common meaning free of misunderstanding.

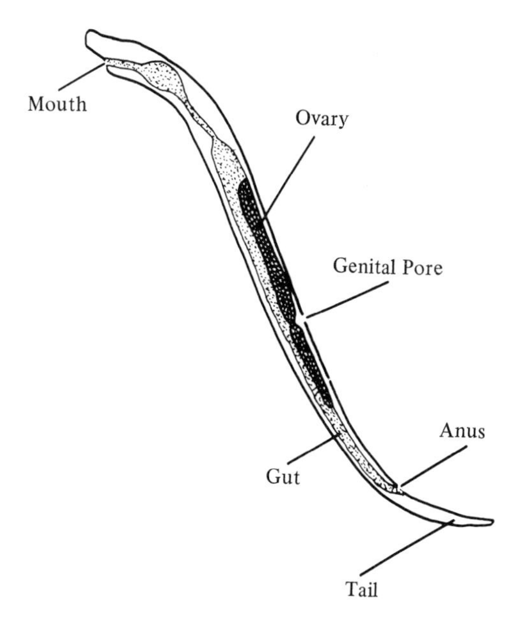

Figure 81 **Nematode Worm**

The system of naming animals and plants is **Linnaeus's binominal system,** based on the Latin language. Each organism is given a generic name, which has a capital initial, followed by a specific or trivial name which has a small initial; e.g. *Carassius auratus,* the Common Goldfish. The generic name may be abbreviated to its initial after its first mention, thus the goldfish becomes *C. auratus.*

NOTOCHORD. A cartilaginous rod present in young vertebrates, becoming the vertebral column in the adult.

NUCLEUS. Body present in cells, containing chromosomes.

NUTRITION. The intake of nourishment (food), which is important to all living beings and is variable according to the needs of the species.

NYMPHAECAE. Water-lilies. *See under* **Plants.**

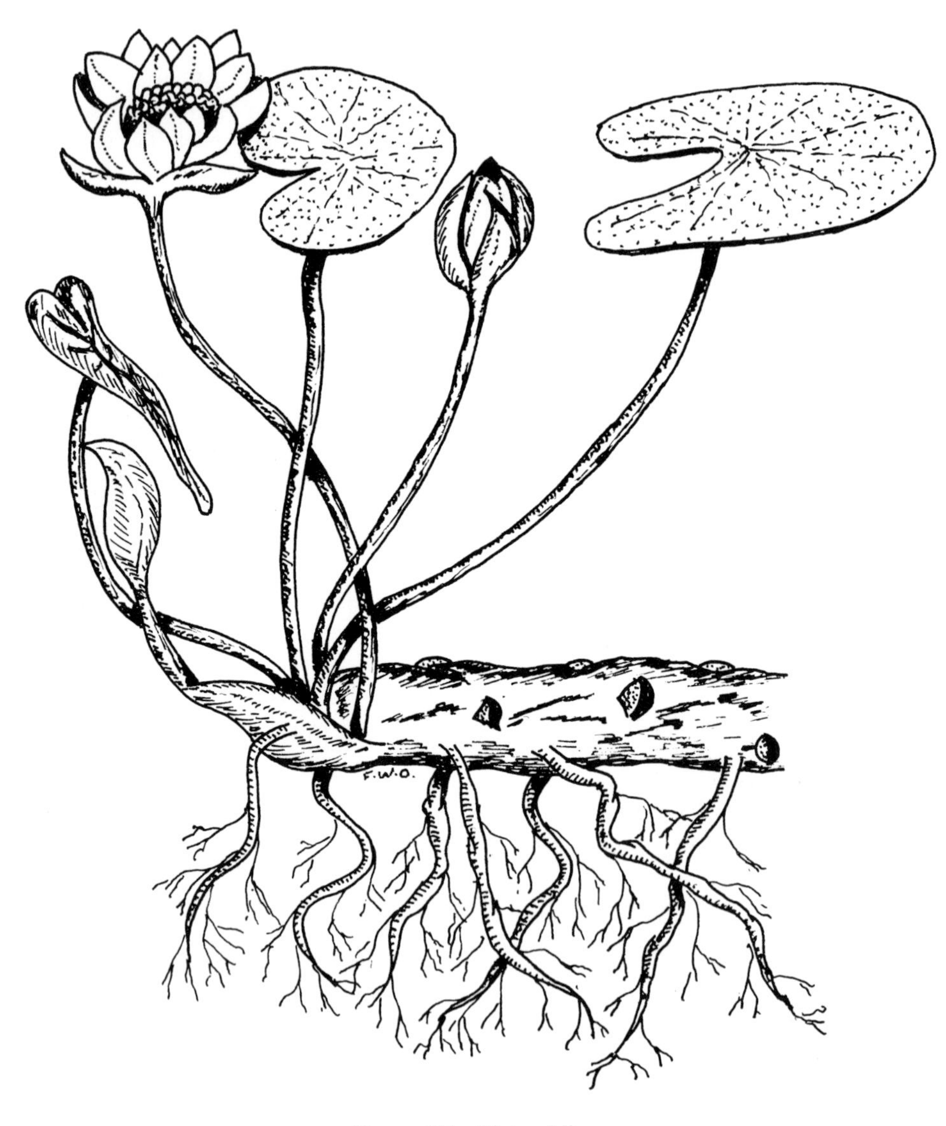

Figure 85 **Water Lily**

O

ODONATA. Dragon-flies. Order pertaining to the phylum of HEXAPODA. Predatory insects with strong biting apparatus, who are also excellent fliers. They possess large eyes in a motile head. The legs are tilted forward and used for resting and catching prey. The front and rear wings move independantly of each other, beating up and down. The larvae are aquatic, and extremely predatory, commonly known as **Water-tigers.** *See* **Predators.**

ŌGON. *See* **Koi.**

OLIGOCHAETA. A class of mainly freshwater worms, but includes the Earthworms and White Worms. They are characterised by having a ring-shaped gland, which encircles the body like a belt, and bristles placed simply in lateral rows.

OLIGOPHAGOUS. Animals having a restricted range of diet.

OMBROGENEOUS. Growing in wet conditions.

OMNIVORE. Eating both animal and vegetable food.

OPERCULUM. The gill-cover of fishes. *See* **Anatomy of a Fish.**

OPPOSED. Botanical term for leaves placed opposite to each other on the plant stem.

ORANDA. *See* **Fancy Goldfish.**

ORDER. One of the groups in the classification of live animals.

ORENJU ŌGON. *See* **Koi.**

ORFE. Common name for *Idus idus.* A popular ornamental fish, of which there are golden and silver varieties. *See Cyprinidae.*

ORGANISM. Any living animal or plant, irrespective of size.

OSMOSIS. Adjustment which equalises the difference between the individual concentrations of two differently composed liquids through a separating membrane. This happens through the skin of a fish when it is taken from freshwater and placed into saltwater. The dissolving medium, water, passes from the weaker concentration to that of the stronger one. The water content of the body is upset, becoming more saline than normal, and this can result in a ponderous influence on the health.

OSTARIOPHYSI. The order of Bony fishes containing the Carp family and the loaches.

OSTRACOD. Class of crustaceans belonging to the sub-phylum of CRUSTACEA. *Cypria* is the freshwater genus; it is bean-shaped with a shell made up of two parts. They are small in size, have no heart and only a single eye. Due to the hard shell they are not relished as a fish food.

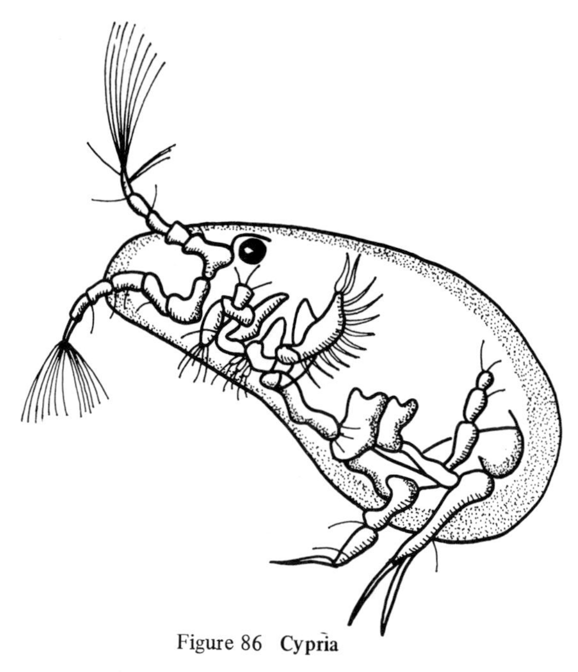

Figure 86 **Cypria**

OVARY. The female reproductive gland **(gonad)** which produces eggs **(ova).**

OVIPAROUS. Animals which produce eggs from which the young hatch after they have been laid.

OVIPOSITOR. A specialised egg-laying organ.

OVUM. Egg. *See* **Egg, Development of.**

OXBOW. A loop in a river, cut off from the main

stream by silt banks, which eventually becomes a pond.

OXYGEN. A tasteless, odourless, colourless gas with the chemical symbol **O** *(oxygenium),* which is essential for combustion and respiration. Together with carbon dioxide it permits the circulation of gases between animals and plants, which is a necessary condition for living.

Despite the need for oxygen it must not be too high, and there are upper and lower limits. In water the percentage should not fall below the minimum required to sustain life. If it should fall to around this dangerous level the fishes will become breathless, they will gulp atmospheric air at the water surface and the rate of breathing will increase. Despite the efforts to obtain a greater intake of oxygen they are unlikely to succeed and carbon dioxide will accumulate in the body and the fish may very well die. A rising temperature will increase the oxygen requirements of the fish whilst, at the same time, the water will not be able to hold the same oxygen as at a lower temperature. Thus, two unfavourable factors arise which can be very detrimental, especially if the biological conditions are unfavourable, such as too dense a growth of plant life, too much light, or an excess of decaying matter.

If, under such conditions the dissolved oxygen is used up, it can only be replenished at a very slow rate. In such cases the water should receive aeration to speed up the rate at which the oxygen is replaced. Whilst this will enrich the water it will not remedy poor biological conditions.

When the oxygen content reaches too high a level and the water becomes over-saturated with oxygen, the fishes will at first raise their oxygen consumption, by moving their gill covers more quickly. Normal breathing will be resumed after some time. Under intense sunlight water plants may produce an over-abundance of oxygen and, under certain conditions, this can prove lethal. An indication of danger is evident from the accelerated gill movements, which, after a time cease as a sudden, complete stoppage sets in. Strong secretions of mucus and blood may also be seen on the gills and fins and bubbles may also appear on the latter. Immediate help must be given before it is too late. This may be given by transferring the fish to fresh water of the same temperature, or an alternative is to expel the excess oxygen by applying very strong aeration. Aeration not only assists water to absorb oxygen, it also helps to dissipate it. Water both absorbs and dispels gases at its surface; therefore, if water receives aeration it forms a current which turns the water over and presents a larger amount to the surface, thereby assisting in the relief of both oxygen conditions.

P

P. Abbreviation for pectoral fin.

PALMATE. Hand-like, divided into fingers.

PANICLE. Botanical term for branched inflorescence.

PARAMECIUM. A microscopic unicellular, often found in infusoria cultures, pertaining to the *CILIATA.* Commonly known as the **Slipper Animalcule** from its slipper-like shape, it is an excellent first food for baby fishes. Culture by placing dried vegetation, such as Lemna, hay or sliced potato into jars which are filled with one half tap water and one half water from a pond or established aquarium. Stand in a well lit position but not in direct sunlight, and within a few days the Paramecia should be seen as a dusty, moving cloud in the water.

PARASITE. An animal or plant which lives on or in another being (the host), feeding upon its elements. External parasites are known as **ecto-parasites**; those which live inside their host are called **endoparasites.**

PARATYPE. A specimen which is described at the same time as the holotype, and can be substituted for the latter if it is lost or destroyed.

PARR. A name for a young Salmon from the time that it absorbs its yolk sac until it becomes a smolt, after approximately two years.

PARTHENOGENISIS. Virgin birth. Frequent phenomenon in lower animals, such as micro-crustaceans, where reproduction takes place through unfertilized eggs. This method of reproduction is the result of accommodation to extreme conditions which could be a danger to the survival of the species if the single remaining females were unable to reproduce without fertilization by males.

PEARLSCALE. *See* **Fancy Goldfish.**

PECTINATE. Comb-like.

PEDUNCLE. The tail of a fish; it lies between the vent and the caudal fin. In botanical terms it is the common stalk of a cluster of flowers.

PERCH. *Perca fluviatillis. See Percidae.*

PERCIDAE. The Perch family. In British waters there are two freshwater and one estuarine species. They belong to one of the most advanced groups of the Bony fishes; their most obvious characteristic being the presence of two dorsal fins separated by a narrow space or deep notch, the first being composed of stiff spines, the second of soft rays. There are stiff spines at the beginning of the pelvic and anal fins. The ctenoid type scales are tough and firmly held in the skin, the fish feeling rough

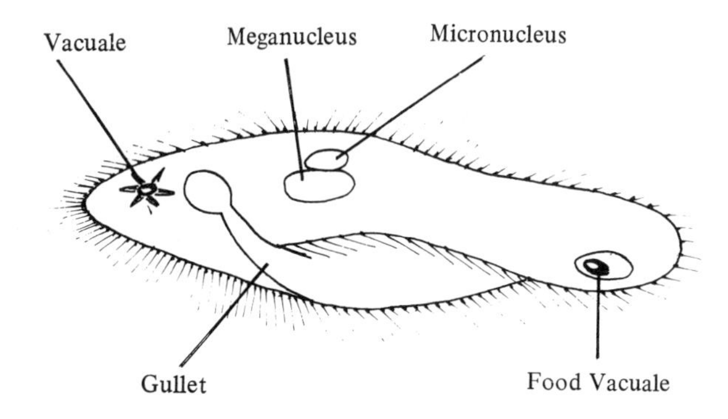

Figure 87 **Paramecium**

to the touch. The mouth is large, with numerous bristle-like teeth (including canines) proving it to be carnivorous and not suitable for keeping with other fish. The gill covers are spiky. Their diet is composed of small fish and frogs; they will also take worms and shrimps.

Spawning occurs during April and May, when the female deposits long strands of a jelly-like substance containing the eggs. These strands, which can be up to 3 feet (0.9m) long, are draped around plants, rocks and other suitable matter. The fry hatch out in around two or three weeks, after

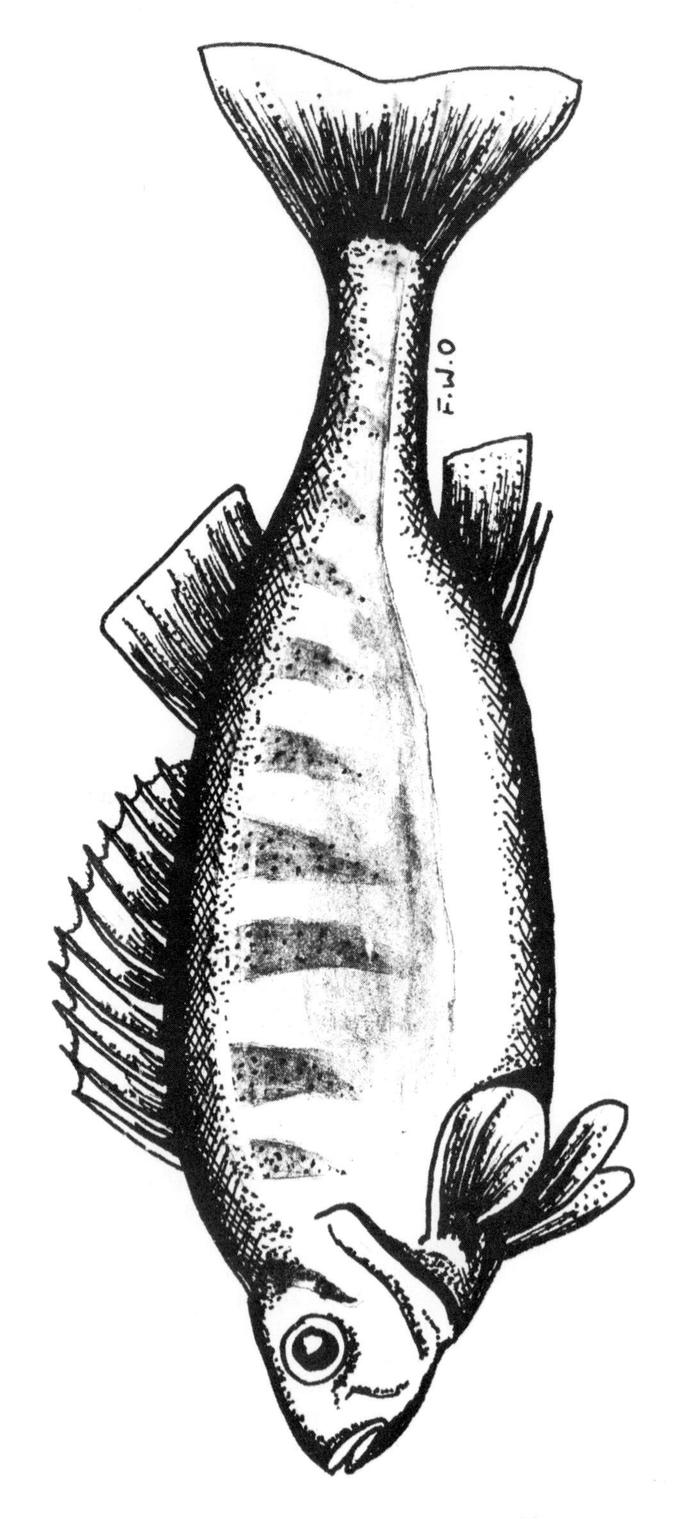

Figure 88 **Perch** *(Perca fluviatillis)*

which development is quite rapid, and by the end of the year they will usually have reached a length of 3 to 4 inches (76-102mm); they become sexually mature when three years old.

Perca fluviatilis– **The Common Perch.** Occurring throughout Europe, North America, and Siberia, this fish is widespread over most of the British Isles. It has a most striking appearance with an olive green back shading into yellow sides and a white belly. The first dorsal fin is marked with a black spot at its end; the anal and ventral fins can vary from orange to scarlet. Across the back there

Figure 89 **Pope or Ruffe** *(Acerina cernua)*

are usually five or six dark bars. The Perch is one of the most handsome of British freshwater fishes; the average adult has a length between 6 to 12 inches (152-305mm).

A gregarious fish – often shoals numbering from fifty or more can be seen in the wild – it prefers still waters, or those with slowly flowing current, which have plenty of water plants, tangled roots, bridge piles, and similar places of concealment where it can lurk in wait for smaller fish, which will be seized as they pass by.

Perch are very hardy, and small specimens may be kept in aquaria. However, they should be kept with their own kind and all be of a similar size.

Acerina cernua– **The Pope or Ruffe.** A rather localized fish, mainly found from the southern to the middle part of England. Rather more thick-set than the Perch with the slightly flattened belly of the bottom-living fish. It prefers fairly deep water and keeps to the bottom, where it feeds upon small crustacea, worms, various larvae, fish spawn and fry. The general colour is olive grey, fading into a whitish belly, with numerous dark markings. The belly fins are yellow. It has a large eye with a mauve iris. Both fins and gill covers are supplied with needle-sharp points.

Morone labrax– **The Bass.** During summer this fish can be found in the brackish waters of estuaries, especially on the south and west coasts of Britain. It may swim up-river for many miles for the purpose of spawning. The body is silvery, with a silvery blue back. Young Bass grow rapidly, being large enough to leave the inshore waters with the parent fish on the approach of winter.

Stizostedion lucioperco– **Pike-Perch or Zander.** A continental species which is shaped like a Pike and marked like a Perch. It has the two typical dorsal fins of the Perch group. The body is dark grey on the back shading to a silvery belly; there is no dark spot on the first dorsal fin. This is a ferocious fish, with large teeth, which kills for the sheer love of killing and not merely to satisfy a hungry appetite. Introduced into British waters, it has proved detrimental to the native species in some areas. Grows to around 20 inches in length.

PERCOIDEA. Sub-order of Perch-like fishes belonging to the order of *PERCOMORPHI.* Within this group are, amongst others, the ***Centrarchidae*** and the ***Percidae.***

PERCOMORPHI. A large and varied order of Bony fishes. They have a generally well developed, partly spiny, dorsal fin and pelvic fins set forward on the chest.

PERENNIAL. Of three or more years duration.

PERMANENT EGGS. Large eggs produced by many lower animals, such as Daphnia, which have hard shells and are rich in yolk. These fertilized eggs are able to withstand long periods of drought or extreme cold, thus ensuring the survival of the species.

PETOILE. A leaf-stalk.

PETROMYZONTIDAE. The lampreys. The body is eel-shaped, without scales. There is no sign of pectoral or pelvic fins, only the tail and two dorsal fins. They are parasitic on fish; having a round mouth, with many horny teeth and a strong tongue armed with sharp horny spikes. They attach themselves to their victims by means of their sucking lip, and use the tongue to rasp away the flesh, at the same time drinking the blood.

Spawning takes place during the summer. A nest is made in a gravelly and sandy bed; by means of the sucking mouth the pebbles are removed (for this reason they are often known as **Stone-suckers**), the stones being moved to the downstream side of the cleared area. Eggs are laid in the sand and then covered over with more sand. Usually a large number of lampreys share in the nest building and spawning. After spawning they are so weakened that they die. The larvae hatch out in ten to fifteen days and live in the mud banks and, at this stage, are called **Pride** or **Mud Lamprey.** After three or four years they change into the adult lamprey, are a few inches long, and begin their swimming existence.

Petromyzon marinus– **The Sea Lamprey.** This is the largest species and grows to a length of 2 feet, and can reach 3 feet (0.9m) in some specimens.

Petromyzon or *Lampetra fluviatilis*– **The Lampern or River Lamprey.** Can reach 16 inches (41cm), but 1 foot (0.3m) is the usual length. It is a uniform brownish or greenish colour on the back, fading down the sides to a white or silver belly. The front dorsal fin is separated from the second, which is somewhat triangular in shape and joined to the tail fin.

Petromyzon or Lampetra planeri– **The Brook Lamprey.** The smallest species, it is about the length and size of a pencil. Apart from its size, it resembles the preceding species, except that the front and second dorsal fins are joined together, the second having a rounded edge.

pH. Potential of Hydrogen. A scale (from 0 to 14) is used to measure the degree of acidity or alkalinity of soil and water by calculating the negative logarithm of the hydrogen ion concentration. An ion is a particle of an element carrying a charge of electricity. pH 7 indicates neutral.

PHAGE (or Bacteriophage). A virus which destroys bacteria.

PHANTOM LARVA. Transparent larva of the Phantom Midge. *See* **Live Foods.**

PHANTOM MIDGE. A member of the same family as the Mosquitoes, ***Culicidae.*** The adults are not

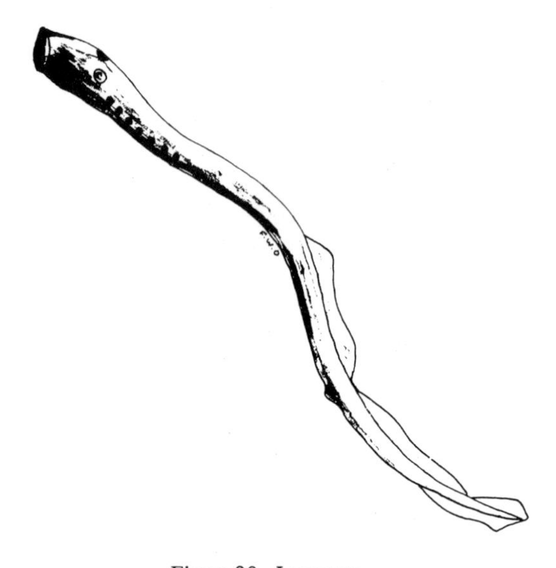

Figure 90 Lamprey

blood-suckers. Females lay their eggs in flat discs of up to 100 eggs, arranged in a spiral.

The larvae are carnivorous, grasping their prey with modified antennae. They are quite transparent and rather difficult to see, their air bladders being the most noticeable part. The creature remains in a motionless horizontal position, at varying depths, and absorbs oxygen from the surrounding water through its skin. The pupae are similar to those of the Mosquito (*see separate section*), and the adult flies emerge in the spring. The larvae make excellent live food. *See* **Live Foods.**

PHENOLOGY. The study of the seasonal changes and their effect upon animals and plants.

PHENOTYPE. The characters of an individual organism, determined by environmental effects upon the genotype.

PHOENIX. *See* **Fancy Goldfish.**

PHOTOSYNTHESIS. The process by which plants use sunlight to synthesise carbohydrates and carbon dioxide with the aid of chlorophyll. *See* **Assimilation.**

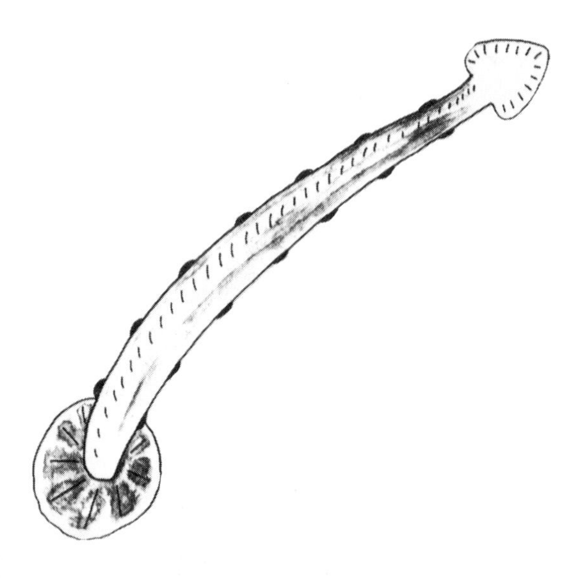

Figure 91 **Common Fish Leech** *(Piscicola geometra Linne)*

PHOXINUS PHOXINUS. The Minnow. *See Cyprinidae.*

PHYCOMYCETES. A class of mostly one-celled and aquatic fungi which includes the well known *Saprolegnia* that attacks weak and injured fish, showing up as white fungus patches.

PHYLOGENY. The history of a species' evolution.

PHYLUM. The top group in the zoological classification of animals which is sub-divided into classes.

PHYSIDAE. The Bladder Snails. Of the sub-class of **Lung Snails** or ***PULMONATA***. The shell has a few spiral turns, the last being the largest. All Bladder Snails are small with thread-like antennae, and live in a freshwater environment. They eat meaty foods and the spawn of other snails. *See* **Molluscs.**

PHYSIOLOGE. The study of the organs and functions of organisms.

PHYTOPHAGY. The eating of plants and other vegetable matter.

PIGMY SUNFISH. Common name for *Elassoma evergladei. See under* ***Centrarchidae.***

PIKE. *Esox Lucius.* The only member of the Esocidae to be found in British waters. *See* ***Esox Lucius*** *for description.*

PIKE-PERCH. *See under* ***Percidae.***

PILOSE. Botanical term meaning covered with long soft hairs.

PINNATE. Leaflets arranged in opposite pairs on a midrib like a feather.

PISCES. The Bony fishes – a class of cold-blooded, gill-breathing, aquatic vertebrates with bony skeletons and an outer covering of scales.

PISCICOLA GEOMETRA LINNE. The Common Fish Leech. It occupies all kinds of freshwaters, and sucks the blood of Carp, their relatives, and similar fish. It is brown with black cross bands, roundish in section, and measures about 4 inches (102mm) when fully stretched. Cocoons of eggs are laid on aquatic plants.

PISTIL. The female part of a flower.

PLANARIAN. Free-living flatworms, mainly found in freshwater, although some can be found on the sea shore. They can reach a length of 1 inch (25mm) but most species are much smaller. They are nocturnal predators and will destroy fish eggs.

PLANKTON. Floating organic life found at various depths in water. Unlike necton, which swims, plankton drifts with the action of wind and water currents. Freshwater plankton consists mainly of animal and plant unicellulars and micro-crustaceans. Animal plankton is known as **zoo-plankton**; vegetable plankton as **phyto-plankton**; and freshwater plankton as **limno-plankton.**

PLANORBIS. The well-known **Ram's Horn Snail.** *Planorbis corneus Linne* is the most popular species for the aquarium because of its harmless nature. It may be brownish-black or the more attractive red variety, known as **rubra.** The shell is laterally compressed and evenly coiled, into a round flattish form. Eggs are laid, in longish cushions of jelly, upon plants, stones and the like. *See* **Molluscs.**

PLANTS. Living organisms devoid of the powers of locomotion, sensation and digestion. Some of the more popular aquatic and waterside plants are listed below.

Acorus– Striking, aquatic perennials with sword-like leaves, which are aromatic when bruised, growing in shallow water or waterlogged margins.

A. calamus– The Sweet Flag, which grows to a height of 3 feet (0.9m) and bears small, yellowish flowers. The variety *pusillus* forms 2-3 inch (51-76mm) tufts of leaves whilst *variegatus* has 2-foot (0.6m) long leaves, striped with cream.

A. gramineus– This species reaches 1 foot (0.3m) and has grass-like leaves. On the *pusillus* these reach 3 inches (76mm), whilst *variegatus* reach 1 foot (0.3m).

Alisma– **Water Plantain.** Aquatic plant with small flowers borne in loose panicles, and plantain-like leaves. Prefers shallow water or waterlogged position.

A. gramineum– Has submerged grass-like leaves and pinkish-white flowers.

A. lanceolatum– Grows to around 1½ feet (0.4m), and has pale pink flowers.

A. parviflora– Possesses leaves up to 1½ feet in length and white flowers.

A. plantago-aquatica– The **Great Water Plantain** which reaches up to 3 feet (0.9m) and has pale, rose-coloured flowers.

Anacharis– Submerged aquatic plants, of value for their oxygenating properties. They have small leaves and form dense growths. *See* **Elodea.**

Aponogeton distachys– **Water Hawthorn.** The common name is derived from the vanilla-like fragrance of the flowers. It has a similar mode of growth to the water-lilies. Originating from the South African Cape of Good Hope, it is hardy enough to withstand the average British winter in the sheltered pond.

Butumus– Flowering rush found in Britain, Europe and Asia.

B. umbellatus– The only species, it grows to between 2 and 4 feet (0.6-1.2m) with sword-like leaves and bears umbels of rose-pink flowers. It prefers to grow in boggy ground or water up to 6 inches (152mm) deep.

Calla– A native of Europe, north Asia and north-east America. It prefers pond edges, and has heart-shaped leaves.

Figure 92 Great Water Plantain *(Alisma plantago)*

C. palustris– The only aquatic species of the above, known by the common name of **Bog Arum.** It is hardy and bears small, white arum-type flowers and grows 6 to 9 inches (152-229mm) tall.

Caltha– A small genus of moisture-loving perennial plants which grow at the borders of streams, ponds and lakes throughout Europe and North America.

C. leptosepela– Grows to 1 foot (0.3m), with white flowers.

C. palustris– The **Marsh Marigold** or **Kingcup.** Reaching around 1 foot (0.3m) in height, it has heart-shaped leaves and butter-yellow flowers. The variety *alba* grows to 8 inches (203mm) with a white, single flower; *nana plena,* 8 inches (203mm) with double flowers.

C. polupetala– Has large leaves and yellow flowers that can be up to 3 inches (76mm) wide. Can grow up to 2 feet (0.6m) if conditions are suitable.

Cardamine pratensis– British plant of moist meadows and swampy places. Commonly known as **Lady's Smock,** this attractive plant has pale pink or lilac flowers, which look white if seen in a

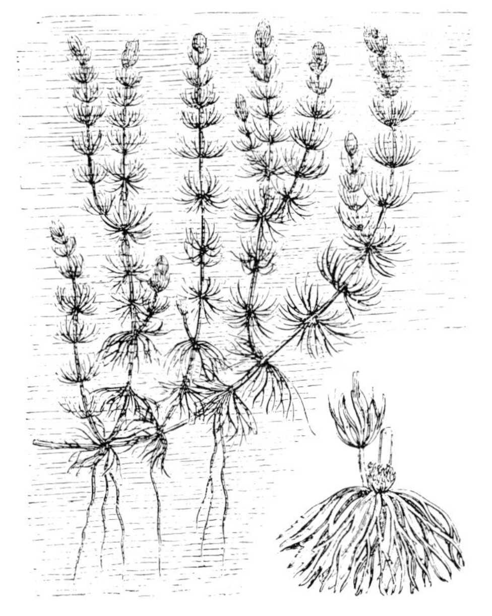

Figure 93 Hornwort *(Ceratophyllum demersum)*

mass. Lying close to the wet ground, runners carry radical leaves which are cut up into a variable number of distinct, more or less rounded, leaflets from which tiny rooted plants develop. The erect stems rise to about 1 foot (0.3m) high, carrying leaves which are longer and narrower than those on the ground stems, and terminate in flowers that can be ¾ inch (19mm) across. The seed-pod is about 1 inch (25mm) long, slender and upright.

Ceratophyllum demersum– **Hornwort.** A plant with the curious habit of never developing roots. It is a submerged aquatic that prefers a water temperature in the lower 60°F (15°C) range. A many-branched bare stalk, dark green and stiffish, carries the needle-like leaves which are arranged in whorls around the stem. Shows a distinct seasonal cycle; the plants tend to die back during the winter.

Eleocharis acicularis– **Hair Grass.** Partly to completely submerged aquatic plant. Growing from a trailing root-stock the plant forms tufts of filliform stalks, each grass stalk developing its own root system.

Elodea canadensis– (Originally classified as *Anacharis canadensis.*) A submerged water plant with much branched stems thickly dressed in narrow lanceolated leaves; an excellent oxy-genator which forms dense masses.

E. densa– Similar to, but stouter than, *E. canadensis.* The single stem is sparsley branched with narrow, lanceolated leaves growing in whorls around the stems.

Eriophorum– Related to *Scirpus,* this **Cotton Grass** is a small perennial plant which prefers moist, boggy areas. The tufts of elongated bristles surrounding the spikelets in summer give the plants a cottony appearance.

E. alpinum– Grows to 1 foot (0.3m)

E. augustifolium– Native British plant, growing to 15 inches (38cm).

E. latifolium– Up to 1 foot (0.3m) tall.

E. vaginatum– Native British plant, reaching a height of 1 foot (0.3m).

Fontinalis– Aquatic mosses often employed by aquarists in their coldwater aquariums.

F. antipyretica– **Willow Moss.** Slender flexible stems closely clad with tiny, oval, dark green leaves. It grows in tufts, affixed to various solid objects such as stones, usually in running water. A British native, growing submerged.

F. gracilis– Another native of Britain, it is usually considered a variety of the preceding species. It is much more slender and often has a reddish tinge.

Glyceria– Perennial, water-loving grasses which flourish in marshy places and are useful for water-side planting.

G. aquatica– The only species worth culti-vating, it is a British native which grows to a height of around 4 feet (1.2m). The leaves are smooth and pale green. The variety *variegata* is much more striking, the young leaves being flushed with pink and striped with longitudinal white lines. Both can be grown in deepish water.

***Hottonia palustris*– Water Violet.** A perennial aquatic plant, native to Britain, which will grow in water up to 18 inches (46cm) deep. Dense masses of finely divided, light green foliage are formed. During the summer, slender stems bearing pale lilac flowers are thrust above the water surface.

***Iris*–** A large genus of bulbous, creeping, and tuberous rooted perennials of which a number prefer boggy conditions. Planted in a sunny position at the edge of ponds, streams or the 'bog garden' they will make most attractive subjects.

I. foetidissima– Height to 2 feet (0.6m); has lilac-blue flowers followed by seed capsules which, during winter, will expose orange seeds.

I. pseudacorus– Height 2-3 feet (0.6-0.9m); has bright yellow flowers.

I. sibirica– Height 2-3 feet (0.6-0.9m); flowers being blue, purple and white in colour.

I. kaempferi– Height up to 2 feet (0.6m); has flowers of varying shades of lilac, pink, blue and white.

***Juncus*–** A large genus of annual or perennial, mainly rhizomatous plants. For the most part these bog inhabitants are coarse-growing, rampant plants of little ornamental value.

J. effusus spiralis– **The Corkscrew Rush** is perhaps the best of the *Juncus* for garden use, the twisted stems growing to around 18 inches (46cm). The variety *vittatus* has yellow striped leaves which can reach a height of 3 feet (0.9m).

***Lagarosiphon muscoides*–** Very similar in appearance to *Elodea densa;* often wrongly called *Elodea crispa.* The stems are erect, single and sparsley branched. Dark green, crispate leaves encircle the stout stem giving the vague appearance of a tube. A submerged aquatic which needs plenty of light and mildly alkaline water.

***Lychnis flos-cuculi*– Ragged Robin.** A perennial of the wet meadow, bog or ditch. The reddish stem reaches a height of about 2 feet (0.6m), the upper part being rough and sticky. Lance-like leaves grow directly from the root-stock and are stalked; those on the reddish stem are not. The rosy-pink flowers are much divided and borne in loose terminal panicles. The extreme diameter of a flower is about 1¼ inches (32mm).

***Lycopus europaeus*– Gipsywort.** Found around the margins of ponds and along the banks of ditches and streams, this perennial plant may be found amongst the other vegetation. The stem is square and rises to around 3 feet (0.9m) in height. The elliptical leaves have deeply cut margins and grow opposite to each other. The bluish-white flowers, which are spotted with purple, are small and stalkless being produced in dense whorls from the axils of the leaves.

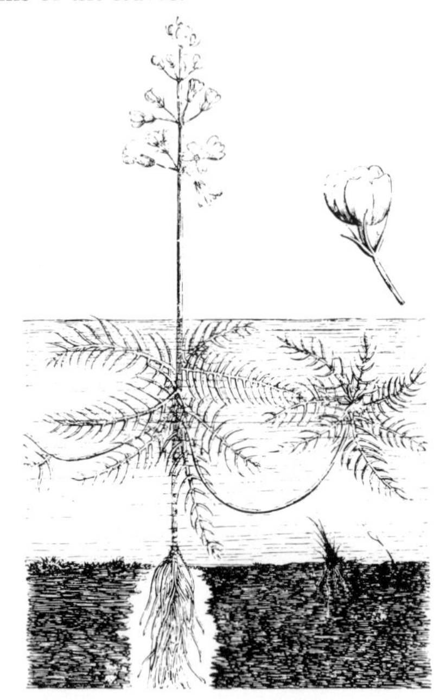

Figure 94 **Water Violet** *(Hottonia palustris)*

***Lysichitum*–** Hardy vigorous marsh plants, having large ornamental spathes and spadices. Large leaves develop fully after flowering.

L. americanum– Possesses spathes up to 6 inches (152mm) high, and pale yellow flowers contained in a greenish to golden-yellow, evil smelling, 6-inch (152mm) long spadix. Fully developed leaves reach 2½ feet (0.8m) long.

L. camtschatcense– Similar to *L. americanum* but odourless, with white spathes.

***Lythrum salicaria*– Purple Loosestrife.** Often

found frequenting marshy areas and the banks of streams. A perennial growing to a height of 3-5 feet (0.9-1.5m). Branched stems carry opposite, or whorled, lance-shaped leaves. Flowers are bright reddish-purple, about 1 inch (25mm) in diameter, and form a dense terminal spike.

Mentha aquatica– **Water Mint.** Abundant in Britain, this perennial can be found growing on the edges of streams and in wet, marshy areas. It has a creeping root-stock from which square stems rise to a height of around 18 inches (46cm). These are densely branched. The opposite leaves are stalked,

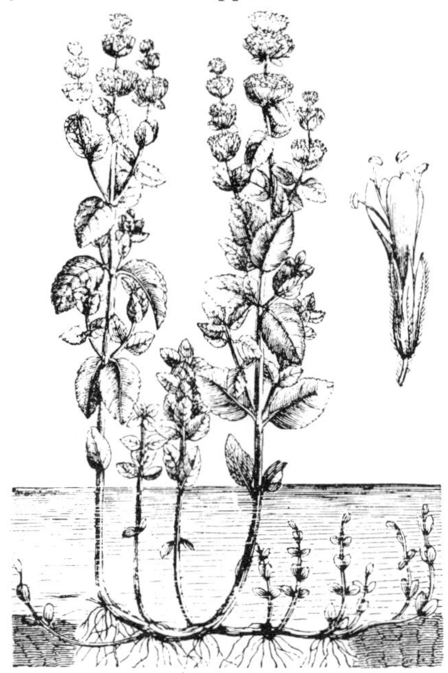

Figure 95 **Water Mint** *(Mentha aquatica)*

ovate, deeply indented and hairy. The lilac or purple flowers are small, forming dense whorls and often seen as long spikes of blossom.

Menyanthes trifoliata– **Buckbean.** Perennial aquatic herb. The leaves are broken into three, smooth, oval leaflets, and grow alternately. The broad base of their stem originates from a thick, creeping root-stock. The flower spike carries from three to twelve blossoms which are pinkish outside and white inside; the five stamens are a reddish colour.

Mimulus– Genus of hardy annual, half-hardy perennial and hardy perennial plants, bearing showy flowers. Most prefer a moist sunny position. Commonly known as **Monkey Flower** or **Monkey Musk** because the flower is thought to resemble a monkey's face.

M. luteus– Perhaps the best known of the *Mimulus.* A perennial with yellow flowers, it reaches a height of 1½ feet (0.4m).

M. ringens– Height up to 2 feet (0.6m); violet to white flowers.

Myosotis palustris– **Water Forget-me-not.** Growing near or in water, this perennial is a rampant grower. Slender, light green, spoon-shaped leaves grow from a sturdy stem attached to a creeping root-stock. The flowers are about ½ inch (13mm) across and light blue in colour with a yellow eye.

Myriophyllum– **Water Milfoil.** About forty species of these submerged aquatics are distributed almost all over the world. They have single, sometimes thinly branched stems, with leaves either alternate or opposed, often arranged in whorls and divided into linear segments. The plant can form dense masses and has a strong root system. Needs plenty of light and prefers alkaline water.

M. spicatum– Has branched stems with whorls of four or five feathery, pinnate leaves that are olive-green in colour. The stems are reddish-brown and the plant requires a high percentage of calcium in the water.

M. alternifolium– Does not grow as long as *M. spicatum,* nor does it develop winter buds. It demands a peaty growing medium, plenty of light, and acid water. It is a difficult plant to cultivate under articial conditions.

M. verticillatum– Similar to *M. spicatum,* but prefers slightly alkaline water.

Nuphar– Genus of some twenty-five species of aquatic hardy perennials. All have floating leaves with flowers held above the water. Most are best suited to still water, the floating leaves making them ideal for shallow water.

N. advens– **Common Spatterdock.** Has yellow flowers which do not fully open and cordate leaves which rise above the water.

N. japonica– Possesses golden-yellow flowers held well above water. Arrow-shaped leaves lie on the water surface, the submerged leaves having

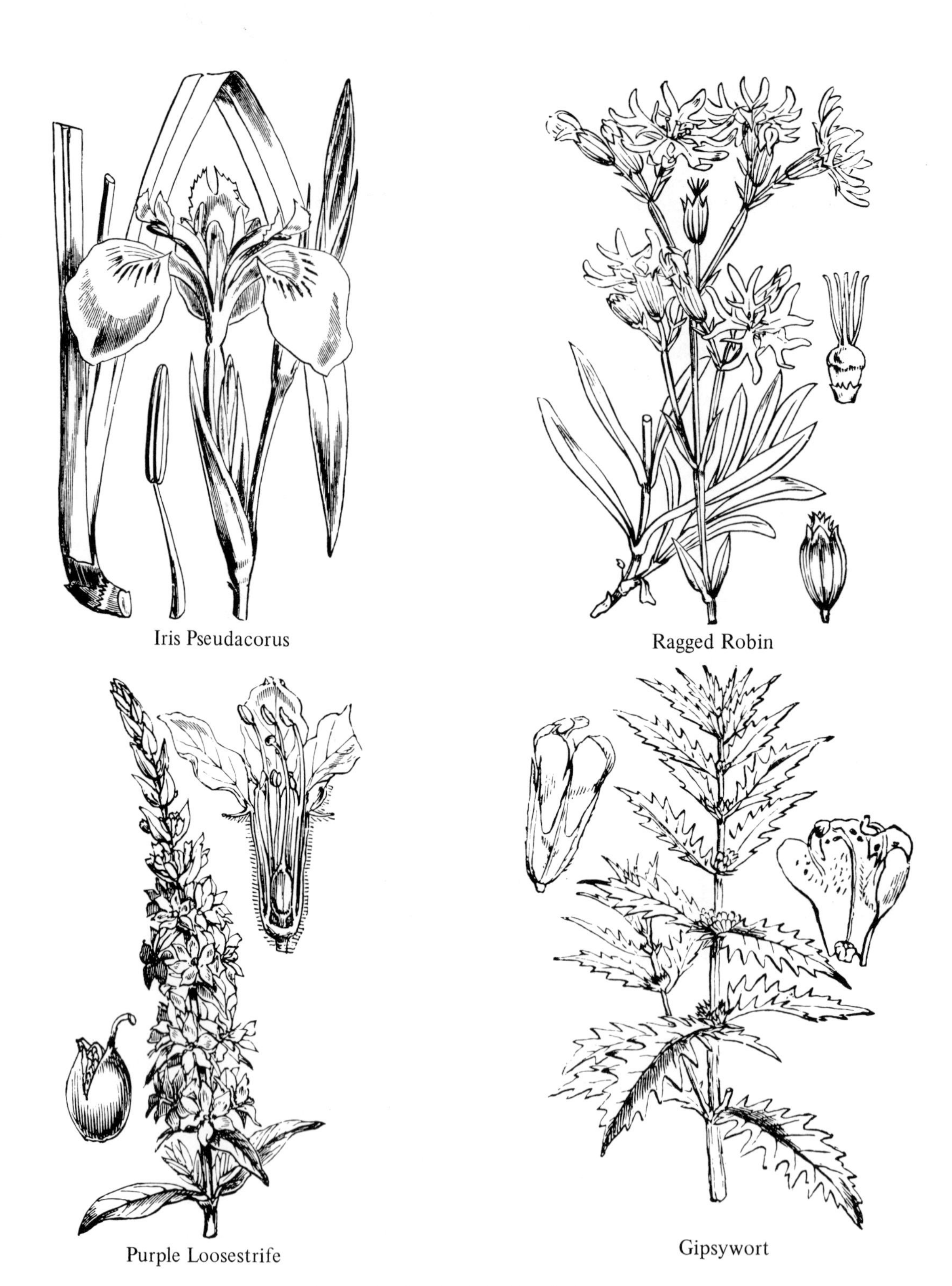

Figure 96 **Plants of the Pond edge**

undulating edges.

N. lutea– **The Brandy Bottle.** The leaves measure 8-12 inches (203-305mm) across and are sometimes held above water. Has slightly fragrant yellow flowers.

N. pumila– Very similar to, but smaller than, *N. lutea.*

Nymphaecae– **Water-lilies.** One of the oldest type of plants; fossils of the water-lily have been found as far back as the Upper Cenozoic period. It was known to the Pharaoh's and flowers of the Blue Water-lily (*N. ceorulea*) and the Egyptian Water-lily (*N. lotus*) accompanied those Egyptian King's of long ago to their last resting places. Von Linne bestowed the name of *Nymphaea* upon the water-lily after the Greek goddess of springs – Nymphe.

The cosmopolitan *Nymphaea* may be found in nearly all temperature zones, except for those that are very cold. It reaches its grandest in the warmer areas of the world. In 1802 the botanist, **Haenke,** discovered the worlds largest water-lily in a back-water of the river Amazon in Bolivia. In 1838 the name *Victoria amazonia* was bestowed upon the giant aquatic, in honour of Queen Victoria, the reigning British Monarch. Later another species, *V. cruziana*, was found in a cooler region of the Argentine. There is little to distinguish between the two species, apart from the difference in temperature requirements.

The *Victorias* have pads up to 10 feet in diameter, with upturned edges, and float on the water surface. The upper leaf surface is smooth and green, whilst the underside is purple and has numerous thick projecting veins containing cells filled with air, giving buoyancy to the large leaf-pad.

The flowers are about 14 inches (35cm) in diameter and white turning to pink in colour. They partially open during the first night and close the following morning; the following evening they open fully and have a strong perfume. The flower sinks after pollination and the fruit ripens in the water, taking around six weeks to mature. Strong spines protect the stems, leaves and flowers.

American horticulturists have produced many beautiful hybrids of the more easily managed types of water-lily, but none of these can compare with the Frenchman, Joseph Bory Latour-Marliac. During his lifetime he produced a vast number of spectacular hybrids – a legacy that the present day water-gardener still enjoys. He died in 1910 taking his closely guarded secrets with him. Among the hybrids produced by this genius are plants suited to waters of shallow depth and others needing water of considerable depth. Of the many varieties the **'Laydekeri'** hybrids were named, by Marliac, after his son-in-law, Maurice Leydeker, and form a colourful group well suited to cultivation in shallow water.

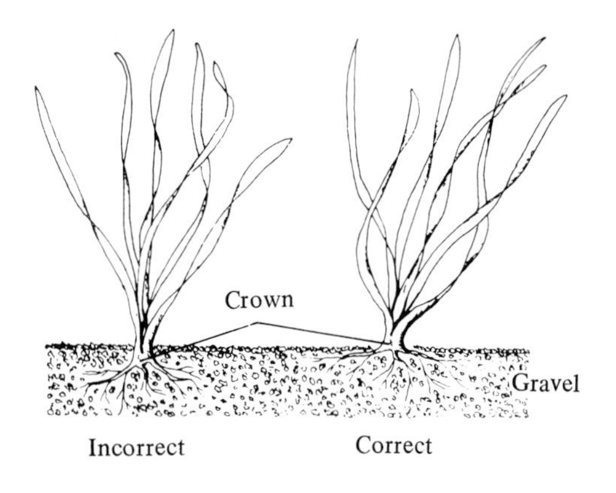

Rooted plants, particularly *vallisneria* and *sagittaria,* should be planted with the crown above the gravel surface to prevent rotting.

Figure 97 **Correct Planting Depth for Submerged Plants**

The following is by no means a comprehensive list of all the many species and varieties of water-lilies that are available, it merely mentions a few of the more popular and easily obtained types. They are listed under the depth of water which best suits them, and it should be borne in mind that many of those intended for deeper water may also succeed in a shallower depth, but may well over-crowd the pond; those intended for shallow planting are unlikely to do well if planted out of their depth.

6-12 inches (152-305mm)– 'Candida', white

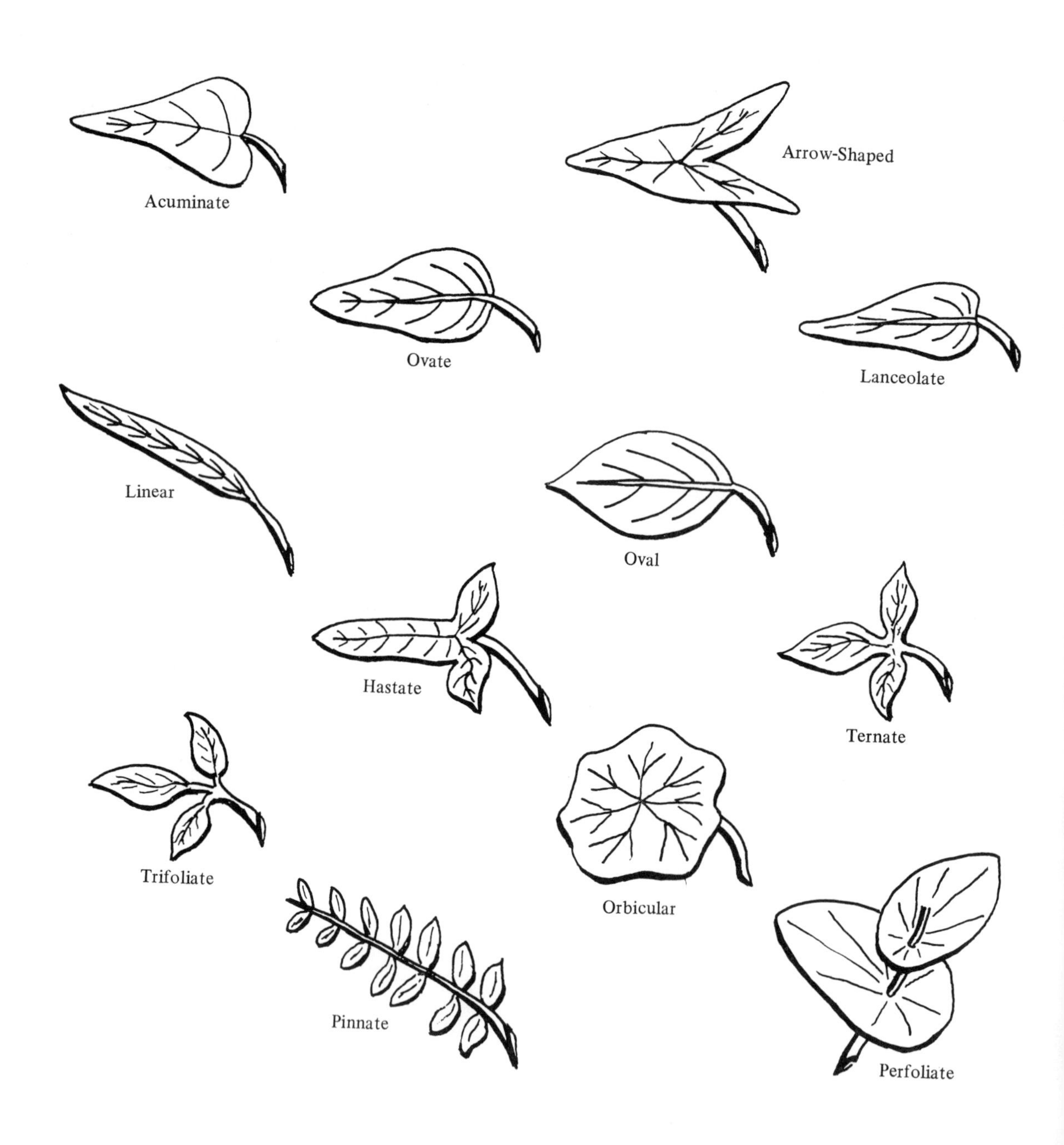

Figure 98 **Leaf Types**

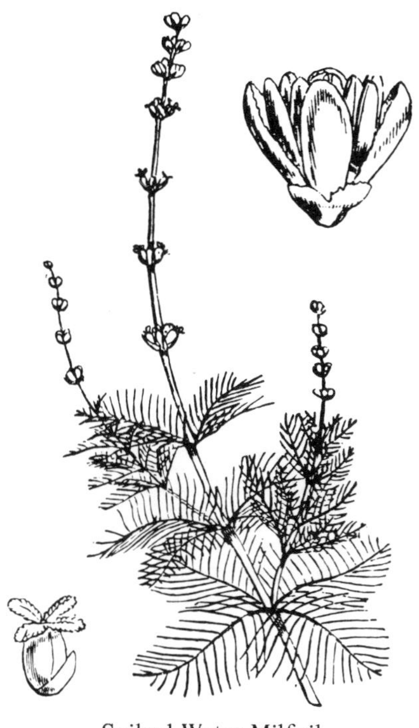

Spiked Water-Milfoil

Water-thyme

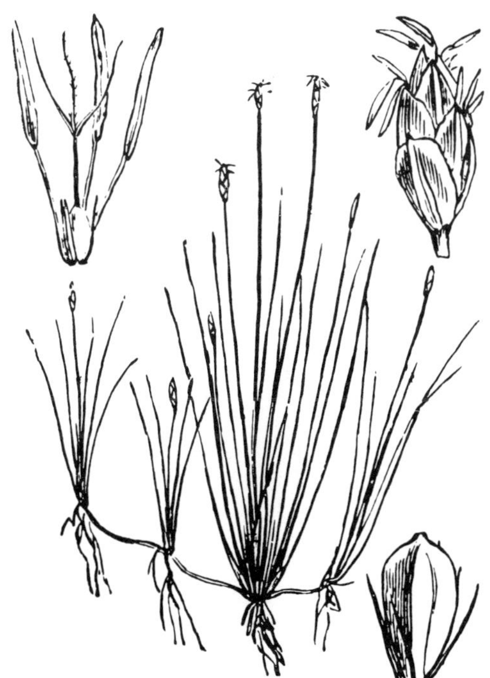

Eleocharis

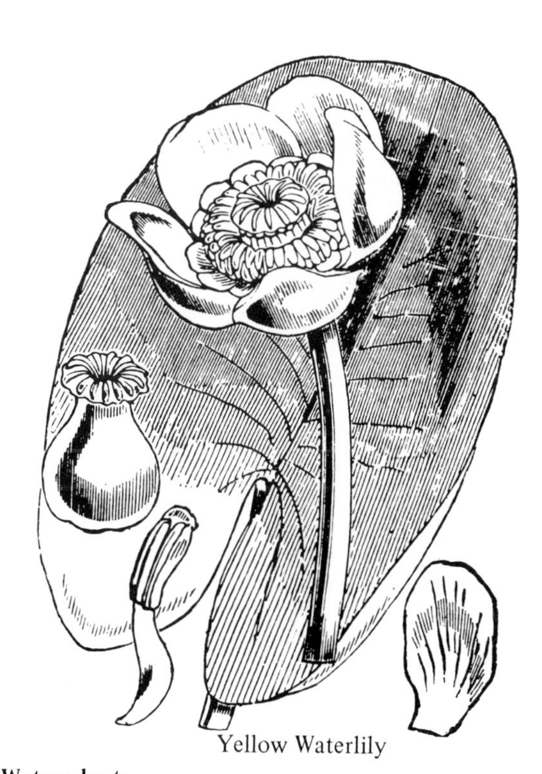

Yellow Waterlily

Figure 99 **Water plants**

with yellow centre; 'Laydekeri Lilacina', pink; 'Froebelii', bright red; 'Graziella', reddish-copper turning to orange-yellow; 'Pink Opal', deep coral-pink; 'Pygmaea Helvola', yellow.

12-24 inches (30.5-61cm)– 'Albatross', white; 'Escarboucle', crimson; 'Esmerelda', rose-white, mottled and striped deep rose; 'Marliacea Alba', white; 'Sunrise', yellow; 'Sultan', cherry-red stained white; 'Vesuve', purple-red.

24-36 inches (61-91cm)– 'Nuphar Lutea', yellow; 'Nymphaea Alba', white; 'Picciola', amaranth-crimson; 'Virginalis', snow-white.

Figure 100 Common Arrowhead ***(Sagittaria sagittifolia)***

The *Oderata* and *Tuberosa* types have long fleshy rhizomes which should be set under 1 inch (25mm) of planting medium leaving only the crown exposed. Tubers of the *Marliacea* group are large and rounded with fibrous roots, these should be planted vertically with the roots spread out and the crown above the medium. The Laydekeri group have a similar, but smaller, root-stock to *Marliacea* and are best set in a semi-horizontal position with the crown exposed.

Nymphoides– Aquatic perennials, some hardy some tender, with broad leaves, heart-shaped at the base, which float on the water surface. Prefers to grow in shallow water.

N. aquatica– Fairy Water-lily; white flowers.

N. indica– Water Snowflake. A tender plant with white flowers that have yellow centres.

***Pontaderia cordata*– Pickeral Weed.** A hardy aquatic perennial which prefers water from 6-12 inches (152-305mm) deep and reaches a height of 2 feet (0.6m). Has heart-shaped leaves and spikes of blue flowers.

***Pulicaria dysenterica*– Common Fleabane:** Common plant of marshy places. Perennial. Erect, branching, downy stems rise to a height of about 1 foot (0.3m). The leaves are wrinkled and downy, of an oblong heart-shaped and with toothed edges. This plant has a bright yellow flower-head.

***Ranunculas*–** A large genus of some 400 species, including a number that are native to Britain, such as the Common Buttercup.

R. aquatilis– **Water Crowfoot.** Found in both pond and stream. The floating leaves are kidney-shaped, divided into three lobes and three leaflets; the submerged leaves are finely divided into stiff, hair-like segments. Possesses small white flowers on upright stalks.

R. lingua– **Great Spearwort.** Prefers a boggy position. Grows to a height of 2-3 feet (0.6-0.9m) and has large yellow flowers.

***Sagittaria*– Arrowheads.** Found growing wild as swamp plants and in ponds, streams and shallow rivers. They prefer sunny places and adapt to the depth of the water, where they root in the mud. Leaves may be submerged, floating, or aerial; often all three will develop. Underwater leaves are long and ribbon-like; elongated, ovoidish, green leaves float on the water surface. These leaves have a reddish reverse, the green upper face becoming mottled with purplish-brown spots. A forked spike carries flowers which are snow-white with coal-black anthers. This plant will grow in water from 6 inches up to 2 feet (0.6m) deep.

S. subulata– Submerged species with ribbon-shaped leaves which are often bent, their length ranging from around 2 inches (51mm) upwards, according to the water depth. Young plants develop on runners from the parent plant. This species appears in three forms: *Forma gracillima* rarely forms floating leaves, but can develop submerged leaves up to 3 feet (0.9m) long; *Forma natans* can form floating leaves, and submerged leaves up to 12 inches (30.5cm) long; *Forma pusilla* is the smallest, with leaves approximately 4 inches (102mm) long – in shallow water the tips of the leaves become oval.

S. macrophylla– Swamp plant with leaves shaped like arrow heads, carried on long stems. Can grow to 3 feet (0.9m) tall with white flowers.

S. sagittifolia– **Common Arrowhead.** Similar to above, with a height of around 18 inches (46cm).

S. sagittifolia var. japonica– As preceding plant, but possessing double white flowers and growing to a height of 2½ feet (0.8m).

***Saururus*–** Perennial plants of bog and water. The flowers are produced in dense drooping spikes, about 5 inches (127mm) long. Will grow in water up to 4 inches (102mm) deep.

S. cernuus– Has dark green, heart-shaped leaves up to 6 inches (152mm) long and fragrant white flowers. Height – up to 2 feet (0.6m).

S. chinensis– Growing to a height of 1½ feet (0.5m), it has yellowish-white flowers and ovate leaves up to 4 inches (102mm) long.

***Scirpus*–** The old Latin name for a reed or rush. The narrow, upright growth of these plants makes a good contrast with the broad leaves of other plants along the border of a stream, pond or in the bog-garden. They should be planted in water up to 4 inches (102mm) deep.

S. albescens– Variegated, green and white stems, grows up to 3 feet (0.9m) high.

S. cernuus– Height 6-12 inches (152-305mm); a tufted plant with drooping stems.

S. lacustris– **The Bulrush.** Height up to 6 feet (1.8m).

S. prolifera– Height about 1 foot (0.3m).

S. tabernaemontani zebrinus– The porcupine, quill-like leaves can grow to 4 feet (1.2m) in length and are transversely banded in green and white.

***Spiraea ulmmaria*– Meadow Sweet.** Found growing along the edge of streams, rivers and in wet meadows. The stout reddish stems grow to 2-3 feet (0.6-0.9m) tall with leaves that are interruptedly pinnate. Large, dense cymes of minute flowers can be seen that are yellowish-white and sweetly perfumed.

***Thalictrum flavum*– Meadow-Rue.** Largest and most striking of the British species. A plant of the swampy banks of rivers and streams. Growing from 2-4 feet (0.6-1.2m) tall, the stems are stout and furrowed. The smooth leaves are broken into three stalked divisions, and each of these into paired leaflets which are wedge-shaped ending in three lobes. The plant has bright yellow flowers.

***Typha latifolia*– The Great Reed Mace.** Rising to a height of 6-7 feet (1.8-2.1m), this perennial is a common sight around lakes, ponds and on river banks. The grass-like leaves are long and narrow, sheathing the stem which bears the well known spike or 'mace'. It is a common mistake to call this plant the Bulrush, a name rightly belonging to *Scirpus lacustris.*

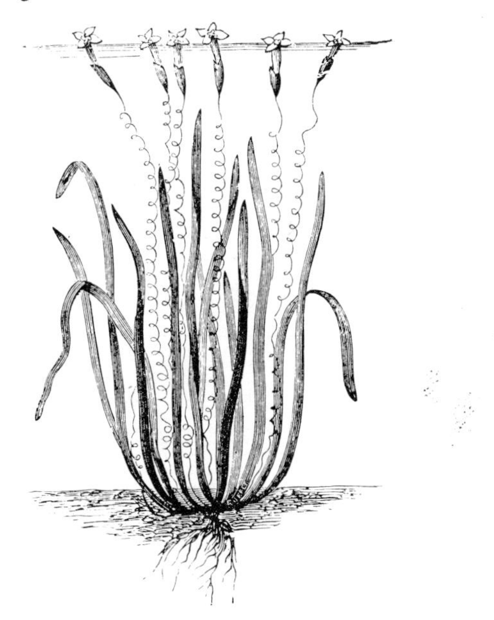

Figure 101 *Vallisneria spiralis*

T. minima– **The Small Reed Mace,** height up to 1½ feet (0.5m).

***Vallisneria*–** A popular plant for the home aquarium, it has a similar appearance and mode of reproduction to *Sagittaria.*

V. gigantea– The largest of these plants, it does not tolerate low temperatures very well. Leaves may reach up to 5 feet (1.5m) in length with a width of 1 inch (25mm).

V. spiralis– The ribbon-shaped leaves range in length from 8-36 inches (20.3-91cm). This plant prefers slightly acid water and bright light.

V. spiralis torta– Not as hardy as the foregoing, it has corkscrew twisted leaves.

Water Starwort. (*Callitriche palustris*)– Spreads rapidly and enjoys cold water. The underwater leaves are linear; the floating leaves are lanceolate and form a rosette on the surface. Easily propogated from shoots and cuttings.

PLATYHELMINTHES. These flatworms are a phylum belonging to the PROTOSTOMIA. They possess a flattened body and occur in various shapes and with different manners of living. Of particular interest to the aquarist are the ***PLANARIANS*** and the ***TREMOTODA,*** which includes *Dactylogyrus* and *Gyrodactylus,* together with some forms of the tapeworm. They may be permanently, or transitionally, parasitic in fishes.

Figure 102 **Water Starwort** *(Callitriche palustris)*

PLEUSTON. Small floating vegetation forming mats of green on or near the water surface.

POIKILOTHERMIC. 'Cold-blooded' creatures, such as fish, in which the body temperature varies with the surrounding temperature; as opposed to the 'warm-blooded' animals which maintain a constant body temperature.

POISON METALS. Metals that, when in contact with water, can create poisonous conditions that can be lethal to fishes, especially in the small enclosed area of an aquarium or ornamental pond.

Iron and steel are dangerous, copper and brass are extremely poisonous, as is nickel but to a lesser extent, and zinc is invariably lethal. Aluminium can also be dangerous if the water contains calcium. Water drawn through newly laid metal pipes can be an unsuspected cause of metal poisoning, and the consequent death of fish.

Poisoned fishes may exhibit the following signs: restless and unusual movements; breathlessness; listing at various angles; lying on the back or side; shimmying; convulsions; changes in colour; lethargy and death. Little, if anything, can be done to save a poisoned fish.

POLYEMBRONY. The division of an egg into two or more animals, as with identical twins.

POLYMORPHISM. The occurrence together, within the same habitat, of two or more sharply contrasting varieties of an animal or plant species in sufficiently large proportions to make it quite evident that the rarest is not being maintained by recurrent mutation.

POLYPHAGOUS. An animal that eats many kinds of food.

POMPON. Variety of goldfish. This word is sometimes wrongly spelt as Pom-Pom – a type of World War II naval gun. *See* **Fancy Goldfish.**

POND. Small sheet of inland freshwater.

POND, ORNAMENTAL. By its very nature an ornamental garden pond is virtually a permanent feature. Therefore, careful consideration should be given to the size, design, siting and method of construction before construction starts. A pond built for Goldfish may well be much too small for the comfort of Koi; these large fish require quite spacious swimming areas to a depth of, say 5 feet (1.5m), whereas the Goldfish pond need have a deep point of no more than 2 feet (0.6m). These deep regions provide an area of safety to which the fishes can retire during the coldest months of the year; other areas of the pond can be of less depth.

A pond should not be placed where it is in permanent shade; although it is impossible to bring sunlight to such a pond, it is always possible to devise some form of shading for a pond which may receive too much sunlight.

Trees should be avoided for it is possible for their roots to damage a pond and, in any event, they will shed their leaves into the water. The leaves of some trees and bushes can be toxic to fish: laburnum, laurel, holly and rhododendrons are particularly dangerous in this respect. On the whole, therefore, it is better to site a pond in an open position.

Ideally, the chosen position will afford some protection from any winds blowing from the east or north, allow the early morning, and possibly the late afternoon and evening, sun to caress its surface, whilst shading from the heat of the mid-day sun.

The shape of the pond may be of formal or informal design, but, whichever is decided upon, it should blend in with its surroundings to form a unified and harmonious whole. A well planned pond should give pleasure to all who see it, and encourage the visitor to linger in contemplation of its charm. In order to try to achieve these objectives the proposed pond should first be planned on paper.

First prepare a plan, drawn to scale, showing the boundaries and main features of the garden. Next prepare a scale-size cut-out of the pond. The cut-out can then be tried in various positions, on the drawing, to decide the best place to site it, at the same time making sure that it is neither too small nor too large for the size of the garden. When a satisfactory size, shape and location have been arrived at, it can be roughly marked out, life-size, by pouring sand (or laying a garden-line) to the outline of the pond in its proposed position. Standing back the effect can be studied; if any slight alteration is thought necessary, this can be attended to quite easily.

Commence excavating the hole by first digging a trench to the shape of the marked outline, thus providing an easily recognised area within which to work. If a very large pond has been planned it may well be worth hiring the services of a mechanical digger to carry out the bulk of the work; although expensive it could save many hours of back-breaking toil. As the work proceeds, shape the excavation into the desired shape and depth, from shallow to deep – leaving shelves for the plants not much deeper than 12 inches (30.5cm) below the eventual level of the water surface.

Fibreglass shells are preformed into various pond shapes. However, they are seldom deep enough to allow the fishes to over-winter in safety during a really cold spell. Installation presents no difficulties; the shell is sunk into a hole of suitable size, levelled, and finally firmly infilled around the sides. It is then ready for stocking with plants and fishes.

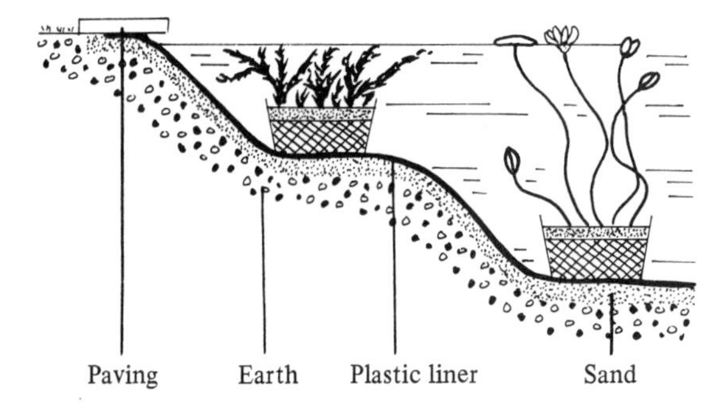

Figure 103 Section through 'Liner' pond, with paved edge.

The modern method is to use a **pond-liner,** which merely involves lining the excavation with a plastic sheet; it is much less arduous than constructing a concrete pond and has the advantage that it can be put into use immediately. The choice of liner is the main factor which decides the permanency of the pond, and care must be taken, at all times, not to puncture it.

Broadly speaking there are three types of pond-liners. The cheapest and least satisfactory is polythene. **Polythene** has the great disadvantage of deteriorating after a few years; it rots above the water-line where it is exposed to the air. This material is really only suitable for temporary use and should be of at least 500 gauge quality and preferably black.

Much more suitable for ponds are the tough, nylon mesh **reinforced pvc liners.** This material wears well and has a greater resistance to being punctured; it is very often available with a pebble design on one side and plain blue on the other.

Best of all are the **butyl liners** which have an indefinite life and are very tough. Butyl has a great advantage in that it is possible to join it by electric

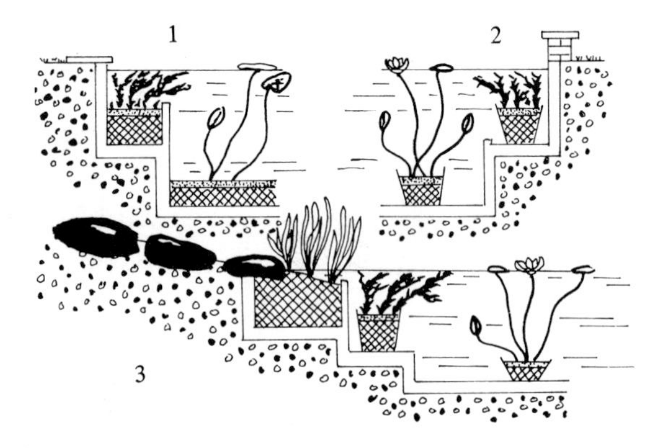

1. Ground level pond with paved surround. Gravel covered loam in planting trough and on base.
2. Dwarf wall surround. Gravel covered loam in baskets.
3. Pond with rockery and bog area.

Figure 104 **Section through Concrete ponds**

welding, or the use of a special adhesive and tape, and so create various shapes. It is the most expensive type of liner but well worth the cost, in view of its virtually trouble-free long life. Being flexible, plastic liners are unaffected by ground movement, freezing, or the effects of contraction and expansion caused by temperature fluctuations.

In order to determine the size of liner required the length and width should be measured. Measure the maximum dimension of the base and up the two opposing walls to their highest points. Both total measurements should have an additional 2 feet (0.6m) added, this is to allow a 12 inch (30.5cm) overlap all round, to be covered by the surround.

Having prepared the excavation, carefully remove any sharp stones or other objects that might make a hole in the liner. Next lay a 2 inch (51mm) layer of soft sand over the bottom; an alternative is to line the excavation thickly with several newspapers. Lay the liner over the excavation, allowing it to drape down, checking that there is an equal overlap all round. Place a few bricks, or other weights around the overlap to hold it in position.

The pond can now be slowly filled with water from a garden hose. As the weight of the water pulls the liner down, and moulds it to the shape of the pond, gently pull and ease the liner into position trying to disguise any folds or creases that may form. Care at this stage will add much to the appearance of the finished pond. Leave the weights to hold the flap in position until a permanent surround can be placed around it.

Although turves may be replaced over the liner overlap a far better method is to lay paving; this will make a firm area for walking on during inclement weather.

When the paving has set firm and hard the pond should be emptied, to rid it of any impurities or fallen soil, and then refilled after filling the planting troughs with compost.

The concrete pond is still very popular despite the hard work involved in its construction; it can be built to practically any size, shape or depth, and there is no fear of puncturing it.

If the pond walls are nearly vertical, shuttering will be required to hold the concrete in position, and should be constructed of strong material that will not give with the weight of the concrete. It must be well braced and have spacers to hold the shuttering at least 6 inches (152mm) away from the inner face of the excavation. These spacers are removed after the concrete has been poured, and the concrete must be tamped well down to remove any air-pockets. The base is laid after the shuttering has been removed, but before the poured concrete has really hardened, after which it is finished as described later.

Sloping walls allow the concrete to be 'battered'

into place. This requires a stiff concrete mix which is thrown firmly against the walls and base; it should be firm enough to stay in place, and then is battered with the back of a spade. Continue over the whole area of the excavation, building up a depth of around 3 inches (76mm). The following day repeat the process to build the concrete up to a 6-inch (152mm) thickness. Any reinforcing material can be sandwiched between these two layers.

Whichever method is used, the concrete mix should be in the proportions of 1 part cement, 2 parts clean sharp sand and 3 parts washed coarse ballast – all measured with a bucket. Mix thoroughly in the dry state until the colour is uniform and free of streaks of grey or red. Make a depression in the agglomeration and then pour a little water on it, continue mixing and adding a little more water as required. The concrete should not be sloppy as a stiff consistency is required (and firmish if it is to be 'battered'); test by plunging and withdrawing the shovel – if it leaves ridges it is about right. The concrete must be laid as soon as possible after mixing.

As soon as the concrete has become firm, but not hard, a coat of the same concrete mix should be trowelled overall to a thickness of 1 inch (25mm), this layer need not be too smooth and is better left a little rough. The following day a finishing coat should be applied to a thickness of ½-1 inch (13-25mm).

The finishing coat, which is rendered over the complete face of the concrete, is a stiff mix of 1 part cement to 3 parts clean sharp sand plus a waterproofing powder. This rendering must be completed in one operation and trowelled smooth, care being taken to avoid or eliminate any air-bubbles that may appear. When this coat has set firm, cover it with damp sacks, or something similar, to slow down the drying period. Allow the pond to harden for about a week before filling it.

New concrete contains a considerable quantity of lime which must be got rid of before the pond is safe to use. Lime is highly toxic and will prove fatal to fish and most plants. It is possible to apply various sealants to the concrete, in order to prevent the free lime entering the water. However, if these coatings become damaged the lime will be waiting to leak into the water with predictable results.

The oldest, and still the safest, method of preventing this requires a little more hard work. Fill the pond with water, leave it for a week, then, with a stiff brush, thoroughly scrub it all over. The pond should then be emptied and any sediment removed. Continue to give the pond this treatment for around eight weeks, then test the pH value. If the alkaline content appears to be within a safe range a poor quality fish may be used as a final test. If at the end of a week the fish is still alive it

Figure 105 **Ivy-leaved Duckweed** *(Lemna trisulca)* showing mode of growth.

can be assumed that the water is safe; if, however, the fish dies or the pH test gives a high alkali reading continue to change the water until it becomes safe.

An alternative method of solid pond construction is to use either **bricks** or **cement blocks**; this is an ideal method to adopt when constructing raised ponds. Commence by making a form from battens. This should be slightly larger than the required outside measurements for the proposed pond. Pour the same concrete mix, as used for the previous pond, into the form to act as the foundation and base, making sure that it is level in all directions.

Whether using concrete blocks or hard house bricks they should be thoroughly soaked before use. Lay a line of mortar onto the concrete base after it has set, and commence laying the walls. For obvious reasons during this work use a spirit-level until the required height is reached. Leave the inside joints a little rough to act as a key for the rendering; the outside can, however, be neatly pointed – unless the exterior is to be rendered over.

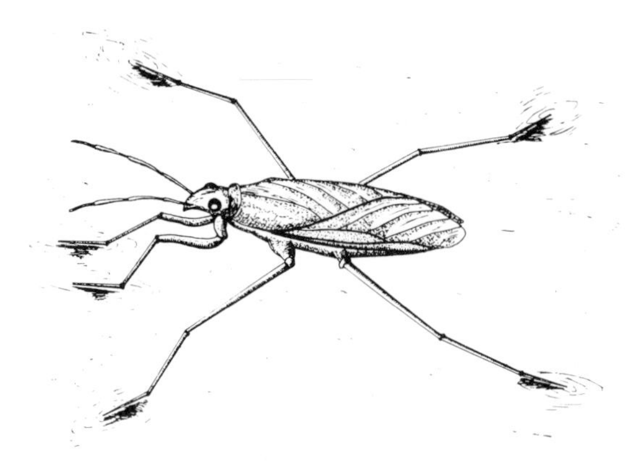

Figure 106 **Pond Skater** *(Gerris lacustris)*

Allow the mortar to set for a day before applying the rendering to base and walls in one operation – as described for concrete ponds. At this stage any capping can also be placed into position. It may be that, prior to rendering, the interior surfaces will require wetting – rendering is not successful if laid on a dry surface, and is liable to break away with time.

Cure the rendering, to remove the free lime, before putting the pond into commission.

The planting medium most suitable for ponds is a good turfy loam; the top spit from a meadow would be perfect – providing it has not been sprayed with any weed or pest-killer. Place the loam into the containers, or the built-in trough, and gently firm down. Cover with a 2-inch (51mm) layer of well washed gravel or stone-chippings, to prevent the fish stirring the muddy loam into the water.

Before placing any plants in position they must be thoroughly clean and sterilized in order to avoid introducing any possible infection or parasite – it will also prevent the inclusion of snails which are unnecessary in a pond. A list of suitable plants will be found under the heading **Plants.**

POND SKATER. Sometimes called **Water Strider.** Slender, elongated, predatory, water surface bug, often seen gliding over the water surface of ponds, ditches and slow streams. They feed upon insects which fall upon the water, but do not harm under-water life. *See* **Water Bugs.**

POND SNAILS. A general term for freshwater Pulmonata snails, especially applied to the genus *Limneae,* and particularly to the Great Pond Snail, *L. stagnalis,* which has a spiral shell up to 2 inches (51mm) long and is sometimes carnivorous – it may even attack newts and fish if given the chance. *See* **Molluscs.**

POPULATION. The total number of beings in a given area.

PORRECT. Botanical term meaning pointing forward and outward.

POWAN. *Coregonus clupeoides. See* ***Coregonus.***

PREDATORS. Creatures which attack, kill and eat others.

PREDATORS OF FISH. Those that cause damage or death. The large predators, such as cats, other animals and some birds can be avoided, in the ornamental pond, by stretching a net above the water surface. However, there are some predators which are not so easy to avoid, so the best rule of safety is to remove any creature, large or small, whose habits are not known.

Predators should be removed and killed immediately they are seen. To ignore them is courting trouble, for many can cause considerable

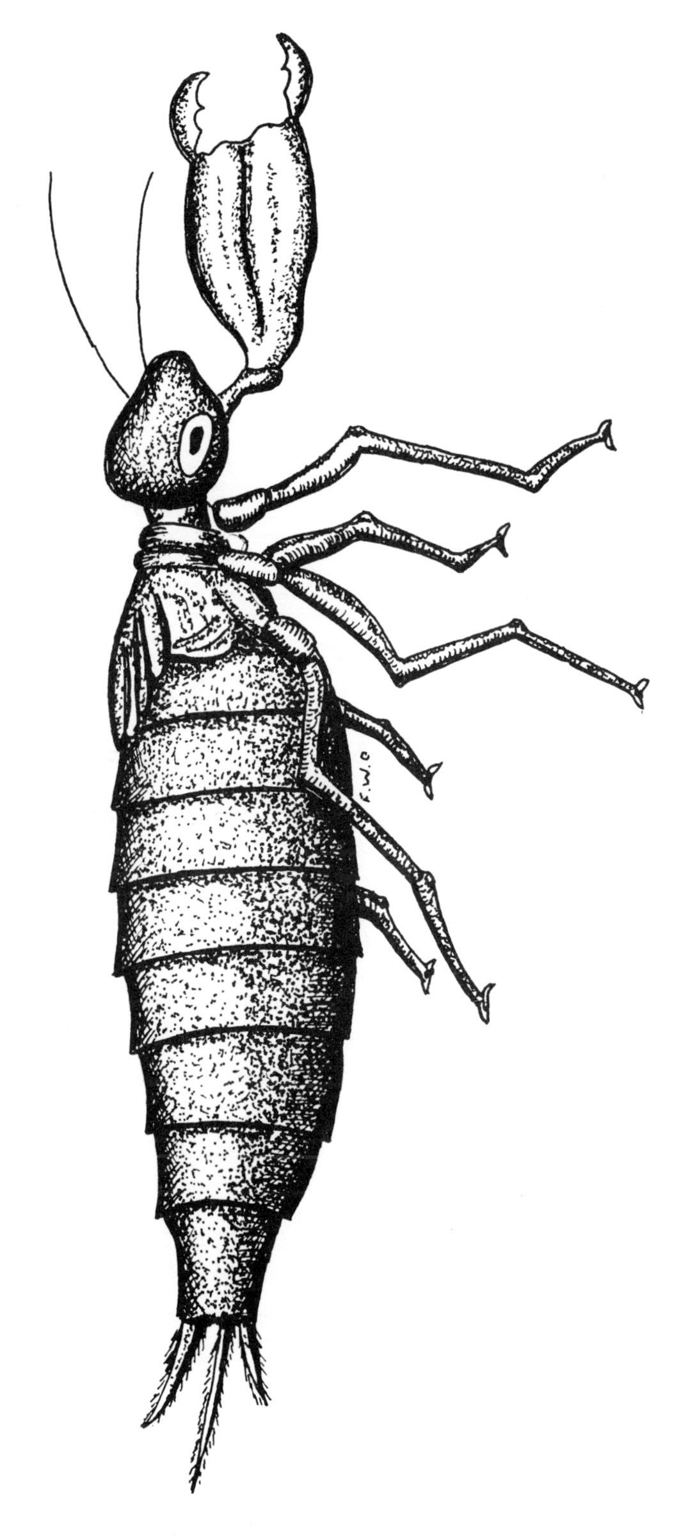

Figure 107 **Water-Tiger** – the larva of the Dragon-Fly.

damage to a fish – even if they do not kill it.

Alder-Fly– The common Alder-fly is a familiar sight around ponds, lakes and streams during May and June. Their larvae remain in the water for up to two years, and spend much of their time crawling in the bottom mud. Brown in colour, the larvae grow to a length of 1 inch (25mm). They attack smaller creatures, seizing their prey in powerful mandibles.

Great Diving Beetle– A vicious beetle that will readily attack quite large fish. If anything the larvae are more vicious than the adult. *See* **Dytiscus.**

Great Silver Beetle– The adult is omnivorous and will not harm fish. However, the larvae are strictly carnivorous and can attain a length of 2¾ inches (70mm).

Water-Boatman– These creatures swim upside down, and can be recognised by their two, long, oar-like legs. They will not hesitate to attack creatures larger than themselves.

Water Scorpion– Looking like a dead leaf, this aquatic bug lurks in the mud of shallow water at the edge of ponds. The front legs are modified to grasp its victims in a vice-like grip; the juice then being sucked out of the prey.

Water-Tiger– The larval stage of the Dragon-fly. Normally sluggish, this creature lies in wait until its victim comes within striking distance. This extremely vicious creature is most aptly named.

Stick-Insect– Related to the Water Scorpion, it has a stick-like body. It has similar habits to those of the Water Scorpion.

Hydra– These constitute a danger to small fry only. They are difficult to remove from an aquarium. One method is to stir into the aquarium one teaspoon of ammonia to every four gallons of water. Leave for forty-eight hours before emptying and then flush to remove all traces of ammonia. Before giving this treatment the fishes should be placed in a separate container.

The creatures mentioned are those most commonly encountered, a number are covered in more detail elsewhere in this book, under their specific headings.

PROTOPLASM. A protein jelly which is the physical basis of life found in all living cells. Protoplasm maintains life by incorporating different substances from its surroundings into its own being, and eliminating all unwanted matter.

PROTOZOAN. The most primitive phylum of animals; they are among the oldest forms of life on earth and consist, mostly, of microscopic single cells or units of protoplasm which perform all the vital functions. Fundamentally, the cell of the protozoan differs from that of multicellulars in that it is a closed unit which is able to exert all necessary manifestations of life. It achieves all

Figure 108 **Water Crowfoot** *(Ranunculus aquatilis)*

those functions for which the multicellular organism must employ a great many highly specialised cells. The PROTOZOA comprise four classes; ***FLAGELLATA, RHIZOPODA,*** the parasitic ***SPOROZOA*** and the ***CILIATA.***

PRUINOSE. Botanical term meaning with a white bloom.

PUBESCENT. Botanical term meaning covered with short soft hairs.

PULMONATA. Sub-class of the Gastropods containing, amongst others, most of the freshwater snails. They have lungs instead of gills and, unlike the superficially similar operculates, have no operculm. *See* **Molluscs.**

PUNGENT. Botanical term meaning equipped with a point sharp enough to puncture the skin.

PUPA. The third, non-motile stage in the metamorphosis of many insects, in which the creature becomes chrysalis-like.

PURACHINA ŌGON. *See* **Koi.**

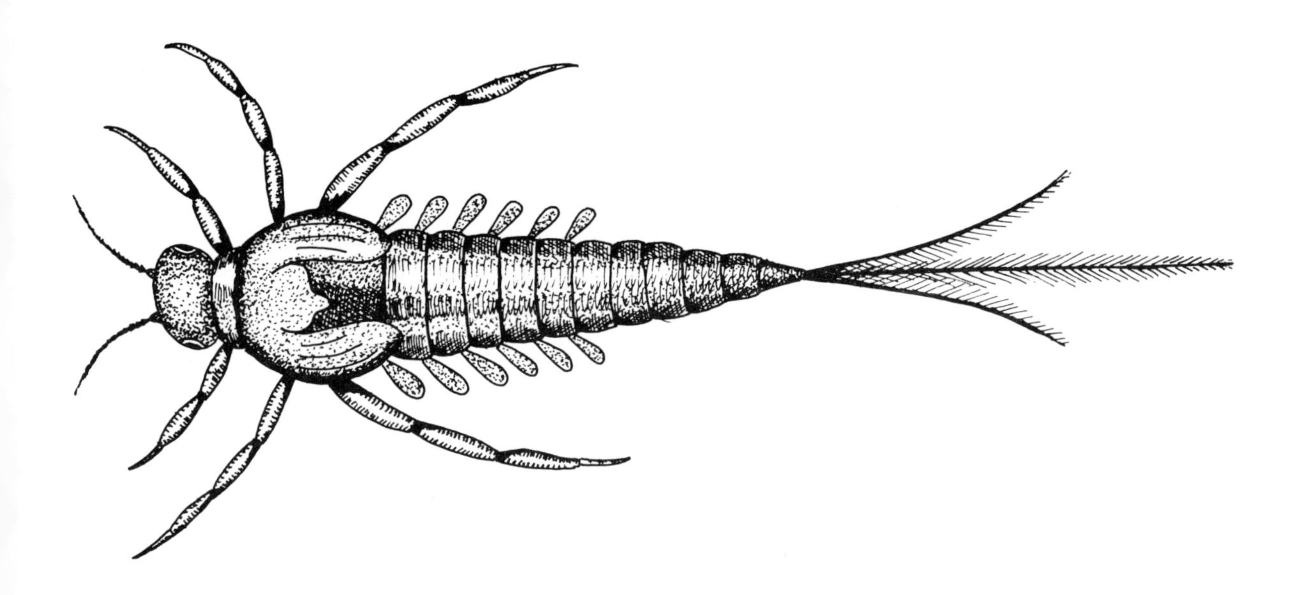

Figure 109 **Mayfly Nymph**

Q

QUILLWORT. Common name for *Isoetes:* a species of flowerless plants with tufted leaves. There are three species, two growing in acid water on the bottom of lakes or pools and the third preferring turf near the sea.

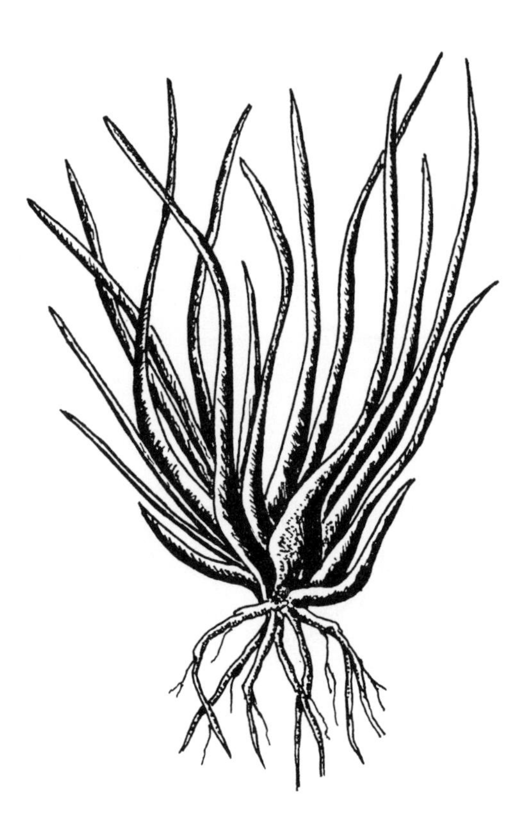

Figure 110 **Quillwort** *(Isoetes lacustris)*

R

RACE. A geographical subspecies, being a group of members of a species which differ from their fellow members, but are able to interbreed and produce fertile young.

RACEME. A simple flower cluster on an elongated stem.

RANUNCLEACEA. The Buttercup family. *See next entry.*

Figure 111 **Common Reed**

RANUNCULUS. Of the *Ranunculacea. R. aquatilis Linne,* commonly called Water Crowfoot. Swamp and aquatic plants that, because they do not survive long in the artificial conditions, are unsuitable for the aquarium. *See* **Plants.**

RAM'S-HORN SNAILS. Freshwater snails with flattish spiral shells, often kept by aquarists. *P. planorbis* is the most common and widespread; more local is *P. corneus* which can reach a length of 1 inch (25mm) across its shell. *See under* **Molluscs.**

RECENT. That of the present time.

RECESSIVE. The hereditary factor which, although present, is superseded by one that is dominant.

REDCAP. *See* **Fancy Goldfish.**

REDD. The gravel spawning bed of Salmon.

REED. Tall, swamp living grasses, forming extensive reed-beds in both fresh and brackish waters. They carry plume-like, purplish flower heads.

REEDMACE. Common name for *Typha. See under* **Plants.**

REGENERATION. The ability to replace lost or mutilated parts of the body. Fishes will, generally, replace missing scales or sections of fins.

REMEDIES. Although some remedies were mentioned under the section **Complaints of Fish,** there are a number of other treatments which can be applied. The following list of chemicals have all been found useful in treating against fish diseases.

Acriflavin– Effective against White Spot, Tail and Fin Rot, and Slime Disease. Use the deep orange-coloured, neutral acriflavine which is in the commercial form of small tablets. Dissolve one 3mg tablet in 330cc of hot water. Keep the solution protected from light. Vigorously stir 10cc into each gallon of water used. This treatment will last for a period of three days, after which the water should be changed and a further three days treatment given on the sixth day. Temporary sterility is produced by this chemical; however, normal fertility will be restored after several months.

Ammonia– 10 parts, by volume, of household ammonia is diluted with 90 parts of water. This may be used at the rate of 22½cc to each gallon of water, or the strength can be increased, for obstinate cases, to 45cc per gallon. When used against Skin and Gill Flukes, the fish should be bathed for between five and twenty minutes. Remove the patient if it appears to be adversely affected.

Chloromycetin– Use at a rate of 60mg to each gallon of water, and/or by adding 1mg to each gramme of food. Immerse the fish in the bath for three days, change the water and repeat the treatment after another three days. This chemical has been found to be effective against disease caused by bacteria and some protozoans.

Formalin– For use against Skin and Gill Flukes. Add one part, by volume, to 99 parts, by volume, of water. Add 165cc of the stock solution to each cubic foot of water. The fish should then be left in the bath until cured. Alternatively, the strength can be increased to a stock solution of 10 parts of formalin to 90 parts water, added at the rate of 25cc per gallon. Infected fish should be bathed for no longer than thirty minutes. Formalin is available in two strengths; only the **32% v/v** strength should be used. It must be free of paraformaldehyde – a whitish sediment which can be toxic to fish. It must not be used in a tank which has recently been treated with methylene blue, and the water to be treated should have a temperature of about 65°F (18°C) to avoid the risk of a secondary infection by fungus.

Friar's Balsam– Used to protect wounds by drying the area, then swabbing balsam over the entire area with cotton wool on a matchstick. Repeat until the wound heals.

Hydrogen Peroxide– Can be used at full strength, for initial treatment of very bad ulcers. Roll a little cotton wool onto a matchstick, dip into the peroxide, and gently swab the necrotic walls of the ulcer to cauterise the infected flesh.

Iodine– Mix 50% iodine to 50% water. Use by swabbing over areas infected by fungus, wounds or sore spots. Keep well away from the gills and eyes.

Malachite Green– Used against fungus, especially that which attacks fish eggs. It must be of the zinc-free, medical grade and must not be used in contact with zinc or galvanized iron. Prepare a stock solution of 1g of pure malachite green in 500cc of distilled water. This is added to the bath at the rate of 9cc to each gallon of water. For the treatment of eggs the strength of the stock solution is halved. Treat for no longer than one hour. This chemical can prove toxic if prolonged treatment is given.

Methylene Blue– Must be of medical quality only. The stock solution is made by dissolving 15g in 100cc of hot water. This is added to the water at the rate of 2cc per gallon, or in bad cases at double the amount. Used as a permanent bath in the treatment of White Spot, Skin and Gill Flukes and other gill complaints. With time the blue colour will fade from the water. Plants may be badly affected.

Phenoxethol– An oily liquid, slightly soluble in water, which is effective against various infections including Fungus, Tail and Fin Rot, some worm infections and Ichthyophonus Disease. Prepare a stock solution of 1cc of phenoxethol dissolved in 99cc of water. Add 90cc of the solution to each gallon of water. Dried food can be soaked in the stock solution and fed to the fish, in combination with the bath, for treatment of internal worm and other infections. The fish can remain in the bath until cured.

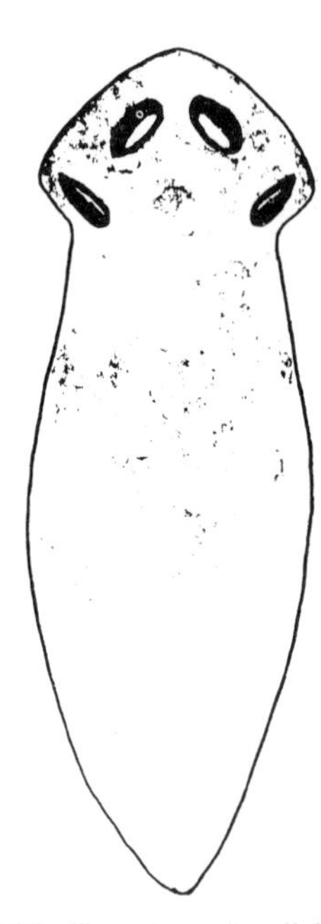

Figure 112 **Planarian** – free living flatworm

Potassium Permanganate– Useful for treating some complaints, especially in the open pond, and for disinfecting purposes. Never add the chemical directly to the water, always prepare a stock solution first. Dissolve 15g in 99cc of distilled water. This should be mixed into the water to be treated at the rate of 2cc per gallon in a fully planted tank or pond, or 4.5cc per gallon for a thirty minute bath. Some species of fish may be adversely affected; therefore, any distressed fish should be removed to fresh water immediately.

Salt– Do not use table salt. Obtain sea salts or cooking salts which are free of additives. Although suitable for use against a number of complaints, salt is generally used to combat fungus. Can be used as either a short-term, or long term bath.

For a bath of fifteen to thirty minutes duration add 5oz (142g) of salt to each gallon of water,

Figure 113 **Chromatophores** (pigment cells)
The cells on the left have concentrated pigment granules, whilst those on the right are fully expanded.

mixing it well in. If the bath is to be for an indefinite period add the same amount of salt but in small amounts, so that the fish can adapt itself to the gradual increase in salinity. Spread the salt additions over a twelve hour period until the total of 5oz (142g) has been added. The return to fresh water must be equally gradual, by changing one third of the salt water each day for freshwater, until after four changes the fish can be returned to fresh water. *See* **Complaints of Fish.**

RENIFORM. A botanical term meaning kidney-shaped.

REPRODUCTION OF FISH. The aim of reproduction is to maintain the stock of the species. When the progeny of the parents mature into male and female adults, and produce a further generation which, in turn, reproduce more descendants thereby ensuring the continuation of the species, it can be considered that the aim has been achieved.

Reproduction is influenced by specific conditions affecting the fish's surroundings; i.e. water temperature, length of daylight, or some other specific conditioning factor. The act is exclusively sexual, and fish are always disexual. If the specific conditions are fulfilled the males and females become sexually ripe and capable of reproduction. As a general rule the different species have their own well defined spawning periods.

During this time their behaviour pattern changes and, frequently, they develop external signs which show them to be ripe for spawning. The females increase their girth, due to the developing spawn, whilst the males often exhibit strikingly intense colours, or other characteristics such as a whitish rash (**tubercles**) on the body, head or fins. During spawning the external signs usually become much more intense.

In general the female fish lay unfertilised eggs, fertilization taking place in open water when the males simultaneously release **'milt'** containing spermatozoans. The number of eggs, their size, and the ratio of destruction form a balance. The eggs and alevins are defenceless against the many dangers to which their surroundings subject them. In order to protect them against total extermination there are two possibilities: either the eggs and alevins are produced in such great numbers that some are certain to survive, or the parents will protect them until they are able to stand a good chance of surviving the dangers of their environment.

Instinctively, fish spawn in places which afford the best protection for their eggs. In many cases the fish spawn in the shallow water, whilst in other instances the depths near the bottom are preferred. There are others which undertake long migrations to reach the spawning site. In nearly all instances, the chosen spawning site is very different to the areas normally frequented by the fish.

The aquarist who wishes to breed fish under artificial conditions should study the natural environment and the conditions which trigger them into sexual ripeness. As near as possible, these factors should be recreated for the fish if they are to be encouraged to spawn. Not all species, however, will respond in an artificial environment.

Young fish should be chosen, so that they can become acclimatised to the new conditions, and grow to sexual maturity therein. Ensure that they are healthy and free of any parasites. Do not use any specimen that is not a good, typical example of its kind – the alert fish breeder will develop an eye for those fishes which are good specimens of their kind.

RESISTANCE. The ability to withstand disease, which may be inherited or developed.

RESPIRATORY ORGANS. In fish, mainly the gills. The gills are positioned at the hind, central to lower end of the head. They are protected by hard bony plates which form the moveable gill covers (**operculi** or **opercles**). The gills themselves are supported by a number of specific bones, collectively called the gill arches. Blood vessels fill the skin folds which sit upon the gill arches and draw oxygen from the water that passes in over them via the mouth and out through the gill slits. An excessively rapid movement of the gills indicates a lack of oxygen in the surrounding water.

RETINA. Tissue at the back of the eye containing the light-sensitive visual cells.

RHIZOME. The usually thick stout root-stock, or storage stem, of such plants as the irises and water-lilies.

RHIZPODA. Phylum of unicellulars or protozoa, characterised by their method of stretching out and retracting their 'mock feet' to obtain locomotion. There are no permanent organs for feeding or locomotion, *Amoeba* is numbered among this large class of minute freshwater, marine, soil and parasitic animals.

RHODEUS AMARUS. The Bitterling. Member of the ***Cyprinidae*** originating from the area of Central Europe to Russia; it is not a native of British waters. A high-backed, laterally compressed, active little fish. Reaching a length of around 2½ inches (64mm); it has a short dorsal fin, longish concave anal fin and deeply forked caudal. Normally the body is a bright, shiny silver with a luminous green colour appearing on the centre of the caudal peduncle. During the breeding season the male assumes a mantle of reddish, bluish and violet colours over the silver body. At this time the female develops an ovipositor, a yellow to crimson tube of up to 2 inches in length (51mm), which remains visible for a few days.

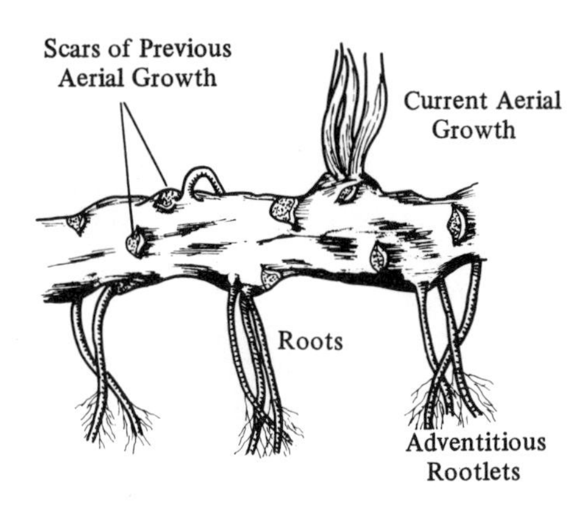

Figure 114 Rhizome of Water-Lily

It is a peaceful species which enjoys the company of its fellows. Aquarists are attracted to this fish because of its interesting breeding habits.

The spawning procedure, which takes place during March and May, involves a mussel which acts as a host to the eggs. The *Unio pictorum* Mussel (*see* **Molluscs**) is the usual host. The spawning female deposits her eggs into the intake siphon of the mussel. Fertilization takes place as the male hovers over the bivalve and releases his milt. The sperm-bearing milt is drawn into the

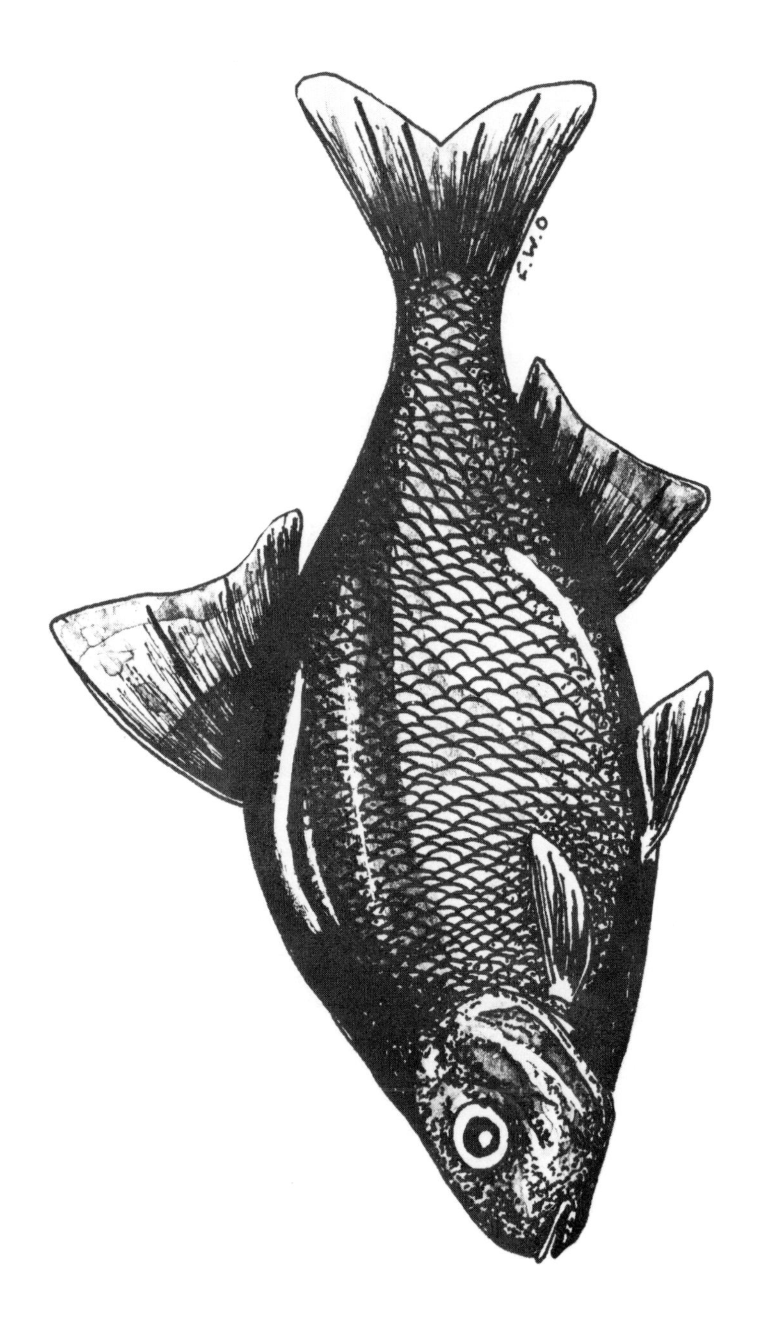

Figure 115 **Bitterling** *(Rhodeus amarus)*

intake siphon where it fertilizes the eggs. After spawning, the female's ovipositor is retracted.

The eggs and fry develop amongst the gills of the mussel until, eventually, the fry are expelled through the mussel's siphon into the open water.

Due to the close relationship between this fish and the mussel it can quite often be found to be infested with the mussel's parasitic young – the glochidia.

RHYNCHOBDELLODEA. Super family of the order of leeches (*HIRUDINEA*) which are found predominantly on cold-blooded vertebrates. They perforate the skin with a long, protactile trunk and suck the blood of their victim. Probably the best known species is *Piscicola geometrea,* the Common Fish Leech.

ROACH. *Rutilus rutilus. See under* ***Cyprinidae.***

ROTIFER. The Wheel Animaculae – tiny aquatic animals, the majority living in freshwater. Most are free-swimming, whilst others attach themselves to animals or plants; some are parasitic. Despite their small size they are not unicellular, as might be supposed, but somewhat highly developed multicellular animals. Rotifers are often found in 'infusoria' collected from a pond.

RUDD. *Scardinius erythrophthalmus. See under* ***Cyprinidae.***

RUGOSE. Botanical term meaning wrinkled.

RUNNER. A creeping stem, or stolon, that grows above ground from the parent plant to form a new, rooted plant.

RUNT. An undersized fish which remains dwarfed.

RYUKIN. *See* **Fancy Goldfish.**

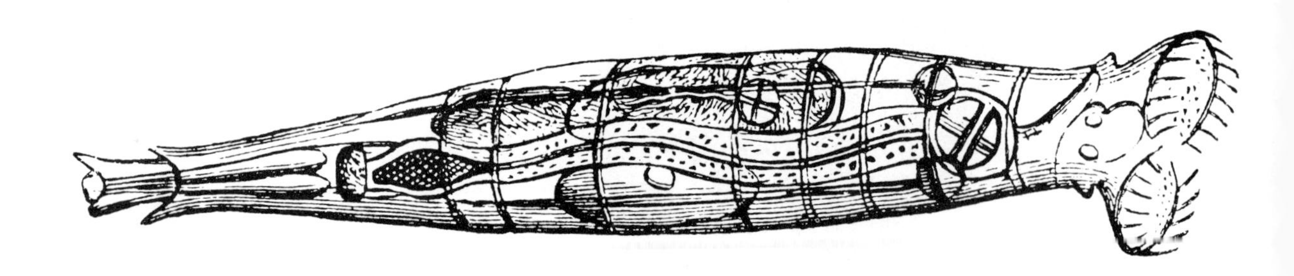

Figure 116 **Rotifer**

S

SACCATE. Botanical term meaning pouched.

SAGITTARIA. Genus of swamp and aquatic plants. Growing submerged and partly semi-emerged, the submerged leaves being narrow and strap-shaped. Reproduction is by seeds and runners. *See under* **Plants.**

SAGITTATE. Botanical term meaning arrow-shaped.

SALIENTIA. Order of those amphibians which lack a tail: the frogs *(Ranidae)* and toads *(Bufonidae)*. *See* ***Amphibians.***

SALMON. *See* ***Salmonidae.***

SALMONIDAE. Important family of Bony fishes containing the Salmon, Trout, Char, Grayling and other species of whitefish.

Salmo salar– **The Salmon.** Salmonids are found in the sea and freshwater; it is thought to be a marine fish which is slowly evolving into a freshwater living fish. The life of the Salmon is spent partly in the sea and partly in freshwater. They enter freshwater to spawn, usually between September and February, although it is not uncommon for Salmon to run up rivers at other times of the year. Great perseverance is shown by the fish as they surmount rapids and leap up falls of up to 10 feet (3m) high. They segregate into pairs at the spawning ground – a gravelly bed, in water with a depth of from 2 to 3 feet (0.6-0.9m). Eggs are deposited in a scooped-out trough, which is called a '**redd**'. The eggs are covered with gravel, after which the pair rest before again spawning. This continues until the female has no further eggs left in her. Once the spawning is over, the fish swim feebly back to the sea. At this stage the spent fish are known as **kelts.** They are very weak and thin and may die; survivors do not eat until they have regained the sea.

The orange coloured eggs are roughly a ¼ inch (6mm) in diameter and take from five weeks to five months to hatch, depending upon the temperature. The **alevins** are about ½ inch (13mm) long when they hatch out but by the time the yolk sac has been consumed they have grown to about 1 inch (25mm) in length, and begin to seek food. At this stage they are called **parr.** The parr remain in the shallows, growing to around 6 inches (152mm) during the two years that they live there. After a time, two to three years, the fish is gripped by the instinct to migrate to the sea; it is then known as a **smolt.** The smolt is carried down the river, often tail first, into the estuary and from here they quickly enter the sea.

Once in the sea, the smolt feed upon Sand-Eels, young Herrings and Sprats. They are greedy feeders and grow rapidly, for when they return to

Figure 117 **Salmon Parr**

the river, after twelve months in the sea, they will have reached a length of not less than 16 inches (41cm) and is called a **grilse.** At this stage it will have all the characteristics of the adult Salmon. Grilse come up from the sea in quite large shoals, their average length being 2 feet (0.6m). Many grilse do not ascend the rivers in their first year, but remain at sea until they are nearly four years old and finally gain the title of Salmon.

Salmo trutta– **The Common Trout.** Found all round the British Isles, in suitable lakes and rivers. It is less graceful than the Salmon and is subject to extreme colour variation. In general, the non-migratory Trout are brownish, often called **Brown Trout** whilst **Sea Trout** are silvery. The spawning habits are similar to those of the Salmon. In some Welsh estuaries there is a variety known as the **Skewen** which attains a large size and may be mistaken for a Salmon.

Salmo iridens– **The Rainbrow Trout.** This species originates from the U.S.A., in the

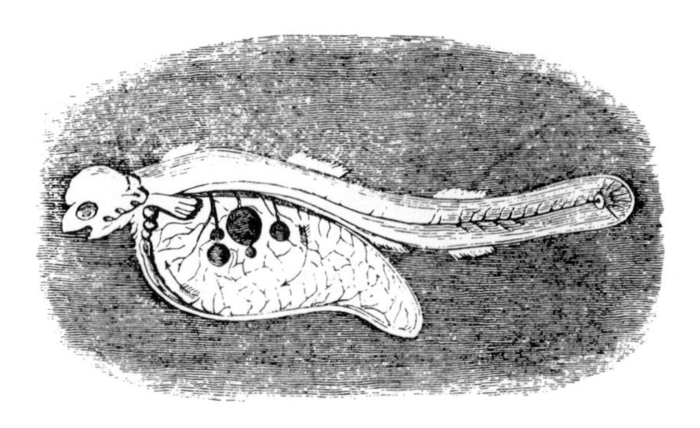

Figure 118 **Salmon alevin**

Sacromento River, and has been acclimatised in British water for many years. It is a migratory species and, unless in landlocked waters, will make its way to the sea. It is a spring spawner, laying its eggs during March and April.

Salvelinus– **The Char.** This genus is a member of the ***Salmonidae.*** Specifically coldwater fish, Char have been found in British lakes at over 1,500 feet above sea-level, and a temperature above 59°F can prove fatal. They are shy, deep-water fish with a somewhat obscure life-history. Spawning takes place from November to February, although different species have different habits and spawning times. They spawn in shallow water, forming redds or spawning beds in a similar manner to Salmon. Hatching takes place in about ten weeks.

Char vary greatly in colour, from bluish-grey, or bluish-black to olive green or brownish. The abdomen is silvery white, orange or crimson, depending upon the locality, age and sex of the fish. There are a number of different species of Char.

Salvelinus willoughbii– **The Windermere Char.** Reaches a length of up to 12 inches (30.5cm). It has a slightly oblique mouth, at the end of the snout, the lower jaw taking up not more than two-thirds of the head.

Salvelinus lonsdalii– **The Haweswater Char.** Grows to around 6 inches, and has a protruding lower jaw that takes up more than two-thirds of the head.

Salvelinus struanensis– **The Struan Char.** A bottom feeder that grows to about 9 inches (229mm); it has a blunt snout and feeble teeth in the mouth below.

Salvelinus killinensis– **The Haddy Char** (also known as **Killin Char**). Can reach a length up to 16 inches (41cm), it is deeper than the Struan.

Salvelinus maxillaris– **Large-Mouthed Char.** Average size about 10 inches (25cm). Characterised by its very large mouth which extends beyond the eye.

Salvelinus mallochi– **Malloch's Char.** Up to 1 foot in length, it has a small head and mouth.

Salvelinus gracillimus– **The Shetland Char.** Average length is 8 inches, it has a slender body, blunt snout and large fins.

Salvelinus perisii– **The Torgoch or Welsh Char.** Length about 9 inches (229mm). It has a pointed snout, large mouth with a long lower jaw and large fins.

Salvelinus colii– **Cole's Char.** Length between 9 inches (229mm) and 1 foot (0.3m). Very similar to the Windermere Char.

Salvelinus grayi– **Gray's Char.** Has a deeper and more compressed body than Cole's Char; it grows to between 10 and 12 inches (25-30.5cm).

Salvelinus trevelyani– **Trevelyan's Char.** Differs from Cole's Char by having a longer head, pointed

Figure 119 *Top:* **Salmon** *(Salmo salar)*
Bottom: **Trout** *(Salmo trutta)*

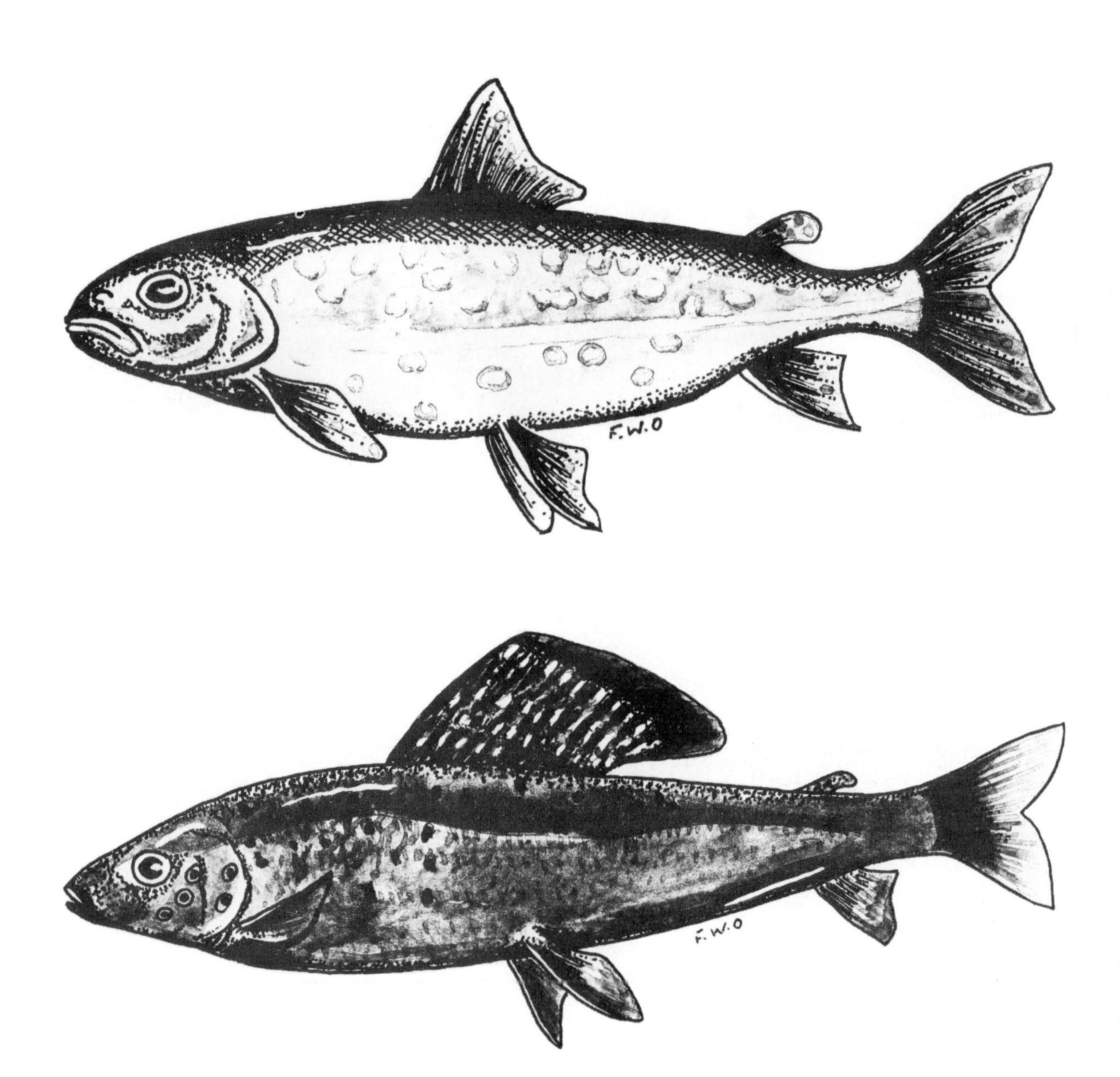

Figure 120 *Top:* **Char** *(Salvelinus)*
Bottom: **Grayling** *(Thymallus vulgaris)*

snout with strong teeth, and a narrow forehead.

Salvelinus scharff– **Scharff's Char.** Similar to Cole's Char, but having a sharper snout, smaller mouth and rounder body.

Salvelinus obtusus– **Blunt-Snouted Char.** Length about 8 inches (203mm), with a rather flat, narrow forehead and a short round snout.

Windermere Char live in several Lake District Lakes.

Haweswater Char inhabit Haweswater where they feed at the surface on flies.

Struan Char are found in Scotland's Loch Rannoch and the Haddy in Loch Killin.

The Large-Mouthed Char can be found in Loch Stack.

Malloch's Char may be seen in Sutherland's Loch Scourie.

The Shetland Char is the only Char in Shetland, it is found in Loch Girlsta.

The Torgoch lives in Welsh Lakes near Llanberis and in Llyn Corsygedol in Merionethshire.

Cole's Char has been found in waters from Kerry to Donegal in Ireland.

Gray's Char lives in Lough Melvin Fermanagh.

Trevelyan's Char has been found in Lough Finn in Donegal.

Scharff's Char may be seen in Lough Owel, Westmeath.

The Blunt-Snouted Char inhabits Southern Ireland's Loughs Acoose, Dan, Killarney, Luggala and Tay.

***Thymallus vulgaris*– The Grayling.** A member of the Salmon family. Probably Britain's most beautiful freshwater fish, but absent from Ireland. It has a long dorsal fin, which is beautifully coloured, and a small adipose fin. The body is elongated with a sub-terminal mouth. The iridescent body colours can be all shades from deep purple to shimmering pink. The eye has a deep blue, pear-shaped pupil.

Grayling and Trout are often found together in the same river. Preferring swift-running streams with plenty of water and a stony bottom, the Grayling is a spring spawner. From March to May eggs are laid on a gravel bottom in shallow water. The eggs are not quite as large as peas, and the young hatch out within a few weeks. Grayling feed upon crustacea, molluscs and insect larvae.

SAPROLEGNIA. The well known fungus which attacks weak and/or injured fish. It also attacks dead organic substances. *See* **Fungus** *under* **Complaints of Fish.**

SAPROPHAGOUS. An animal that feeds on decaying plant material.

SAPROPHYTE. A plant that derives nourishment from decaying organic matter; e.g. most fungi.

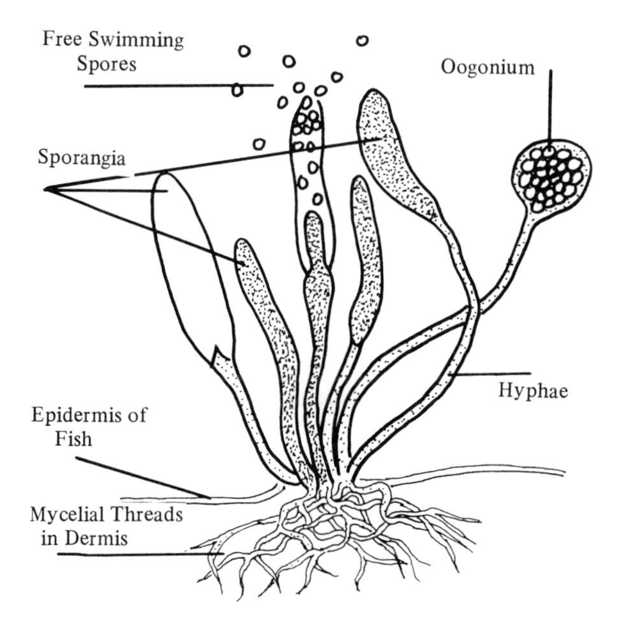

Figure 121 **Saprolegnia**

SCALES OF FISH. These are the present day remnants of the 'armour-plate' worn by the earliest fossil fish. As fish evolved they became more active and faster swimming, and the continuous mail-like covering became more flexible. This was accomplished by breaking it up into smaller sections, and in time these smaller sections evolved into the protective covering which the majority of present day fish wear.

The scales are formed from dead material, much like the human fingernail, and no matter how large the fish grows the number of scales remains constant. Except to replace a missing scale, no further scales will be added to the original number.

The scale is composed of two layers: a flexible fibrous lower layer, and an upper layer of a clear, bony,dentine deposit. Whilst the thickness of the scale does not increase, the upper layer grows at the edge to increase its diameter. For this reason a scale is thickest immediately under the original scale plate. The forward end of each scale is embedded in the cutis and the free after-end develops to overlap the front end of the scale which lies behind it. The visible part of the scale is only a small section of the whole.

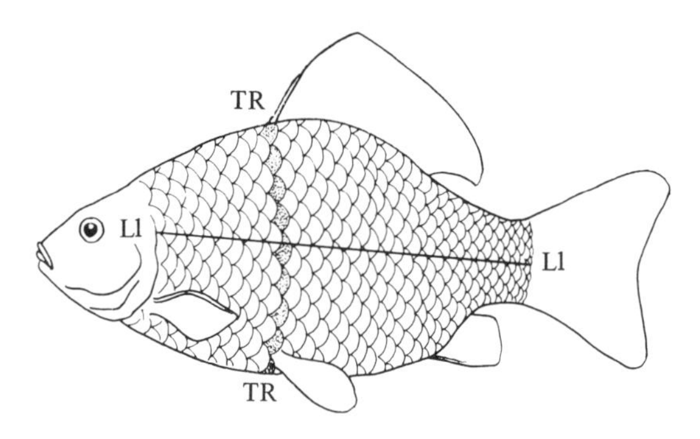

Ll. Lateral line TR. Transverse line

Figure 122 **Diagram to illustrate Scale Counting**

As the fish grows, the scales must also grow in order to continue to overlap. This is accomplished by the individual scale adding new rings of dentine around its edge, in much the same way that a tree grows. Where this new material is added to the after-end of the scale it shows in irregular, poorly marked accretions. However, the larger portion has clearly defined rings throughout its life.

Whereas a tree adds a ring for each year of its life, the growth rings on the scale of a fish will vary according to the seasons, the food supplies and the activities of the fish. A skilled observer can tell not only the age of the fish, but how many times it has spawned, and the length it reached in each year of its life.

During the warm months, when food is plentiful, a fish tends to feed well and grow rapidly. This means the scales must also grow quickly and so the growth rings are widely spaced. In cold weather food is scarce and the fish grows slowly, if at all. This results in the rings being close together and appearing as a dark band, known as **annual checks.** By counting the number of annual checks the age of the fish can be determined.

The scales are transparent and grow only on the body of the fish, from behind the gill-covers to the root of the caudal fin. *See* **Skin of Fish.**

SCHELLY. *Coregonus stigmaticus. See under Coregonus.*

SCHOOL. A term applied to communities of fish which swim closely together, sometimes in large numbers. Young fish tend to school together as a form of protection. *See* **Shoal.**

SCLEROPAREI. The order of Bony fishes with mailed-cheeks which includes the Sticklebacks.

SECRETION. The product of a gland.

SELECTION. In the fish breeding programme, selection must play an important part as it replaces the natural selection which takes place in nature. Selection for health, size, vigour, colour and various other factors ensures the continued quality, or improvement, of the stock. Failure to exercise selection will lead to a gradual degeneration in the quality.

SENSORY ORGANS OF FISH. All animals have senses which make them aware of their surroundings. However, fishes have developed some additional senses for use in their aquatic environment. Despite this the senses may be grouped into those of touch, smell, hearing, sight, and taste. There are some differences of opinion regarding the exact nature of these senses, but it is obvious that they must differ to some extent from those of the terrestial animals.

The organ of smell is not used for respiration but it does have the ability to smell certain odours which may attract or repel it.

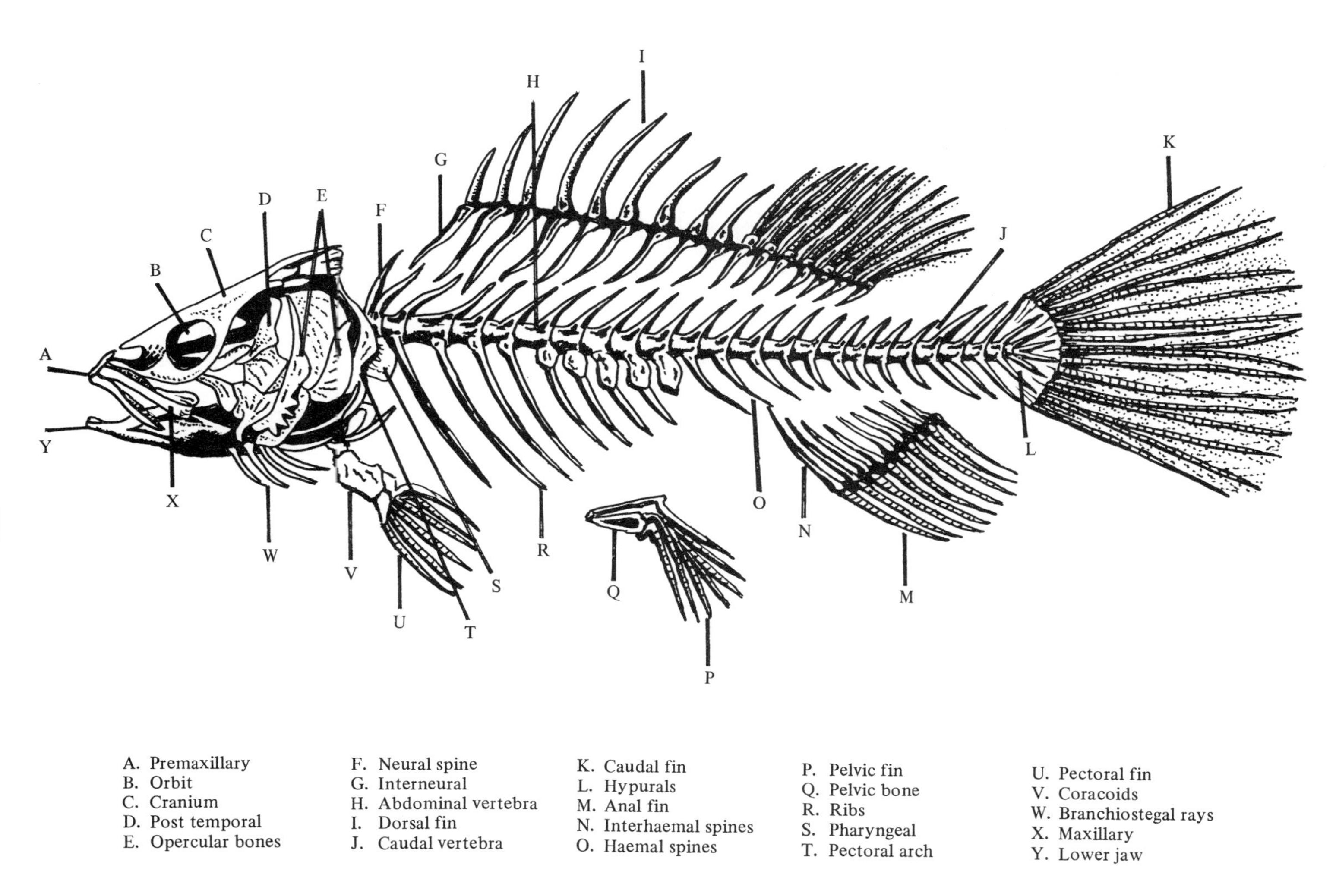

A. Premaxillary
B. Orbit
C. Cranium
D. Post temporal
E. Opercular bones

F. Neural spine
G. Interneural
H. Abdominal vertebra
I. Dorsal fin
J. Caudal vertebra

K. Caudal fin
L. Hypurals
M. Anal fin
N. Interhaemal spines
O. Haemal spines

P. Pelvic fin
Q. Pelvic bone
R. Ribs
S. Pharyngeal
T. Pectoral arch

U. Pectoral fin
V. Coracoids
W. Branchiostegal rays
X. Maxillary
Y. Lower jaw

Figure 123 **Skeletal Features of Bony Fish**

The faculty of taste is, no doubt, slight since most fishes swallow their food rapidly. Nevertheless there are taste buds situated within the mouth and on the palate.

In all fish, the skin of the head passes over the eye, becoming transparent where it enters the orbit. The eye is subhemispherical, the cornea being quite flat, thus it presents no resistance to the water when the fish is swimming and, being level with the head, is less liable to injury.

Instead of being lens-shaped the eye lens of a fish is globular or spherical; therefore, the range of vision is rather restricted. Adjustment of sight to a greater or lesser distance is not accomplished, as in land animals, by altering the shape of the lens. Instead, with the aid of a special muscle, it is achieved by moving the lens further from or nearer to the retina. This may only give perfect sight up to about 3 feet (approx. 1 metre), and imperfect vision to around 30 feet (9m). In some varieties of Goldfish the eye protrudes greatly – giving much reduced vision.

The auditory organ is much simpler than ours. In fishes the external ear and middle ear are entirely missing, and the inner ear consists only of a labyrinth with three semicircular canals. The labyrinth is delated into one or more sacs containing the ear-stones or **otoliths**. There is no cochlea. In many Bony fishes there is a connection between the auditory organ and the air bladder. The hearing is almost, if not entirely, non-existent, the organ acting chiefly as an organ of balance.

The senses of touch are located mainly around the lips, and in the barbels of bottom feeders. Vibrations are also sensed by the lateral line. *See* **Lateral Line,** *also* **Anatomy.**

SESSILE. Without a stalk.

SHANNON POLLAN. *Coregonus elegans. See under Coregonus.*

SHIRO BEKKO. *See* **Koi.**

SHIRO MUJI. *See* **Koi.**

SHIRO UTSURI. *See* **Koi.**

SHOAL. Term applied to a number of adult fishes swimming in a group; shoaling affords some protection from predators.

SHŌWA SANKE. *See* **Koi.**

SHŪSUI. *See* **Koi.**

SKELETON OF FISH. The skeleton of a fish is either cartilaginous or else more or less ossified. This fact serves to differentiate between the two great groups: the Cartilaginous fish and the Bony fish.

The dorsal spine is the main supporting part of the skeleton, and is divided into the trunk and tail parts. The latter part lends the necessary firmness to the caudal (tail) fin, which is important for locomotion, and bends upwards at the root of the caudal fin carrying the supporting bones for the fin rays.

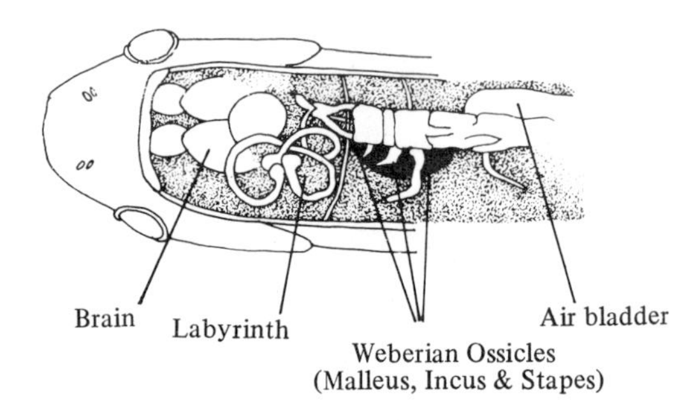

Figure 124 **Sound Reception Organs of Fish**

The **dorsal spine** is made up of a number of vertebral sections which allow a degree of flexibility. These are connected on the upper side to vaulted pieces which enclose the spinal marrow. The vertebral bodies carry extensions downwards, through which runs the great body artery. Connected with these are a series of thorny extensions, which rise from the upper vertebral vaults, and also in the tail part from the lower ones; there are also the link pieces of the vertebrae, and finally ribs enclosing the ventral cavity.

The front part of the dorsal spine is connected to the skull. The principal bones of the upper skull are the **frontal** and the **parietal**, both being in pairs. The lower skull is composed, amongst others, of the **ethmoids**, the **pterygoids**, the **sphenoids**, the **orbitals**, and the **hyomandibular.** The rear of the skull is closed by the **occipitals.** On each side of the skull the gill openings are closed by the gill covers, which consists of an **operculum** and **sub-**

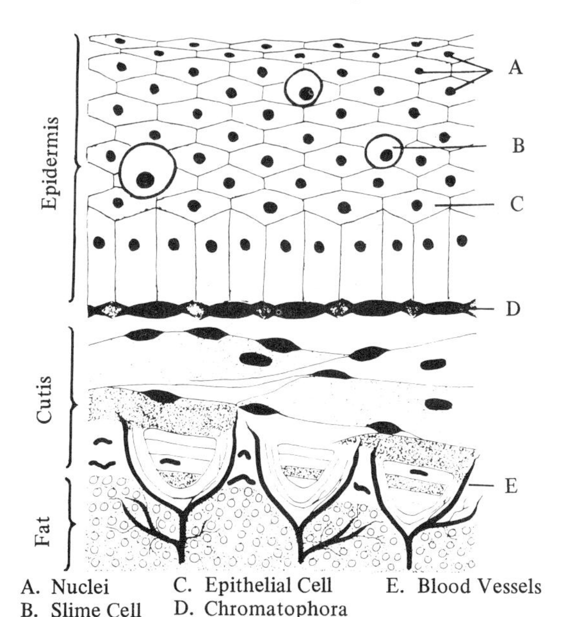

Figure 125 **Section of Fish's Skin**

operculum. The upper jaw is made up of the **maxillary** and the **premaxillary**; the maxillary also serves as the base for the barbels of bottom feeders. The premaxillary acts as the real jaw. The lower jaw, or **mandibular bone,** consists of three separate bones: the **dental,** the **articular** and the **angular.**

Unpaired fins are deeply imbedded in the muscle tissue on triangular fin carriers, they also have some support from the upper and lower thorny extensions of the vertebral column. The paired pectoral fins are carried on a special shoulder belt.

SKIN OF FISH. The skin of fishes consists of two distinctly differentiated layers: the **epidermis,** or upper skin, and the **cutis,** or lower skin.

The epidermis is composed of several layers of large soft cells. Beneath these are the mucous cells which make the skin slippery. The epidermis presents a form of defence for the cutis, against the influences of the ambient water.

The cutis consists of several layers of conjunctive tissue. It is richly supplied with blood vessels and nerves and also contains the organs for the sense of touch and the pigmentation cells (*see* **Colour of Fish**). Depending upon the species, the cutis may be either naked or else provided with scales, spikes, bony plates etc. Generally fishes have scales which are typical of them. These may be formations of different construction: either bony plates, which are hard and possess an enamel-like gloss, or thin flexible scales (*see* **Scales of Fish**), which insert in a scale pocket in the cutis and are generally covered by the epidermis.

The scale structure differs greatly in the different groups of fishes, and is taken into consideration when classifying species. **Scale counts** are made by counting the number of scales along the lateral line (or an imaginary line along the middle of the side of the body), which gives the number of scales in the length of the fish. The scales are also counted along a line from the front ray of the dorsal fin to the first ray of the pelvic fin. The number from the dorsal fin to the lateral line is the **dorsal (upper) depth,** and from the lateral line to the pelvic fin is the **ventral (lower) depth**; referring, of course, to the number of scales not the true body depth of the fish. These scale counts are called the **lateral line count** (often abbreviated to Ll.,), and the **transverse line count** (Tr). The scale 'formula' for the Roach would be given as:

Ll. 42 – 45. L.tr. 7½ – 8½/6½

This is interpreted as: scales along the lateral line **(Ll)** between the head and caudal fin number 42 to 45, whilst **L.tr.** signifies that from the dorsal fin to the lateral line there are 7½ to 8½ scales, and from the lateral line to the pelvic fin there are 6½ scales.

The number of scales remain constant throughout the life of the fish. *See* **Scales of Fish.**

SMOLT. The name for young Salmon parr which, after a period of about two years, turn silvery and migrate to the sea. When this stage is reached they are known as smolt.

SPATULATE. Botanical term meaning shaped like a wooden spoon.

SPAWN. The totality of eggs from frogs, toads, bivalves and fishes. Fish spawn is also known as roe whilst still in the body.

SPAWNING. The act of the female shedding eggs and the male fish actively fertilizing them.

SPECIATION. The evolutionary process by which a species is created.

SPECIES. The smallest group in the classification of living things. The members of a species can interbreed, whereas it is not usual for members of different species to cross breed.

SPERM. Compound substance containing the semen cells produced by male animals and capable of fertilizing the female eggs.

SPERMATOZOON. Microscopic, highly motile, flagellated male gamete. (Plural: spermatozoa).

SPHAGNALES. The order of bog mosses.

SPINY LOACH. *See Cobitidae.*

SPORE. The reproductive cell of plants.

SPOROZOA. A class of minute parasitic animals, some species being dangerous disease germs. Includes *Eimeria (Coccidi),* the origin of coccidiosis, and *Plasmodium* which causes malaria and which is passed to man after spending part of its life in Mosquitoes.

STAMEN. The male organ of a flower.

STAMINODE. A sterile stamen.

STELLATE. Botanical term meaning star-shaped.

STENOTOPIC. Applied to organisms which have only a restricted range of distribution, as opposed to eurytopic.

STERILE. Incapable of reproducing.

STICKLEBACK. *See Gasterosteus.*

STIGMA. That part of a flower carpel which receives pollen.

STIMULUS. The action of some factor which excites an organism and causes a reaction to result.

STIPITATE. Botanical term for organs with very short stalks.

STIPULE. Small, generally leaf-like, appendage at the base of a leaf stalk.

STOLON. A shoot which bends to touch the ground, then roots and produces a new plant at the point of contact.

STONE LOACH. *See Cobitidae.*

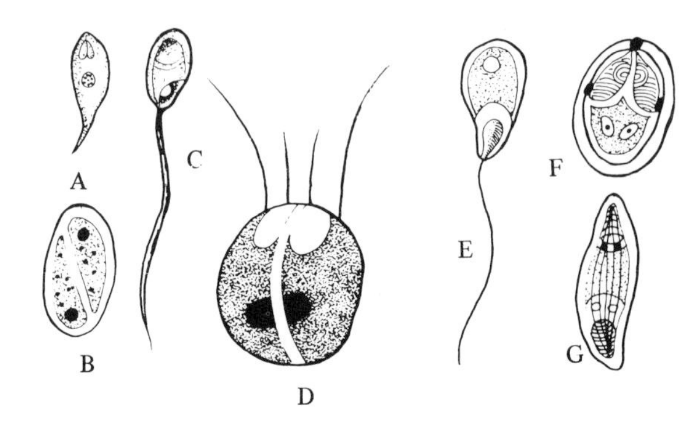

A Henneguya creplini
B Eimeria gasterostei
C Plistophora typicalis
D Sphaerospora mascovica
E Myxobolus exiguus
F Myxobolus cyprini
G Myxidium lieberkühni

Figure 126 **Sporozoan Parasites**

STRATOITES ALLOIDES. *See* **Water Soldier.**

STRIATE. Botanical term meaning ridged.

STYLE. The stalk which rises from the ovary of a flower and bears the stigma.

SUB-FAMILY. A category in the classification of animals and plants. It is intermediate between a family and a genus and is characterised by having names ending in *-inae,* instead of *-daeas* in families.

SUB-GENUS. Subdivision within a genus.

SUBMERGED. Underwater.

SUB-ORDER. Category in the classification of animals and plants which is intermediate between an order and a family.

SUBSPECIES. A group with similar characteristics that differs from the species in some minor way.

SUBULATE. Botanical term meaning awl-shaped.

SUNFISHES. *See* ***Centrarchidae.***

SWIM-BLADDER. Also known as air bladder. Always situated above the intestine, it is connected to the gullet of the fish. The bladder allows the fish to adjust its specific gravity weight to the pressure of the surrounding water and thereby maintain its equilibrium. Generally, the swim-bladder is an unpaired sac, often subdivided into lobes, with a smooth-walled inner surface. The bladder is filled with a gas which has a similar composition to atmospheric air.

Young fry develop their swim-bladders during the first few days of their life but in order to do so, they must rise to the water surface to fill the swim-bladder. If the fry are unable to reach the surface within the first days, perhaps through pressure from too great a water depth, the bladder will not be filled and will remain undeveloped and prevent the fish from swimming freely. Not all fish have swim-bladders. *See* **Anatomy of Fish.**

SYNONYM. A scientific name for a plant or animal which has been in valid use for some time and is more popular than the later officialized one. In such a case it is usual to mention both the official name and the synonym.

SYSTEMATICS. An indispensable order-bringing basis, which places all living beings into an externally recognisable relationship. The credit for creating a valid, internationally understood, system of classifying living beings belongs to Linne. *See* **Linne, Charles de.**

Figure 127 **Trout**

T

TADPOLE. The aquatic gill-breathing larval stage of the frog, toad and newt. *See* **Amphibians.**

TAISHŌ SANKE. *See* **Koi.**

TANCHŌ. *See* **Koi.**

TAPEWORM. An exclusively endoparasitic class of flatworms. In fishes they may occur singly or in numbers. Transmission of the worms may be through Tubifex, or through copepods, the fish being either a final or intermediate host. For instance *Ligula intestinalis* starts life in a small copepod, and passes through various freshwater fish before finally infesting ducks and other water birds.

TAXIS. Components of animal behaviour: a directional response to a stimulus which impels a creature in a certain direction. Taxi are closely related with the manner of living, and are combined with the other components of behaviour.

TAXONOMY. Comprising the principles of classification and systematics. *See* **Systematics.**

TELCOST FISH. The vast majority of the Bony fish group.

TENCH. *Tinca tinca. See under* ***Cyprinidae.***

TERETE. A botanical term for a stem which is not grooved or ridged.

THALLOPHYTE. A collective name for bacteria, algae, lichens and fungi.

THALLUS. The vegetative body of the lower plants that do not have the division of roots, stems, leaves etc.

THEROPHYTE. An annual plant which over-winters as a seed.

THORAX. The portion between the head and abdomen of an insect, split into three leg-bearing segments.

TOAD. *See* **Amphibians.**

TOADHEAD. *See* **Fancy Goldfish.**

TOSAKIN. *See* **Fancy Goldfish.**

TRACE ELEMENTS. These are those chemical elements which dissolve in water only in minute quantities and, in traces only, play an important role as catalysts in metabolism. A lack of trace elements may lead to symptoms of starvation, an excess to symptoms of poisoning.

TRACHAEA. The tube system through which arthropods breath, rather than through gills or lungs.

TREMATODES. Class of parasitic sucking worms belonging to the phylum of flatworms. Their characteristics are the sucking discs. *See* **Flukes.**

Figure 128 **Tapeworm** ***(Ligula simplicissima)***

TRICHOPTERA. The Caddis Fly.

TROUT. *See under* ***Salmonidae.***

TUBER. The swollen portion of an underground root or stem. A typical example is the tuber of the water-lily.

TUBERCLE. Sexual character exhibited by some male fishes, such as Carp, when in breeding condition. They have the appearance of small raised white pimples upon the head, gill-plates or pectoral fins depending upon the species.

TUBERCULATE. Botanical term meaning wart-like, or warty.

TUBIFEX. A popular live food for fish, if properly cleaned. It is becoming increasingly hard to find due to the lessening pollution of many waters. They normally live in large colonies in highly polluted water, especially near sewerage, where they inhabit the muddy bottom. They build tubes from body excretions and, keeping their heads inside the tubes, they wave their bodies in lively, snaky motions. If disturbed they very quickly withdraw into the tube. The worms are reddish, up to 2½ inches long, very thin and, when seen in quantity, give the water bottom a red colour. *See* **Live Foods.**

TUBIFICIDAE. Family of worms pertaining to the order of *OLIGOCHAETA,* of which Tubifex is of significance as a fish food.

TURBATRIX. Micro-worms. Formerly known as *Anguillula silusiae,* these worms grow from 1-2mm long and live on bacteria in fermenting vinegar. Micro-worms are an easily cultured live food for baby fishes.

TURBELLARIA. Class pertaining to the flatworms phylum, which includes ***PLANARIA.*** They are small, long-stretching, flatworms with square heads and two or more eyes. They may be white, yellow, brown or black in colour and are nocturnal predators. At all cost they must be kept out of tanks used for hatching fish eggs.

TURION. A bud which falls off an aquatic plant to overwinter in the bottom mud of the water.

TYPE SPECIES. A species chosen as representative of a genus.

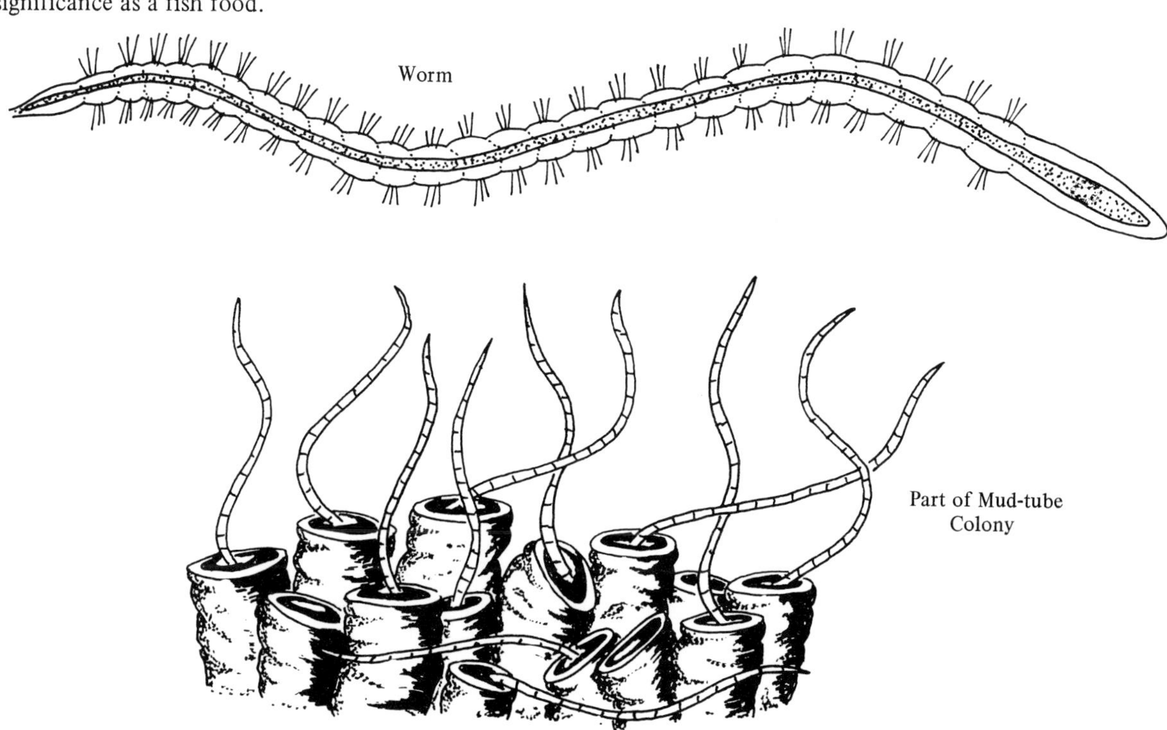

Figure 129 **Tubifex**

U

UMBEL. Botanical term for an umbrella-shaped, compound flower-head; the individual flowers borne on stems radiating from the main stalk like the ribs of an umbrella.

UNIVALVE. *See* **Gastropod.**

UTRICULARIA. Genus of carnivorous aquatic plants of the ***Lentriburiacae*** family. Perennial, submerged plants with finely divided leaves, bearing small bladders. The bladders have a cap which is held closed. However, when a small organism touches the sensitive bristles surrounding the bladder entrance, the cap springs open, water rushes in carrying the creature with it, the cap quickly closes and the water is expelled. The trapped organism is then forced against the digestive glands of the plant.

UTSURI MONO. *See* **Koi.**

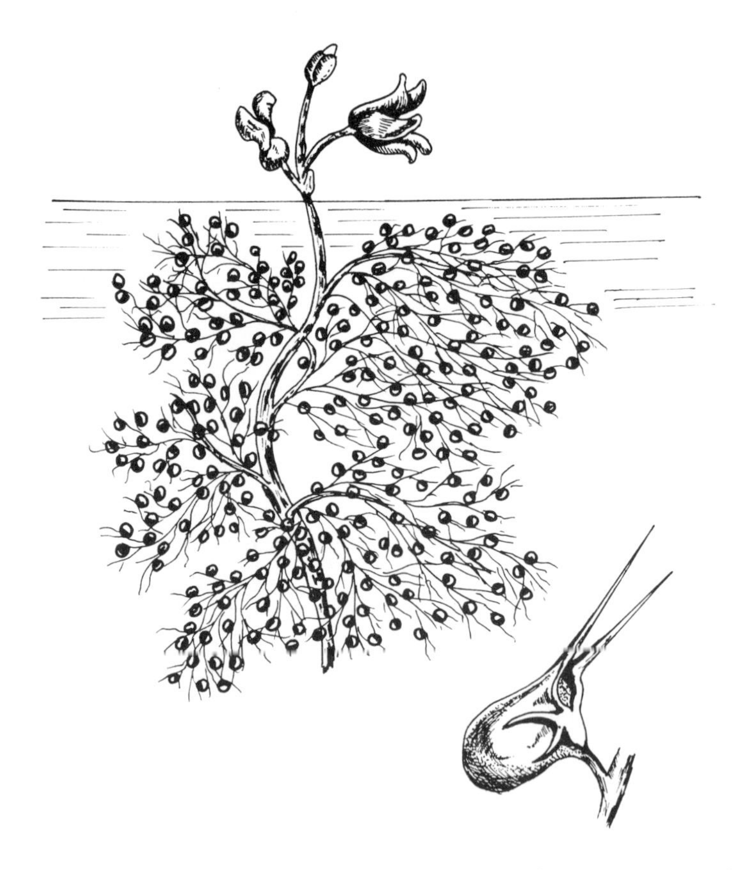

Figure 130 *Utricularia* – **Bladderwort** – showing the flowers and magnified bladder.

V

V. Abbreviation for ventral fin, which is also known as the pelvic fin.

VALLISNERIA. Genus of perennial water plants which are widely distributed over the warmer zones of the world. Some will grow in the colder conditions of the coldwater aquarium. They are hardy plants with ribbon-shaped leaves of a light-green colour which rise from the bottom. New plants arise from runners thrown out by the parent plant. *See* **Plants.**

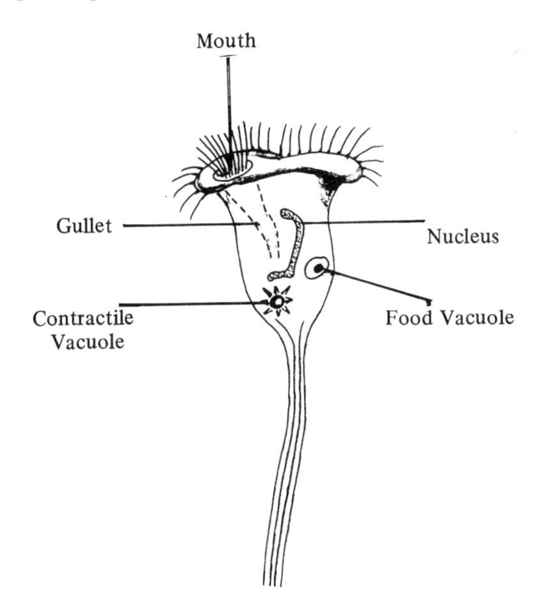

Figure 131 **Vorticella**

VARIETY. Often used to indicate a variation in a species or subspecies. Strictly applied it indicates a distinct form or colour phase occuring either by mutation or maintained state of balanced polymorphism.

VECTOR. A carrier of disease or parasite.

VEGETATION. A community of plants; plant life.

VEILTAIL. *See* **Fancy Goldfish.**

VERMES. An old-fashioned term for all worm-like animals.

VERTEBRATA. The most advanced sub-phylum of the animal kingdom, belonging to the phylum of CHORDATES. Vertebrates have a more or less fully developed, cartilaginous or bony skeleton; possess a firm but flexible dorsal spine which encloses the central nerve cord *(dorsal medulla)*, and a brain in a skull which has moveable jaws. Includes mammals, birds, reptiles, amphibians and fishes.

VERTICAL FINS. Collective name for the unpaired fins: anal, dorsal and caudal.

VIRULENT. Very contagious; very poisonous.

VIRUS. Minute self-reproducing protein particle, sometimes crystalline, sometimes molecular, and small enough to pass through filters which trap bacteria. Parasitic and causing both animal and plant diseases.

VITAMINS. Active substances necessary for the metabolism of animals. Required in only small quantities, a lack of them may cause severe symptoms of deficiency.

VITELLINE MEMBRANE. The membrane which encases the egg.

VOLVOX. Genus belonging to the phylum of FLAGELLATA. They are unicellulars which form colonies beneath a common jelly which may cover thousands of individuals.

VORTICELLA. The protozoan of the order *PERITRICHA.* A colonial and social form of ciliate that is very common in most waters. They attach themselves to water plants, dead sticks, stones and other submerged material, even the bodies of aquatic creatures whose movements they may greatly impede.

Commonly known as Bell Animals, the various species of *vorticella* can sometimes form dense masses, looking at first glance like a fungoid growth. The individual *vorticella* are not connected to each other in any way, each stalk being separately attached to its support. The body of the organism is like an inverted bell, and bears a crown of rapidly vibrating cilia which brings food to the mouth. If disturbed their stalks contract suddenly into a corkscrew shape and the 'head' closes up, only to expand again within a few seconds.

Reproduction is effected by simple division of the 'head', one of the new animals remaining attached to the stalk and the other swimming away to settle elsewhere. Two free-swimming 'heads' may also conjucate.

Figure 132 **Water Frogs**

W

WAKIN. *See* **Fancy Goldfish.**

WATER-BOATMAN. *See* **Water Bugs.**

WATER BUGS. These belong to the large order of *HEMPITERA,* and are members of the sub-order *HETEROPTERA.* Amongst the best known of British water bugs are: *Gerridae,* Pond Skaters or Water Striders; *Nepidae,* Water Scorpions and Water Stick-insects; *Notonectidae,* Water-boatmen; and *Corixidae,* the Lesser Water-boatman.

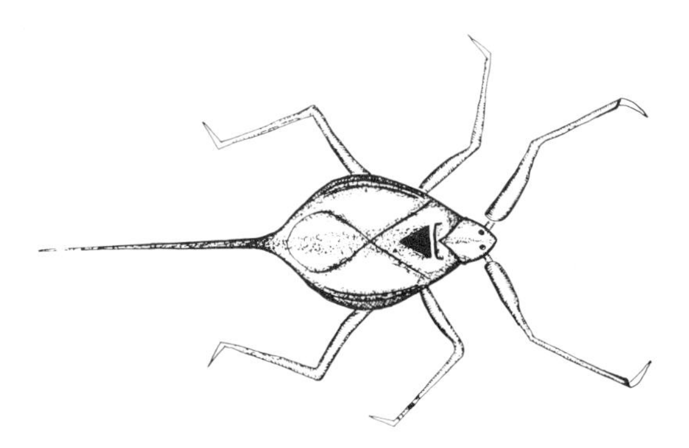

Figure 133 **Water Scorpion** *(Nepa cinerea)*

Gerridae– **The Pond Skater** *(Gerris najas)* is one of the commonest of the ten species comprising this genus and can be seen upon the surface of most lakes, ponds and ditches. It is roughly ½ inch (13mm) long, and with its wide spread legs it may be seen gliding rapidly over the water surface in search of dead or dying insects.

Nepidae– There are two species which are found in Britain and, in appearance, they are quite unlike each other. *Nepa cinerea* **(Water Scorpion)** attains a length of 1 inch (25mm) or more. It is dark brown in colour and flat; lying on the bottom, near the water edge, it looks like a dead leaf. At the rear end is a long tube – often mistaken for a sting – through which the creature breathes by pushing it above the water into the air. The front two legs are modified into limbs capable of grasping and with these they seize their prey and grasp it whilst sucking out the juices of the victims. The second species is *Ranatra linearis* **(Stick-insect).** The body is round and stick-like, growing to about 2½ inches (64mm). Its habits are very similar to its relative; it also has a breathing-tube.

Nontonectidae– The **Water-boatmen** are probably the best known of all water bugs – there are four British species, the most common being *N.glauca.* This bug reaches a length of around ¾ inch (19mm) or slightly less, and is very abundant and widespread. Water-boatmen rest at the water surface and swim in an upside down position. When at the surface the tip of their abdomen and the middle and front legs just touch the underside of the surface film. The body is keeled along the back; the hind legs are long, fringed and oar-like. Water-boatmen will feed upon any living creature that can be attacked, and will have little hesitation in attacking creatures larger than themselves – fish are not immune to their predacious attentions. They have piercing beaks and toxic saliva and feed upon their victims body fluids. Water-boatmen are well able to fly from pond to pond. The young, which hatch from cigar-shaped eggs, are white with red eyes.

Corixidae– The **Lesser Water-boatmen** comprise a large family of thirty-three British species. Although having a similar appearance to the true Water-boatmen, they are smaller and do not swim on their backs. Their backs are flatter and their tail end is blunter and, unlike the true Water-boatmen, the *Coricidae* spend much of their time on the bottom sucking up small particles of organic food matter; they rarely use their beaks to pierce other creatures.

WATERCRESS. The commercial watercress is a hybrid of two closely similar species *Rorippa nasturtium (aquaticum)* and *R. microphyllum;* it should not be confused with the true watercress *(Barberea)*. Widely distributed in shallow moving water.

WATER-FLEAS. Collective name commonly applied to Daphnia and other tiny freshwater crustaceans. *See* **Daphnia.**

WATER INSECTS. *See* **Hexapoda.**

WATER-LILY. Large aquatic plants with floating leaves, growing mainly in still water. Common British species are: White Water-lily, *Nymphaea alba;* the Yellow Water-lily or Brandy-Bottle, *Nuphar lutea,* so named because of the scent of its flowers; the Fringed Water-lily, *Nymphoides peltata,* which is smaller than the true water-lilies. *See Nymphaceae under* **Plants.**

WATER LOUSE. Common freshwater crustacean, related to the Wood Louse, found in the submerged vegetation of ponds and streams. *Asellus aquaticus* and *A. meridianus* are the most common of the species. *See* **Live Foods.**

WATER MILFOIL. *See* **Myriophyllum** *and under* **Plants.**

WATER SCORPION. *Nepa cinerea* – a widespread water bug, superficially resembling a scorpion, having an elongated body with a 'tail', which is actually a breathing organ. *See* **Water Bugs.**

WATER SOLDIER. *Stratoites aloides* – a free-floating aquatic monocotyledon. Floating upon the surface of still freshwater, its white flowers rise from the middle of a tuft of sharply toothed, sword-shaped leaves. During the cold months it sinks below the water surface.

WATER SPIDER. *Argyroneta aquatica* is the only spider that lives in water, constructing a web to form an underwater bell which it fills with air gathered from the surface.

WATER STARWORT. *See under* **Plants.**

WATER STICK-INSECT. A long thin water bug, *Ranatra linearis,* which is closely related to the Water Scorpion. *See* **Water Bugs.**

WATER TIGER. *See* **Dragon-fly.**

WEBERIAN OSSICLES. A bony linkage formed by the first vertebrae of a fish, providing contact between the ear labyrinth and the swim-bladder, which characterizes the order of the ***Ostariophysi.***

WHIRLIGIG BEETLE. A genus of small water beetles, comprised of twelve different species, that gyrate round one another on freshwater surfaces; the ***Gyrinidae.***

WHITE SPOT. A prevalent disease of fishes characterised by the appearance of a varying number of white or greyish small spots on the skin. The spots, are in fact, bladders with a diameter of about 0.5-1mm, containing one or more parasites. The parasite is a protozoan which rotates in a lively manner.

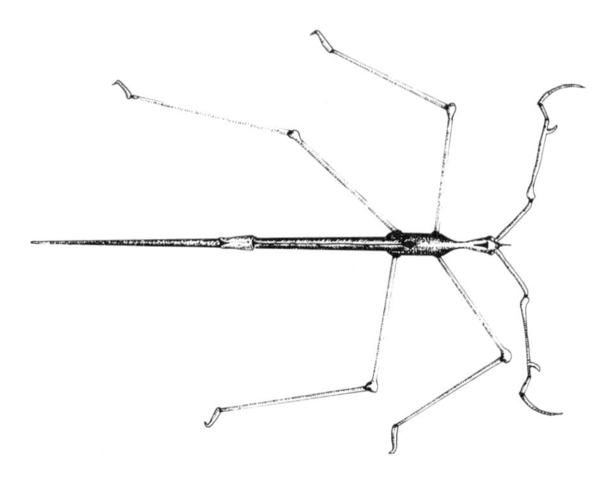

Figure 134 Water Stick-Insect *(Ranatra linearis)*

The parasite penetrates the upper layer of the skin of the fish where its movements irritate and cause the augmentation of epithelial cells, so that it becomes covered with a layer of skin. Within this 'cover' the parasite feeds on red blood corpuscles.

When, after a few days, the parasite becomes full grown, it bores through to the exterior of the fish, and falls to the bottom.

Having left the host, the parasite covers itself in a jelly-like cyst. Within the cyst the creature rapidly divides itself into numerous youngsters, the speed of the process depending upon the water temperature. Within about thirty-six hours of the adult parasite having encysted, the young will be seeking a new host. Infection, and reinfection, of a fish can be so rapid and heavy that the fish will become severely weakened and will die.

The young parasites must find a new host within a few days, if they fail they also will die. *See* **Complaints of Fish.**

WHITEFISH. *See Coregonus.*

WHITE WORMS. *See* **Enchytraeus.**

WHORL. The ring of leaves or flowers around a stem.

WILLOW MOSS. *See* **Fontinalis** *under* **Plants.**

Figure 135 **Whiteworms** – easily cultured live food for goldfish.

X

XANTHISM. A variation in which the normal colour of an animal is replaced by, or suffused with, yellow. Also known as Xanthochroism.

Y

YAMABUKI ŌGON. *See* **Koi.**

YELLOW FLAG. *Iris pseudacorous,* the native British iris. Widespread in areas of freshwater and marsh. *See under* **Plants.**

Z

ZANDER. *See* **Zandra.**

ZANDRA. Pike-Perch. *See under* ***Percidae.***

ZOOLOGY. The scientific study of animals.

ZOO PLANKTON. Animal plankton.

ZYGOTE. The product of the fusion of two sexual cells, thus the starting point of a new live being.